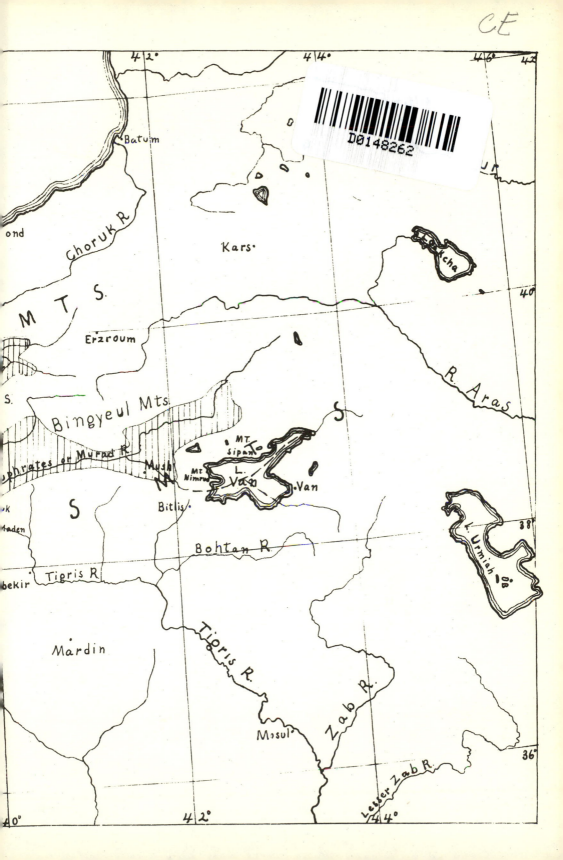

ELLSWORTH HUNTINGTON

His Life and Thought

Ellsworth Huntington

Ellsworth Huntington

His Life and Thought

BY

Geoffrey J. Martin

Archon Books

1973

Library of Congress Cataloging in Publication Data

Martin, Geoffrey J
    Ellsworth Huntington; his life and thought.

    Includes bibliographical references.
    1. Huntington, Ellsworth, 1876–1947. I. Title.
G69.H86M37   910'.92'4 ⌞B⌟   73–5682
ISBN 0–208–01347–4

© 1973 by Geoffrey J. Martin
First published 1973 as an Archon Book
by THE SHOE STRING PRESS, INC.,
Hamden, Connecticut 06514

PRINTED IN THE UNITED STATES OF AMERICA

To
Norma

CONTENTS

ILLUSTRATIONS

A book on Ellsworth Huntington and his work is most timely; indeed it is overdue. Huntington's researches, and the thoughts and hypotheses to which these researches gave birth in his perceptive fertile mind, are one of the abiding influences on the present-day study of human affairs.

Huntington is influencing present-day thinkers even if they are not aware of this, and also even if they are aware of it but dissent from Huntington's ideas. Students of human affairs may agree or disagree with Huntington, but in either case they will be influenced by him, so it is better that they should be aware of him. We are moving towards a unitary study of human affairs in which the arbitrary and obstructive barriers between the traditional separate "disciplines" are being broken down progressively. Huntington was a pioneer in this liberating iconoclastic movement, and, as has happened to other pioneers, he has suffered for being ahead of his contemporaries. Some of his more conventional-minded contemporaries failed to appreciate the importance of his work—above all, they were blind to its significance for the future of his and their common field.

Huntington not only looked at human affairs as a unity; he also looked at them in relation to the natural environment in which mankind has made its appearance on this planet. Today we are waking up belatedly to the truth that this natural environment, which has sustained our ancestors since the beginning of life on Earth, is now in danger of being obliterated by human technology. It is dawning on us that we may be sawing off the bough on which we are perched. Huntington's work is pertinent to this question. The evidence that he found for rhythmical oscillations of natural phenomena has been disputed. (It has not been rebutted, for the question is still open, and the data on which Huntington based his hypotheses are more numerous and more detailed than the accounts of them for which he was able to find room in his publications.)

I have had the good fortune to know Dr. and Mrs. Huntington personally. I have a lasting memory of their kindness to a younger student, and a lasting gratitude for the stimulus that I received from Dr. Huntington at a time when it was particularly valuable

to me. I will mention one characteristic product of Dr. Huntington's work: his pair of graphs of fluctuations in the breadth of
Californian tree-rings and in the levels of the surfaces of Central
Asian lakes. Huntington had a mind that perceived the possible
connexions between things that pedestrian minds, plodding along
in blinkers, overlooked. Minds like Huntington's are what our
present-day world needs.

ARNOLD J. TOYNBEE

There was nothing final about his thought: there was only a ceaseless striving for a wider comprehension. He was fascinated by the search for explanations of the major currents of historical change, of the rise and decline of civilizations. He attracted much attention by presenting unusual interpretations of historical events in vigorous and eloquent prose. But the explanations he offered were "like metal keys attached to kites to attract the lightning." The quickest way toward a wider comprehension of man on the earth was to present a hypothetical explanation for the course of events which would attract sharp criticism. His hypotheses could not be ignored; he did not expect them to be accepted without modification, nor was he angered by the attacks of his peers. He became one of the most controversial figures in the development of geographical thought in America, and one whose misfortune it was to be commonly misunderstood. For to form a judgement about the man and his thinking on the basis of any one of his numerous books is to miss the whole sweep of his ideas. This book is written to provide such a perspective. The man is Ellsworth Huntington.

Ellsworth Huntington (1876–1947) lived and worked during the time that geography was just making its appearance as a professional field in America. William Morris Davis had set forth his concept of geography as an explanatory description of the physical character of the earth's surface, and of man's response to his physical surroundings. Davis suggested that to complement and complete the study of physiography there should be a parallel development of ontography. Huntington, who studied with Davis, undertook to develop ontography. He began a lifelong participation in the emergence of human geography, economic geography, and climatology especially as it affected man. He also looked at man, himself, and began to emphasize the need to apply the principles of eugenics. The exchanges of ideas between Huntington and geographers, ecologists, anthropologists, sociologists, eugenicists, and historians are examined so that Huntington's quest for a wider comprehension of the forces contributing to civilization can be more clearly understood.

Revealed is the nature of geography quite aside from the

matter of definition; revealed, too, is an age when a geographer rarely hid behind a narrow specialism, and undertakings ranged from the local to sweeping visions of world schemes. What has gone before might best be studied and assayed in the context of its time. In criticising writings accomplished at an earlier time, one may do well to remember the words of Isaiah Bowman (letter to Mark Jefferson, September 6, 1936):

> . . . A man wrote me the other day about Davis—had him all sized up from his writing. I told him it was sawdust—that to separate a man's work from his setting was a crime and that professional appraisal apart from biography was lop-sided. It is the same with "problems." Simon-pure geography is a blind-man feeling the elephant's tail.

Ellsworth Huntington left the Harvard Yard in 1903 to travel across Asia on his first major scientific expedition just as the first undergraduate geography "major" was being developed at the University of Chicago, and while the Association of American Geographers was in process of formation. During the next forty-four years Huntington companioned with many intellectuals, and especially with the geographers. He wrote for the popular reader, for the classroom, and for science. This arrangement was forced upon him by economic circumstance. American geographers were growing up, trying to develop a mature geography, and were so diverse in their points of view that Derwent Whittlesey remarked "I am not sure that such a group would subscribe to the Lord's Prayer!" To this group Huntington offered a point of view which became acceptable to some and wholly unacceptable to others. To people in other fields of study he offered a geographic point of view: he provided analysis of climatic change during postglacial time for the historian, advanced causative notions relating to human capacity for the eugenist, unravelled cyclic phenomena for the economist, and offered analysis of the environment and what in it that had meaning for human occupance to the sociologist and anthropologist. George H. T. Kimble has written "There were giants in the land in those days and Ellsworth Huntington was one of them. . . . He dealt with 'age-less' questions. His main 'fault,' I suppose, was in being born out of due time." (G. H. T. Kimble to G. J. Martin, 28 May 1971.)

Huntington did not deal primarily in techniques or studies of local areas or in imports and exports but considered larger matters. He explored continents and honed a point of view which derived legitimately from observations made while on the back of a camel, yak or horse or while riding in a springless cart. He endured much privation as he journeyed in six continents. When he camped at night, perhaps in Asia he committed his daily observations to his diary (and less frequently into letters home). Gradually, out of a myriad of lesser matters there emerged issues of larger moment. Huntington's thought was not developed in the classroom; it was wrought in the crucible of far-flung journeying. As he travelled he observed climates, cultures, and peoples; in Asia, Europe, the Americas, Africa and Australia. He wanted to understand civilization, to write of his understanding, and to be understood.

The genesis of his interest in civilization is obscure: it may owe to family Bible study, to the archeological work of his Harpoot days, or possibly to the Pumpelly-led digs in Central Asia. Whatever the source of his inspiration, it led him to search for clues to the pattern of history which he beheld and whose rhythmic pattern remained less hidden from his view as his life work proceeded. Indeed, his graph revealing historic variations of climate provides an instrument that contributes to an understanding of the strengths and weaknesses, the rise and fall, and the affiliation and diffusion of civilizations. It was both as a student of civilization as well as geographer that he investigated climatic pulsations, established the principle of climatic variability, sought climatic optima, studied the results of natural selection, opted for eugenics, described the qualities of ozone, and investigated cyclic phenomena ranging from chestnuts in Scotland to Wall Street stock prices. In fact, he may have contributed more to thought than he did to geography. One derives from Huntington in relation to one's ability to accede to his thought, without criticism of excrescent detail or disagreement with an environmentalist posture that has been branded determinist. The ordered plan which Huntington perceived for the rise of man implies determinism, and there the ideological squabble may rest. The point is that Huntington recognized man as an incident in the cosmic drama and was able to assign weights to the process of evolution since a Beginning. In positing climate, heredity, and culture as a triadic causation of human progress he refused to countenance the march of civilization as a matter of chance.

The early years of his academic life were given essentially to the study of climate and more particularly to the quest for evidence (and later for the causes) of climatic change in postglacial time. Themes on studies of climatic change and on the relative merits of the earth's climates appear and reappear throughout his lifetime, but are announced particularly in *The Pulse of Asia* (1907), *Palestine and Its Transformation* (1911), *Civilization and Climate* (1915), *World Power and Evolution* (1919), the very much revised *Civilization and Climate* (1924), and the mature summation "Climatic Pulsations" on the occasion of Sven Hedin's seventieth birthday, 1935. His estimate of the importance of climate for mankind led him to a close association with the American plumbing trade and more especially the American Society of Heating and Ventilating Engineers (indoor climate should approach the optimum). Independently he argued that the seat of the United Nations should be located at Newport, Rhode Island. He thought it had the best climate for man in the U.S. He also advised on suitable locations for schools, colleges, hospitals, retired people, business enterprises, and Brasilia. His interest in climate never did pass; the study of eugenics and culture became additions to this first love.

Emerging in the teens of the twentieth century was Huntington's concern with the quality of people. He was concerned that democracy itself was threatened by the rapid multiplication of the less able members of the species, and urged restrictive immigration into the United States. In association with Roland Dixon, Lothrop Stoddard, and Madison Grant, he became a significant force in the American Eugenics Society for a quarter of a century (President, 1934–1938) and announced his interest in the quality of people in works including *The Character of Races* (1924), *The Builders of America* (with Leon Whitney 1927), *Tomorrow's Children: The Goal of Eugenics* (1935), *After Three Centuries* (1935), and *Season of Birth: Its Relation to Human Abilities* (1938).

Culture, the third of his determinants of civilization, he regarded as the field of recorded history. He enjoyed reading history and histories, deplored the historian's omission of a due consideration to the role of environment and biological inheritance, but did not doubt the significance of events and culture in the pageant of man. He was especially thoughtful of the rôle of ideas and inventions in man's progress: he gave attention to the role of the horseshoe in ninth-century Turkey; to the invention of the glass window in fifteenth-century England; and to the development of the boat throughout recorded history. When S. C. Gilfillan announced that man had "climbed with clime" from lower latitudes northward, Huntington accepted the rôle of culture in facilitating such migration. Parts of several of Huntington's books accept culture as a moving force; in particular his critics should read "Climate and the Evolution of Civilization," a chapter in the book *The Evolution of the Earth and Its Inhabitants*, edited by Richard S. Lull (1918), and "The March of Civilization," a chapter in *Europe* by S. Van Valkenburg and E. Huntington (1935).

The papers of Ellsworth Huntington, donated to the Yale University Library by Mrs. Huntington in August 1968, have been processed and the contents entered into a register (edited by Theodore Persons, August, 1970). They are contained in 318 boxes (approximately 135 linear feet) and constitute one of the largest known archival deposits of a geographer. Huntington posthumously remains the most prolific United States geographer; as author of 28 books, parts of 29 others, and over 240 articles, he invites comparison notwithstanding time and place. These papers are part of the trove which is a fundamental source remaining to us from an earlier time in this century, when geographers were elaborating a disciplinal scheme.

Many have scrambled over the body of thought which Huntington offered without regard to the posture of his mind. He advanced theses cautiously, then having warned the reader of his intent, argued the case with reckless abandon, scribing the vision which his extraordinarily fecund mind beheld. Whether one regards unproved or speculative detail as excrescence to the larger offering, or as major blemish which destroys the whole, is strictly the choice of the beholder. Certainly one hears less frequently from those who benefitted from Huntington's thought than from those who carp and criticize.

Biography chronicles the man's interests and reveals that an initial enthusiasm can label an individual in spite of a later shift in intellectual posture. In his first book, *The Pulse of Asia* (1907), Huntington offers a point of view which later won him the label "determinist." Yet few are the people who read the introduction to the 1919 edition of the same book, in which he writes: "the reader must scan these pages with the thought that he is watching a theory in process of construction." Perhaps fewer are those who have considered determinisms in all their variety (a subject still largely unwritten). Arnold J. Toynbee admits that he "was enormously influenced by his (Huntington's) ideas about the relation between human beings and their physical environments. . . . I am not a determinist, and I think this is also a mistaken description of Huntington's position. It was something much more profound and subtle than that." Certainly Huntington never indulged the impressionistic variety of determinism of which he felt Ratzel and Semple were spokesmen. Huntington attempted to measure influence exerted by environment—hence his study of worker productivity in factories. And if many of his peers did not have the time to keep abreast of shifts in his thinking neither could they be expected to wander with him through the complexities of eugenic history, policy, and accomplishment, and the rôle and meaning of culture as contributing to civilization. He was keenly aware that the reading of one small part of his work could lead to misunderstanding. Chauncy D. Harris may well be correct in his assessment: "Most people who criticize him have never read his work."

No, there was nothing final in his thought; there was only a ceaseless striving for comprehension. Frequently he would write an article or even a book knowing that it would tempt substantial criticism. That was part of his concept of the scientific method. They were statements around which thought could flow (nationally and internationally). These statements constituted his thought in embryo, and in process of development, but many readers doubtless considered such works the man's final thought. In corresponding and talking with those who knew him and his work, one realizes that shadows of images and tricks of the memory sometimes combine with facts to produce erroneous conclusions. Oral tradition has it that Huntington was unimpressive in the classroom at Yale; written communication with living members of those classes suggests he was a teacher whose thought is very much remembered. It is interesting to contemplate that half a century ago he was pondering matters including the height of buildings in St. Louis, the preservation of land in trust, salt water marshes, and some threatened creature species. He was a founding member of the Ecological Society of America, its second president, and the first of its members to persist with the term and concept, human ecology. There is much in Hunting-

ton's work that is of value to this age, and ages yet to come. It is
an important task to reveal the man and his thought as they
really were. That is the purpose of this volume.

G. J. M.

ACKNOWLEDGEMENTS

Numerous people have extended kindnesses to the author which he wishes to acknowledge. Mrs. Ellsworth Huntington granted access to her husband's papers, and was most helpful in recalling matters relating to her husband's life and work; Anna Deming and Charles Huntington, daughter and son respectively of Mr. and Mrs. Ellsworth Huntington, managed the details of archival estate, gave of their time freely in recall, and otherwise aided with a critical reading of the manuscript. Mrs. Samuel Fletcher (née Ruth Huntington) and Henry Strong Huntington, Jr., sister and brother of Ellsworth Huntington, both wrote memorable statements entitled "My Brother Ellsworth" for the author.

Many are those who have provided unwritten insights into the life and thought of the man; especially worthy of mention are Mrs. George P. (Mollie) Bakeman, Mrs. Dumont Clark, Clarence A. Mills, George W. Pierson, Karl J. Pelzer, Raye R. Platt, Samuel Van Valkenburg and Stephen S. Visher. Correspondence with Marcel Aurousseau, Richard J. Chorley, Edward R. Dewey, Thomas W. Freeman, S. Colum Gilfillan, Preston E. James, Paul Popenoe, A. Grenfell Price, Carl O. Sauer, John H. Thompson, Arnold J. Toynbee, Edward M. Weyer, and Nathaniel Weyl have been particularly helpful. John E. Chappell, Jr. read the manuscript in May, 1972, and offered valuable criticism; additionally he has corresponded with the author and discussed matters relating to the manuscript during the last six years. John K. Wright gave freely of his time to the author from April, 1965, until his death in March, 1969; his personal discussion of the work, correspondence, editorial assistance, never-failing good humor and encouragement remain deeply appreciated.

The Yale Library authorities provided a desk in the manuscript and archive library, and extended other privileges; the author's thanks are especially extended to Harry P. Harrison, Herman Kahn, David C. Maslyn, and Judith A. Schiff. The Registrar's Office and Alumni Office of Yale also extended their assistance as did numerous former students and faculty. The American Council of Learned Societies provided the funds for a visit to the Paris Geographical Society, the Royal Geographical Society, and the Bodleian Library; those societies were kind enough to grant access to their holdings (especially helpful were Pierre Delvert in Paris, and Mrs. M. B. Hughes in London).

Other institutions which have facilitated this work include the United States National Archives, Beloit College, the American Geographical Society, and the New York Public Library. Especially worthy of note has been the pastoral environment of the Southern Connecticut State College Geography Department under the stewardship of Joseph B. Hoyt. The latter has been a continuing source of encouragement and has otherwise made many helpful suggestions relative to the manuscript. Many more persons have helped with this study who cannot here be individually recognized—to all my thanks.

It has seemed especially appropriate that Arnold J. Toynbee write the foreword to a study of Ellsworth Huntington, his friend and intellectual companion.

ELLSWORTH HUNTINGTON

His Life and Thought

Chapter I

The Early Years

Simon Huntington, his wife, four sons and a daughter, left Norwich, England, for Boston, Massachusetts Bay Colony, in 1633. Simon Huntington died of smallpox before the ship reached Boston. Eight generations later on September 16, 1876, Ellsworth Huntington was born. He was the third of six children of Henry Strong and Mary Lawrence (Herbert) Huntington: Cornelia, 1872; Theresa, 1875; Ellsworth, 1876; George, 1878; Henry, 1881; and Ruth, 1882.[1]

Henry Strong Huntington had been born in New York City on July 15, 1836, where Ellsworth's grandfather, Oliver Ellsworth Huntington, was then in business. His mother, Mary Ann Strong Huntington, died of "consumption" when Henry was four years of age. He was the third of four children, each of the others dying in early infancy. After his mother's death, Henry was sent to live with his aunt, Cornelia Strong, in Norwich, Connecticut, the ancestral home of the Huntingtons. The association was a happy one, for Aunt Cornelia provided for Henry as would a mother. Attendance at the Northampton Boarding School was followed by entrance to Yale University in 1853 from which he was graduated in 1857, a member of Phi Beta Kappa. He taught for a while, endured invalidism for some months, then entered Andover Seminary where he was graduated in 1862. The following year he was ordained minister of the Congregational Church in Warner, New Hampshire, where in 1870 he married Mary Lawrence Herbert of Chicago, Illinois. Two years later he accepted a call to the First Church of Galesburg, Illinois, and remained there until called to Gorham, Maine, in 1877, where he served for ten years.

In Gorham the family lived in the parsonage some three doors and a hundred yards away from the church down a grassy slope. Ellsworth's brother, Henry, writes:[2]

> Our house was white, an excellent piece of New England architecture, with a good-sized barn a few feet from the house

3

at the rear. Back of the house and barn was charming little
Pine Hill, a gentle mound covered with pine needles under the
tall trees, providing a perfect cover for the picnics that the family occasionally had there. . . . In a very pleasant way the atmosphere in our home was religious. We always had a blessing at
meals, and after breakfast we always sat down together in the
back parlor for prayers. Each morning we read a chapter from
the Bible, each of us who had reached the age where he could
read, reading two verses in his turn in the circle. Then we sang
a hymn, then all knelt down each in front of his chair while
father led us in prayer. The time came when our oldest sister
for a few years before she went off to college would play the
music for the hymn on the piano. But we were all perfectly able
to sing without the instrument. Our hymnbook was an old collection dating from the seventies. Sunday mornings we commonly sang a hymn that began, "How calm and beautiful the
morn / That gilds the sacred tomb / Where once the crucified
was borne / and veiled in midnight gloom."

During his Gorham days Ellsworth commenced his formal
education at the local grade school. He exhibited good form in
the three R's, collected postage stamps with zeal, and displayed
remarkable initiative. He saved Judge Waterman's kittens from
drowning, on two different occasions acted promptly in dowsing
fire in the home, and once, in his father's absence, rearranged
the house guttering during a night storm when gutter water
threatened to erode completely the very terrace upon which a
part of the house rested.[3]

When Ellsworth reached the age of twelve his father resigned
from the Gorham Church and moved to Milton, one of the
wealthier suburbs of Boston, where he retained his ministry until retirement in 1907. Within a year of their arrival in Milton,
the Huntington family bought the Shaw House on Highland
Street, two-thirds of a mile from the church, in the center of
town. The dwellings in the township were widely dispersed
among trees and lawns. Mr. Huntington derived great satisfaction from his ministry, while his wife led the typical social life
of a minister's wife, with missionary groups and sewing circles
frequenting her large home.

The Congregational Church numbered some hundred families. A small proportion of the members were of independent
stock but most came from the homes of artisans and of coach-
men and other employees on the estates of the wealthy. The

richer families attended the Unitarian Church, and sent their
children to the Milton Academy, a private school. When the
head of the academy informed Ellsworth's father that he would
be able to accept the Huntington children free of charge, Mr.
Huntington said "no." He wanted his children to attend public
school, as did their church companions.

Thus did the Huntington children attend the Milton High
School, where Ellsworth did well in his studies, besides playing
on the football and baseball teams. He graduated among the
highest in his class.[4] Bible study at church and with the Christian
Endeavour Society, worthwhile table conversation, and the
earnest reading of stories selected by his father also contributed
to Ellsworth's education. On July 18, 1892, he passed the Harvard entrance examinations in elementary Greek and Latin,
French, Plane Geometry and advanced Greek and Latin. Although a Harvard career was planned (despite the traditional
Huntington preference for Yale), Ellsworth was to attend Beloit
College in Wisconsin. When he was graduated from high school
in 1893, the expenses of his intended Harvard undergraduate
study appeared too great for either himself or the family to bear,
his father's income being then only $1100 a year. But on one of
her annual visits to the Milton home Theresa Gaytes, his mother's sister, learned of the predicament and offered Ellsworth
board and lodging at her Beloit home if he would care to study
at the college there. He accepted the invitation, promised to undertake many of the chores in his aunt's house, and his father
prepared himself to honor the tuition of twelve dollars per
semester.

Beloit was settled in the late 1830s by the New England Emi-
grating Company, and, since Beloit College drew its initial faculty from Yale University, it became known as "The Yale of the
West." In the third week of September, 1893, with rather more
than one hundred other students, Huntington began his studies
on the Beloit College campus. The usual humiliation attended
the freshman class, and it may be supposed that Huntington endured a fair measure of the harassment that upper classmen
bestow upon first-year students and that leaves its mark in the
memory though not in the record. The class of '97 hung placards
in Beloit streets offering the "Freshmen's Apology":[5]

> We realizing what a scrawny illmatched verdant motley gang
> we are feel that a most sincere and humble apology is due to
> the upperclassmen especially 96 to faculty trustees alumineses

> & townspeople in general for our existence & attempting to fol-
> low the footsteps of our illustrious predecessors the class of 96
> feeling that we are still out of place among college MEN. We
> beg you to bear with us a little while longer—signed & counter-
> signed   class of '97

Enrolled as a member of the eighteen-man class of '97, in
his first semester Ellsworth took courses in Greek, Latin, Math,
Rhetoric, and Bible study, and when the term ended, on December 22, received an "A" in each of these subjects.[6] It was the
beginning of a splended undergraduate record. Weekly letters
came from his father or mother, and sometimes from a brother
or sister, or even from a combination of the whole or part of
the family. Ellsworth was a good correspondent in return, an-
swering his mother's inquiries regarding domesticities; discussing with his father matters ranging from the meaning of a Christian life, to authors of the day and the politics of the Milton
School Board (of which Mr. Huntington was a member); and
informing his brothers and sisters on college matters. The family
was distressed if Ellsworth's weekly letter did not arrive. Some
six weeks after the opening of the first semester his father wrote:[7]
"We hope such a delay will never happen again—for our boy
seems so very far off, and it brings him nearer to be sure that his
letter will come at the appointed time."

The Rev. Henry Huntington never found it necessary in the
next four years to request another letter from his son. Mr. Huntington exerted a great influence on his "Eldie." Often, he would
write on the vital importance of leading the Christian life.[8]

> Never forget, my dear son, that whatever brilliant or attractive
> qualities any fellow may have, nothing else is half so important
> as his being a sincerely practical Christian.

Ellsworth was soon active in a campus Bible society, the local
branch of the Y.M.C.A., attended church regularly, taught Sunday school for a nearby community, in addition to participating
fully in campus chapel services. Professor Sleeper helped him
with voice training as a tenor in the Beloit Choral Union. He
would receive the prayers of his father's church and, in turn,
pray for the church. The father-and-son correspondence dwelt
much on the meaning of passages from the Bible, and this, together with Bible reading and college examinations, provided

the young Huntington with a sound knowledge of the Holy Lands. As the months passed, Ellsworth began to yearn for the science course rather than his undertaken course in the classics. Correspondence with his father and careful thought and discussion with Professor George Collie preceded a decision to change his course to a more intense study in the fields of anatomy, botany, chemistry, English literature, French, geology, German, and physics. A lesser amount of time was devoted to the ancients. Perhaps, too, correspondence from a much travelled cousin, founding member of the Association of American Geographers, and a practicing geologist, Frederic Putnam Gulliver, encouraged Ellsworth to opt for the science course.

Christmas was spent pleasantly with his Aunt Theresa in Beloit, and Easter with his Aunt Martha in Galesburg. As the end of the first year approached, plans were made for him to spend some weeks with his family at Popham Beach, Maine, but there was doubt as to whether he could afford the journey. He undertook part-time duties in the 24,000 volume campus library to offset summer expenses, but still was obliged to write that he might have to remain in Beloit that summer. His father offered him a job chopping a cord of wood, his brother George offered him the care of the local church, and Deacon Tucker could be counted on to have him drive his wagon occasionally, but it was not until Ellsworth was nominated by the Christian Endeavour Society of Milton as their delegate to the 13th International Convention of Christian Endeavour to meet in Cleveland, 1894, that his expenses were met and homecoming was assured. An August at home and with the family at Arnold Cottage, Popham Beach, followed a three-day stay at the Cleveland convention.

The return of Ellsworth to Wisconsin in the September of '94 inaugurated a more positive study of science under Professor G. L. Collie. The college did not offer any geography courses but from the geology classes at Beloit there had emerged Thomas C. Chamberlin (class of 1866) and Rollin D Salisbury (class of 1887). Ellsworth studied under men who have left their mark in their respective fields: Edward Eaton, History; Joseph Emerson, Greek; William Porter, Latin; Rev. Henry Whitney, Rhetoric and English; Thomas Smith, Math and Physics; Erastus Smith, Chemistry and Mineralogy; Rev. Almon Burr, Pedagogics; Charles Bacon, Astronomy. Hard study, continued service to Aunt Theresa, fifteen hours a week in the library, typing for thirty-five cents an hour Saturday afternoons

and evenings, Bible study and teaching, together with family
correspondence encouraged his father to write,[9] "remember that
recreation also is one of God's laws, and by a proper amount of
it you achieve more good work in the end." After failing to win
a place on the Glee Club, Ellsworth practiced the mile run. A
third place in a college mile event later encouraged his mother
to write,[10] "I do not believe in this violent exercise of running.
It is too hard upon the action of the heart." And again,[11] "Do
not run too hard. Blood vessels have been broken and hearts too
by such violent exercise." Later the young Huntington was to
turn to gymnastics, where he hurt a wrist and broke his nose.

He was very slight of build. His mother had so much trouble
buying him underwear and gloves that would fit that she once
proclaimed that Ellsworth's grandfather should have been a
larger man! She often wrote to her son,[12] "as to your growing—
a wise use of sleep, recreation, work and food will help you in
general development." Nevertheless he was fit and had a constitution that served him wonderfully well in the field throughout
his career. As a young boy he had been bedded by measles in
the Gorham epidemic, the winter of 1887–1888. Not until 1917
did he again go to bed on account of sickness, and then it was
for half a day while thousands were dying of influenza.[13]

Early in 1895 it was made known that the trustees of the
College had unanimously voted to receive women into the college, beginning in the September of that year. The Old Beloit
had disappeared, and the New Beloit was born. There were some
among the alumni and friends of Beloit who were doubtful about
the wisdom of this step, and Huntington wondered whether he
should remain or attend one of the Eastern colleges. His father
advised that he stay:[14]

> A large Eastern college offers some great advantages, but these
> are largely balanced by the opportunity you have at a smaller
> college for more intimate acquaintance with the professors, and
> the larger share which each individual student has in all which
> is going on in the life of the college.

The campus did have a family air about it: students called
faculty members by their first names, and faculty gave the students generously of their time. Perhaps Ellsworth's father was
also influenced in his judgment by his relationship with Edward
Eaton, President of Beloit College, for they were both Yale
alumni and had maintained their acquaintanceship through meet-

ings of the American Board of Commissioners for Foreign Missions in Boston. President Eaton assured Mr. Huntington that he was well satisfied with Ellsworth's progress.

Ellsworth remained at Beloit, residing with the Gaytes family until his graduation in 1897. Semester after semester he concentrated upon his course work, maintaining carefully kept notebooks for each of his courses. His essays attest to a pleasing vocabulary and sense of composition: those extant include "The Migration of Birds," "What will the Republican Party do?," "Giraldus Cambrensis," "The Profit of High Wages," "Competition in the Production of Grain," "The Pulpit as a Teacher in Rhetoric and Oratory," and two without titles. Even his swiftly taken notes were well written, and his felicity of expression won him a place on the college yearbook staff, *The Codex*, and some part time work with *The Round Table*, the longest-established college paper in the country. He began a diary but he did not maintain it throughout his Beloit days. Later he was to become an avid diarist.

During 1896 he developed an interest in roads. He began to accumulate literature on the subject and wrote to his parents of his intention to make a career in this field. Before his graduation Professor Collie "set him at the problem of road building materials of the Rock River Valley,"[15] for Collie had become associated with the Wisconsin Geological Survey (founded in '97) and had become interested in the subject.[16] He and Ellsworth spent considerable time on the study while the latter was still at Beloit, including the summer of 1897. "Experiments with Available Roadmaking Material of Southern Wisconsin," was the title of a paper which Ellsworth wrote and Collie delivered before the Wisconsin Academy of Sciences; printed in the *Transactions of the Academy*, it was Huntington's first publication.[17]

As his undergraduate college career drew to a close, Ellsworth sought employment. Positions with the Massachusetts Highway Commission, the Boston Metropolitan Water System Works, and a school system near Beloit, were the subjects of correspondence which led to nought. He greatly desired a change in his life and wanted most earnestly to travel; as he wrote his father in February, 1897:[18]

> What I want to do is to go abroad, not to Europe but to Africa or South America or Asia, some part of the world where everything is different. I have always thought that to travel through the heart of Africa would be the best possible way to spend a

year. I do not propose anything as radical as that, but what I really want to do next year is to get some sort of a position in some far off land like those I have mentioned. . . . I do not think that I shall ever be satisfied to settle down to work until I have been to some of the *very* foreign lands of the earth. I am willing to wait and see Europe at any time within the next fifty years but the uncivilized parts of the world are more attractive.

His father was sympathetic:[19]

Now what can be done? I learned on Monday that Professor Chas. Hitchcock, of Dartmouth College, (Prof. of Geology) is planning an expedition to Greenland this coming season. (Does that sound rather frigid?!) I know nothing about the particulars, but have written to him, telling about you. How should you like that, if a place can be found for you, where you could earn at least your board? Prof. Hitchcock is an old friend of mine,— and a cousin, you know, of your Grandmama Huntington.

Other letters by his father to Elijah Morse, Representative in Congress, and to Professor Dunning, teacher of Semitic Languages at Yale, were futile, but reassuringly his father added "I shall have the matter constantly in mind, and do all I can." Thus it was that Ellsworth was graduated without knowing his future course. Unable to attend the graduation exercises himself owing to his obligations to his church, his father insisted that Ellsworth's mother attend the ceremony. After members of the family had raised a fund to pay her fare, Mrs. Huntington saw her son awarded a Bachelor of Arts degree with the fiftieth graduating class in the history of Beloit College. Professor Collie later wrote that Ellsworth[20] "took high rank as a student here, especially in science. At graduation he ranked among the first scholars of his class."

As the days after his graduation passed in Milton, Ellsworth prepared the wood pile for the coming winter, plowed the garden, and spent much time with his road-building interest. He thought that a stone crusher should be located "opposite the foot of Highland Street" close to the reservation. Mr. Henry Helm Clayton of the Blue Hill Observatory introduced him to the science of meteorology. A geologist friend, Arthur Tucker, and the State Geologist, L. W. Page, came to investigate his suggestions on the matter of road building and the gathering of needed materials. A geological survey of the section was recommended by the State Geologist and samples of diabase and diorite were sent to Cambridge to be tested.

On September 24 Ellsworth received a letter from James Barton, corresponding secretary of the American Board of Commissioners for Foreign Missions, definitely offering him a position as assistant to the President of Euphrates College, Harpoot, Turkey. The date of leaving was undecided but it was to be prior to October 15. Four days later on September 28 Ellsworth received a telegram from Beloit College: "Beloit sends you to Harpoot with Enthusiasm and earnest Godspeed. Edward D. Eaton."

The missionary board which appointed Ellsworth, knew of the Huntington family. Missionaries sponsored by the Board had frequently spoken or led prayer meetings at the Huntington home. Furthermore, Cyrus Hamlin, founder of Robert College in Turkey, frequented the Beloit campus and knew the Huntingtons and Ellsworth personally. Beloit had a special commitment to missionary work abroad. It was not by chance alone that Ellsworth was destined for Harpoot. Beloit College was pleased to send another missionary to far lands and announced in *The Congregationalist*:[21]

> A good deal of enthusiasm is felt in the college over the appointment of Mr. Ellsworth Huntington of the class of '97, as an assistant of Dr. Gates in the Euphrates College. At Beloit $300 have been raised toward his support. He is a young man of unusually well-rounded character and mental attainments, strong as a student of the classics and of physical science.

Ellsworth had first mentioned the possibility of a post with a mission school in Turkey in a letter to his parents of March, 1897, but the matter had rested until early in September when the American Board of Commissioners for Foreign Missions asked if he could undertake the work if so requested. Evidently Mr. Huntington was quite sure that his son was destined for Harpoot, for on September 16, Ellsworth's twenty-first birthday, he wrote on behalf of the family:

Dear Ellsworth,
    On your 21st birthday we all send you a great deal of love,

and every possible good wish. We also desire to aid in enlarging your *views* of life. The means of doing this are not now at hand but if you will step into Mr. John H. Thurston's, 50 Bromfield Street, and choose a camera which does not cost more than our fortune we should be delighted to pay for it.

Lovingly yours,
All the Family

P.S. Views of *Turks* and *Koords* should be taken at a distance of half a mile.

On the same day, September 16, Ellsworth made a resolve in his diary:[22]

Today is my twenty-first birthday and I have decided to begin now and keep a careful journal of important things that I do, see, and learn. I also mean to keep a regular diary of the events of each day in a separate volume.

Before departing Milton, Ellsworth secured information relating to the geology of Asia Minor from Professor Dale of the United States Geological Survey, blasted some rock locally to obtain samples of road metal, and visited his brother George at Williams College. He then purchased a barometer, thermometers, and enough blanks to maintain a meteorological record of Harpoot for his three intended years, completed his correspondence, and applied for a passport.

On October 7, 1897, he said farewell to his mother, Theresa, and Ruth at the hearth of the home. His father, Cornelia and Henry journeyed to the railway station and saw him aboard the 8:00 P.M. train bound for Montreal.

CHAPTER II

Euphrates College, Harpoot[1]

The next morning, Friday, October 8, Huntington breakfasted in the Richelieu House, Montreal. This was the first visit to a foreign country in a life later renowned for far-ranging and significant travel. He visited the Windsor Hotel in the hope of locating some other members of the group bound for Asia Minor under the auspices of the American Board. He rode the street cars, "wandered around a while and spent half an hour at the Bon Secours Market," took three pictures in order to test his camera, and after meeting the other seven members of the group retired for the night on board the steamship *Labrador*. The next day the *Labrador* sailed to Quebec, allowed the passengers a brief time ashore, then forged its way across an autumnal Atlantic with a human cargo eighty strong. The boat put in at Moville on the Irish coast, October 18; then traversed the Irish Sea within viewing distance of the Isle of Man to dock in Liverpool. The train journey to London took four and a half hours, and was interrupted only by a ten-minute stop at Crewe. Huntington enjoyed the English countryside:[2]

> The greenness and the wetness impress me, and the sheep feeding here and there give a distant tone to the scene. The fields are all beautifully drained and everything looks old . . . it is beautiful. . . .

But frequent ministerings to Mrs. Chambers' children encouraged him to write "travelling with such a party does not give much opportunity to see the country." Ellsworth saw much of London from the top of an omnibus: "I have been past St. Pauls, the Bank, Trafalgar Square, along the Strand, Fleet Street, etc., and in fact begin to feel a good deal acquainted with the center of London." He spent two days in the big city, "purchased copies of Geikie's Geology and Zittel's Palaeontology," and sufficient clothing for his journey to Harpoot, since his trunk had been mislaid in Liverpool. On October 22 the party left

London, journeying via Chatham to Queenborough "where we took the steamer for Flushing." Thence by train the party travelled to Vienna, Buda-Pesth, Belgrade, and Sophia to the Balkan Mountains. Four days after departing London the mission party crossed the Turkish frontier.

Another customs search at Constantinople relieved Ellsworth of further property, "three or four books and some photoplates were taken out of my bag, and it is doubtful whether I shall ever see them again." His trunk had not been forwarded to Constantinople as had been supposed. He was given "some goods from the relief supply to tide over the time till my trunk shall come, blankets, shirts, overcoat, stockings, etc., all new save the coat." After a few hours at the Bible house in Constantinople, Ellsworth joined another mission group journeying into eastern Turkey. The party boarded the French S.S. *Guardiana*, which sailed the party through the Bosporus and into Samsoon the next day. Here memories of the warmth and brightness of his family came to him in contrast to the stark reality and poverty and disease that he now beheld. It was his first experience of this order. "As I stood in my cold bare room before supper, looking out into the darkness and rain I felt more homesick and alone than ever before. It seemed such a hopeless, cheerless task to try to do anything for these poor wretches . . ." In three wagons the party journeyed to Marsovan where Huntington stayed three days with missionaries Mr. and Mrs. Edward Riggs. On the morning of Tuesday, November 9, he boarded a springless cart called an araba, which "on a Turkish road is not a pleasant mode of conveyance." The journey from Marsovan to Harpoot was to take sixteen days, though only thirteen of them were spent in travelling. A Harpootlee, Khachadoor, drove the araba fourteen hours a day through plains and over mountains in inclement weather and gave Huntington his first lessons in the Armenian language, "but the noise and jolting of the araba make it difficult." A three-day rest with missionaries at Sivas enabled him to purchase a spirited horse which he named Mardin, after the town where he bought it. The journey was resumed, the same daily round of events repeating itself, "your morning meal is taken from 3 to 7 A.M. and from that time till 6 P.M. you eat nothing but a lunch which is carried in the pocket." At night three to six hours sleep was taken in a Khan. Always at the Khan, foreigner Huntington would be much discussed, especially his hat. Accordingly he would pass his hat around, reporting, "the gilt trademark seemed to make a great impression." On Thursday, November 25, by starting early in the morning, leaving the wagon to come at its own speed, and riding vigorously, he was able to reach Harpoot in time to take Thanksgiving supper with President Gates and the Barnum family, of Euphrates College. The journey provided him with a rude, but honest, introduction to the circumstances of his life for the next four years. He later wrote an account of his journey entitled, "On the Road in Turkey," and sent it to the editor of the Beloit College *Round Table*, where it appeared in two installments of the college publication during February, 1898.[3]

Euphrates College was financed and founded in 1880 by the American Board of Commissioners for Foreign Missions.[4] Initially the institution was named Armenia College, but the name proved offensive to the Turkish Government. Since the college was located only ten miles from the Euphrates River, the institution was renamed Euphrates College. The missionary board had established numerous schools throughout eastern Turkey which sent students to the college. Yet bitterness between the Turks and the Armenians seriously hindered the work. Periodic massacres occurred, and one took place at Harpoot during 1895. The Turks and Koords killed many Harpootlees and fired several of the college buildings. Numerous martini bullet holes attested the event. Within three weeks of the attack the college had been reopened, and student numbers began to increase. The President of the College, Caleb F. Gates, sought a younger man to help him administer the college. The senior member of the staff, Dr. Barnum, was nearing the age of retirement, and neither lady missionary teachers nor Armenian teachers suited President Gates' need. Hence Gates appealed to the missionary board and his alma mater, Beloit College, for someone to help him. It was to serve as assistant to the President, as well as to be an instructor, that Huntington travelled to Euphrates College, 700 students and 20 faculty strong in 1897.

Harpoot, capital of a province by that same name, clustered about the base of an ancient castle built on a mountainside at an elevation of 4,500 feet above sea level. The castle dominated the city, with rocks rising precipitously from 30 to 300 feet, the whole surrounded by a thick wall, 40 feet in height. Huntington described the place thus:[5]

A city of 20,000 inhabitants grew up near the top of a steep mountain with no room to expand and no fitness for the conditions of modern life. It is like dozens of other Turkish cities which have grown large in narrow valleys, on steep mountainsides, or even on the tops of mountains. Now Harpoot is losing its wealth and influence which are being transferred to a thriving town of 6,000 people on the plain far below. Mezereh is the seat of government and is the center of a growing trade. Harpoot has some advantages. 'A city that is set on a hill cannot be hid,' and the inhabitants of such a city are blessed with a glorious view. From almost every house the Taurus Mts. fifteen or twenty miles away across the smooth plain are clearly in sight, and the air is always good as soon as one gets away from the foul odors of the streets. In winter the plain is often covered for weeks with a cold benumbing fog while Harpoot on its mountain top rejoices in brilliant sunshine. For a college or for residences the situation is eminently satisfactory.

A town typical of Asiatic Turkey, Harpoot was isolated, poor, abounding in squalor and disease, and inhabited by Turks, Koords, Armenians and Syrians. Dozens of wild street dogs, flat roofs of mud houses, and the sound of a Turkish song, "minor and yet sung in a nasal falsetto and sounding like the wail of a ghost mixed with the voice of an auctioneer," characterized the settlement. Work and travel challenged Huntington, not any supposed charm attaching to Harpoot: "Just now the stillness of the night was broken by a few sweet clear notes from some brave bird that dares to make its home in this city of dirt and ignorance and sin." But it was there that Huntington was to labor for the next four years. As assistant to President Gates, he was obliged to make decisions whenever the latter was absent on matters ranging from insubordination, holidays, the hiring of teachers, the ordering of books, the giving of a party, to the curriculum. The post carried much responsibility. When the matron of the girls school lay dying, Dr. Ussher, the medic of the college, asked Huntington to help him in his work.

Ellsworth taught English and the Christian religion to students who varied considerably in age and ability. He made them write many essays, which he would correct, noting in his diary, for example, that "one boy got stuck and so wrote a 'moral' which began, 'Everyman has his own roar.' Another spoke of the 'bleak mountain tops where no insect murmurs and flies can fly.' " Ellsworth also taught geology and geography to some of his pupils. For the geology class he used Ralph Tarr's *Elementary Geology*. Whenever possible he found local examples to replace Tarr's, which were so frequently drawn from North America. He made a list of these examples in his geology notebook, and with them taught what may well have been the first modern geology course in Asiatic Turkey.[6] An entry in his diary for December 11, 1898, reads:[7] "In the evening I looked over a number of geography textbooks with a view to choosing one for the use of the Armenian boys whom I am teaching in that study"; to this end he read John Murray's *Handbook for Travellers in Asia Minor* and George A. Smith's *Historical Geography of The Holy Land*. He also noted with enthusiasm of a modest college library appropriation: ". . . this year we use half of it in buying Élisée Réclus' great work on geography. I ordered the book a month or more ago. . . . It is without question the greatest geographical work ever published." It was a task demanding much care and patience, for the work was never ending. Teachers and staff were constantly in demand. Thus in November, 1898, Ellsworth's sister Theresa arrived in Harpoot to aid the Christian Endeavour work, and to help in the girls' section of the college. Nearly two years later in the summer of 1900 Ellsworth's brother George was to graduate from Williams College and accept an appointment as tutor in Robert College, Constantinople.

Ellsworth derived much satisfaction from his students' progress. He read to them from books of his own choosing, and gave considerable time to Bible instruction. This work was undertaken largely in the morning and early afternoon. Later in the afternoon Ellsworth would take "Geography rides, Geology walks and Botany trips" or go riding with Mr. Barnum or President Gates. While on these local outings he was confronted by an Asiatic poverty which he had not previously witnessed. In his thinking he began to seek ways in which the veil of economic poverty might be lifted, governmental inadequacy overcome, and personal deceit and hypocrisy eliminated. He was particularly concerned with the lack of authority displayed by the government: "the fact is the Turkish government does not govern." This concern preoccupied him the whole time he was at Harpoot. He saw coal deposits but was disappointed to find they were not being exploited. He searched for other minerals whose exploitation might strengthen the economy.[8]

The marble and the quartz syenite may be of value as building stones but they have not been tested. The sandstone is generally poor but west of Pillar there is a dark colored hard variety which seems to be quite durable and fit for building purposes. Good brick clay is found and is especially valuable in a country where wood is as scarce and poor as it is in central Turkey.

His road-building interest was still upon him:[9]

The basalt will be of great value since its proximity enables good and permanent roads to be made at comparatively small cost. An inexhaustible and cheap supply of the best kind of road metal is a potent tho usually unrecognized source of wealth, to a community.

He thought about the possibilities of irrigation to extend crop acreage, and about the matter of controlling the Euphrates and turning its power to the advantage of Asia Minor. "All my spare time this week has been spent in trying to write an article about the utilization of the Euphrates river by making dams. . . ." To that end he read works concerning irrigation on the Nile and the Ganges. On his afternoon or Sunday journeyings Huntington would take delight in beholding[10]

the beauty of this world in which God has put us. In the background were the mountains, clad like Turkish beggars. Their feet are bare and the clothes around the lower leg are merely strips of ragged cloth which hang from the garments farther up like a coarse fringe. The upper garments are very full of holes to be sure, but the number of holes grows less as you get up to the shoulder although they are found even there. But the head is sure to be warmly wrapped up. It is only fair to the mountains to say that their clothes are white and clean which is never the case with beggars.

References abound in his diaries to the beauty of nature, often described at length. His preference for nature untouched by the hand of man prompted him to observe:[11]

There the ruined houses and a hideous cemetery made one glad to look away to the work of God. If I had no work to do I should become a sort of civilized savage, wandering always, be it far or near, for the sake of some new sight of beauty or of ugliness, or some new adventure.

His desire for travel and adventure was to be well satisfied during later summer vacations. Until then, limited journeyings were accomplished in the afternoon. In the evening there came dinner, after which President Gates might read to some of the teachers for half an hour. "The book in hand now is Henry Van Dyke's Little Rivers." The American teachers would gather, always on Tuesday, but sometimes two or three times a week, and hold prayer meetings Quaker style, in which no one led, but all participated. They were very intense meetings and frequently inspired Ellsworth to search his Bible for a particular verse or thought that had come to him as a result of the prayer meeting. "They are the most genuine meetings with God that I ever had part in. There is a good deal in the Quaker way of holding meetings."[12] The meetings were an important part of his life at the college. They revealed the Bible to him and provided a sense of the antiquity of the life around him. A flute played by ragged shepherd boys on the mountain sides inspired the reflection, "it is the same flute that Virgil's shepherds played, the tent and the flocks are doubtless like Abraham's."

Following the evening prayer meeting Ellsworth would retire and read any one of the numerous books he purchased via the mission board agent in Boston, or write letters to his family, President Eaton, Professor Collie, or perhaps the Christian Endeavor Society in Beloit. But such evening activity was hampered by the inadequacy of candle light. Ellsworth did lead the college boys in prayer, but was obliged to accept the services of an interpreter. Not satisfied with that arrangement, he decided to hold services in Armenian.[13]

> I have spent two hours a day or more on it since last Sunday. First I decided to read James 1:1-8 and spent two hours in acquiring the ability to read it in Armenian. Then I looked up a lot of verses and wrote out what I intended to say in English.

His knowledge of Armenian improved rapidly and soon he was able to lead services in that language without a labored preparation. This knowledge and a more limited knowledge of Turkish were to prove very useful to him in the years ahead.

When Huntington or any missionary teacher from the College travelled to a local or distant village, the native population would expect that individual to preach. This encouraged Huntington to write:[14]

> I never felt myself called to be a preacher, but the fact that I am connected with a missionary school makes the people think that I can preach. When I go to a village I commonly hold a service on Sunday because it does seem to encourage and help the people. All the people call me Badvelly, a title which for myself I very much dislike and some add the Turkish title of respect so that my name becomes Badvelly Effendi Mr. Huntington which means literally Rev. Lord Mr. Huntington. I told them that I am not a Badvelly, but they said, "What can we call you? Your name is hard."

While in Harpoot, Huntington began scientific inquiries. He kept notes of local journeys, thus partially satisfying a thirst for exploration, and in January, 1899, he wrote a paper entitled "The Geology of the Harpoot Group of Mountains in Asiatic Turkey." Rewritten in October, 1889, and again in May, 1900, it was sent to Professor Collie in Beloit and to his father in Milton with a request for suggestions for its improvement. The article seemed not to have been published, but it did provide Huntington with an exercise in reducing to simple language the complexity of what he found in the field. He maintained a regular meteorological station at the college long before an official station was sanctioned in eastern Turkey, and was probably the first person to measure the annual rainfall of Harpoot. In a letter to Professor G. L. Collie of Beloit Huntington wrote:[15] "From December 1, 1897, to December 1, 1898, the rainfall was 15.67 inches at Harpoot." Additionally he induced other people to establish stations in eastern Turkey and maintain weather records. On the basis of such meteorological study he published two articles in the *Monthly Weather Review*, to which he subscribed, "Electric Phenomena in the Euphrates Valley"[16] and "The Climate of Harpoot, Turkey,"[17]

In the summer of 1899 Huntington met C. F. Lehmann, Professor of Ancient History in the University of Berlin, who with W. Belck had been sent as the German Archeological and Geographical Expedition to Armenia. The expedition had been planned for 1895, but had been prevented by the massacre and unrest of that year. Lehmann stayed at the American mission, Harpoot, and became a good friend of Huntington. Although Huntington had a working knowledge of German, the two men spoke English, as Lehmann had been a graduate student at Johns Hopkins University. Lehmann sought to date the succession of Chaldee, Scythian, Armenian, Roman, and Arab in eastern Turkey by archaeological evidence. Huntington helped Lehmann assemble his instruments and journeyed with him, searching for castles and other old buildings, taking photographs, making "squeezes" of inscriptions, or sketching them, sometimes with the aid of field glasses. Lehmann's associate, W. Belck, studied ruins near Lake Van. Huntington was fascinated with his first real encounter with practical archaeology and read some of Ritter on the subject:[18] "Ritter sent Schultz who collected 40 inscriptions in 1828. Schultz was murdered by Koords and the work ended till Belck came in 1891. Next expedition was by Belck and Lehmann planned for 1895 but massacres prevented." Huntington and Lehmann journeyed to many an ancient fortification and were well satisfied with their accomplishments. Additionally, with the aid of a sextant, aneroid barometer, a 4¼-inch surveyor's compass fitted with a small telescope, and a pocket azimuth compass, the elevation of 236 locations was established in the vicinity of Harpoot and many soundings of Lake Goljeuk were taken. Resulting from this work were a map of Harpoot that was more accurate than the only existing map (that of Kiepert) and an essay, "The History of Lake Goljeuk, with a brief account of its early connection with the Euphrates and Tigris Rivers." Some months later Lehmann wrote to the corresponding secretary of Harvard University:[19]

I was struck and deeply impressed by the scientific earnestness and ardour, the great desire of study and the faculty and capacity of methodic work developed and exhibited by Mr. Huntington. These qualities are combined with a skill of handling and getting at the bottom of scientific instruments and their scheme, which far exceeds the average abilities of young scientists, and with a good and most noble character.

He helped me to get in order my scientific instruments some of which he had never seen. He managed to determine latitudes with our sextant in an astonishingly short time and, though geologist and scientist by study and inclination, he took a most profound interest in the historical and archeological purposes of our expedition. He gave me valuable hints as to ancient localities which he had noticed on his geological excursions even then, and since I left Charpoot he wrote me three long letters, full of most valuable information.

Later in the summer, after Lehmann had left Turkey, the English Consul, Jones, financed an expedition to Lake Goljeuk to unravel the lake's history. Huntington accepted an invitation to join the party, learned more history of the lake and became well acquainted with the English Consul. In the autumn of 1899 Huntington began to make plans for the following year. He expected to remain a missionary but wished to study geology for two years and then "the various branches of pedagogy, psychology" for another two years. Huntington believed that Christian educators rather than theologians were needed in Turkey. To that end he decided to apply for a scholarship at Harvard University which would enable him to study geology. He wrote to Professor Collie,[20] "I wish to apply for a fellowship in geology and I want to ask you to apply for me as Turkey is so far away and letters are so long in passing to and fro. If I can get a fellowship, well; if not, I will earn my way. I should prefer to go to Harvard."

An application was duly submitted to Harvard and his father secured testimonials on his behalf, but the fellowship was not forthcoming. Nevertheless, Huntington would probably have gone to Harvard to study geology, had not the Turkish Government given President Gates permission to erect buildings needed since the destruction of 1895. Enrollments were increasing substantially, no new faculty had been added and the Barnums were planning to travel in Europe for six months on a well-earned furlough. Hence the Trustees of the College did not wish to see Huntington leave and persuaded him to remain at Euphrates College and aid with the work.

In April 1901 Huntington satisfied a great desire to travel through the canyons of the Euphrates and map the river's course. Eighteen months previously, in October, 1899, he had written to Collie:[21]

I have been on horseback from a point 15 miles west of Palu to Perteg. Where the river passes thro the mountains the road is almost impassable and much of the way west of Perteg there is no road. Every winter and spring when the water is high the people of Akhore float down the river on inflated skins fishing as they go. Akhore, which means stable, is at the end of the plain N.E. of Harpoot. From there to Perot takes 8 or 10 days. At the latter place they deflate the skins and pack the fish for carriage to the market at Harpoot. If I took the trip I could almost complete the map of the bend of the Euphrates. The difficulty will be that the fishermen will be afraid to take me for fear something will happen and they will get into trouble. If, to satisfy the fishermen, I ask for a zaptieh the government will be very suspicious of such an unheard-of pleasure-trip.

The only European reported to have made such a journey was the German general, Von Moltke, in 1838. Since that time the natives claimed boulders had filled stretches of the river, making any such journey impossible. Huntington read an account of Von Moltke's journey, gathered as much information as possible concerning the fishermen who floated down parts of the Euphrates on inflated sheepskins in the manner reported by Xenophon, then persuaded the American Consul, Thomas H. Norton, to accompany him on the journey. On April 12 Huntington, Consul Norton, the consul's orderly—"bristling with knives and pistols"—Bedros (Peter), and Hohaness (John) embarked on their journey. Twenty-eight inflated sheepskins (soaked overnight to render them pliable) were secured in three rows and tied to a framework of young saplings and rope, and after a parting prayer,

a wise precaution in view of future events . . . the raft swung out into the powerful current of midstream . . . the buoyant skins and pliant saplings adapted themselves to every movement of the ever-changing waves without the slighest jar. It seemed the easiest, most idyllic mode of travel that man has ever devised.[22]

Travelling at three to five miles per hour, fourteen inches above the surface of a Euphrates in low water, Huntington viewed birds of a sort unknown to him, blue pigeons, gazelles, gorges and canyons towering 3,000 feet overhead in limestone and marble that dwarfed the raft, several dozen rapids "where the waves are like ocean white caps," rock throwing red-haired Koords, fortresses and a variety of ruins, and water beneath the sheepskins sometimes shallow enough to send rocks through a

Afloat on the Euphrates

skin and at times "as deep as a minaret." At night the group would pull their raft onto a rock ledge and perhaps sleep there, or they might seek the nearest village, if the inhabitants seemed not unfriendly. In the morning they might roast a lamb for breakfast. "Hat-wearer" Huntington mystified natives by writing in his diary, by "bringing long journeys close" (and the viewer's feet, too) with his field glasses, and by daring to negotiate rapids for the sake of the journey alone. He had gathered on board the raft the apparatus he needed to make useful observation:[23]

> The middle of the kelek is occupied by my tripod with compass above and watch hanging below. I record the direction, time, rate of movement, geological formation on both sides, tributaries, villages, rapids, and any thing else that comes to hand. It keeps me pretty busy.

The raft floated 190 miles down the Euphrates, making a total descent of 1250 feet in thirty-seven hours of river travel. Actually the journey took seven days. Huntington was able to determine speeds of travel for given parts of the journey, the rate of descent, and the number of rapids, their location and ferocity. He announced later that "the map as given by Von Moltke needs considerable modification," and assembled the data for a good map, which he later drew. He made notes instantly, allowed diary narrative to wait at most forty-eight hours, was uncommonly well equipped with apparatus, and was able to replace a prismatic compass after losing one as the kellek whirled through a rapid. He took many photographs which he later used to illustrate essays on the journey. Norton and Huntington also found time to make careful study of numerous Hittite ruins during the journey. At Gerger the two men visited a castle begun by the Hittites, occupied by the Greeks and Romans, and finished by the Saracens. There they were surrounded by armed Koords "who stood around and commented in low tones." As Huntington superintended the dig to uncover Greek and Arabic inscriptions, numerous Koords shot at the inscriptions from the castle gate. They had decided that the "hat wearers" were searching for gold, and so were destroying some inscriptions to prevent the strangers finding any more gold. At journey's end Huntington and Norton rode back over the snowy tops of the mountains on their horses, sent to Morfa by prior arrangement; on finally

reaching Harpoot the two explorers were met by acclaiming vil-
lagers who had heard of their accomplishment.

At Euphrates College Huntington pursued his map making
interests. He was quite persuaded that an accurate map of the
country, or any part of it, would augur well for economic development.

> As usual there is a half finished map on my drawing board. As
> before the subject is the vicinity of Harpoot but the present map
> is on a larger scale and contains much more detail. . . . Map
> making becomes more and more interesting with every succes-
> sive map. The definite purpose of this one is to illustrate a thesis
> on the igneous rocks of the Harpoot Mts. which may possibly
> be written three or four years from now, perhaps as evidence
> of qualification for the degree of Ph.D.[24]

Major Maunsell of the British War Office learned of Huntington's map work through the British Consul in Turkey. He paid
Huntington fifteen pounds for a copy of his Harpoot map. Later
he paid ten pounds for a more detailed map of the same area,
then offered him one hundred pounds for three-months work
mapping the Euphrates and the Dersim. Yet Huntington would
not accept the latter offer as he felt "missionaries must not involve themselves in matters of a political character."

Only a few weeks after his journey down the Euphrates Huntington received word that he had been awarded a Harvard University Townsend Scholarship for the year 1901–1902. Mr.
Huntington had renewed his son's application at Harvard and
had submitted Ellsworth's essays "The History of Lake Goljeuk"
and "The Geology of the Harpoot Group of Mountains in Asiatic Turkey" to Harvard's corresponding secretary Richard
Cobb. Additionally Consul Norton had written a letter to Professor F. W. Putnam of Harvard on Huntington's behalf.[25]
Otherwise the application stood as it had been made in 1900,
with testimonials by Messrs. Barton, Collie, Eaton, Gates, Lehmann, and Teele. This time the application had been submitted
to Harvard earlier in the year and additional evidences strengthened his application. Huntington was delighted at the prospect.
The Trustees of Euphrates College, extremely reluctant to lose
Huntington's services, telegraphed him in the first week of June
requesting that he stay another year, but Huntington was anxious for Harvard and geology.[26] Following college commencement, on June 27 he rode to Marsovan where he met his brother

George, and they spent the next ten weeks travelling "the valleys of six rivers, four flowing to the Black Sea and two to the Persian Gulf," concluding "there can scarcely be a doubt that at a very recent period the whole of Asia Minor, at least as far west as Yazgat was submerged."[27]

Early in September he bade farewell to his friends at Harpoot and journeyed to Trebizond. There he reflected on his stay in Asia Minor, recalled the gardens, the flowers and the fruits which he had enjoyed so much on his walks, and entered in his diary:[28]

> This land had a strange strange fascination. For ten weeks I had been traveling almost without stop. Often the roads were hard and there were many difficulties with men and nature that try one's soul to the bottom, yet as I looked back at those high blue mountains and the green valleys I almost wanted to turn back and see what else there is that lies behind them. I think I shall come back to the Orient. I cannot help it. It has seized hold of me.

Leaving Trebizond he took ship through the Bosporus to Constantinopole, where he attended a memorial service for the recently assassinated President McKinley; then he proceeded via Eastern Romania, Cracow, and Breslau to Berlin. Encouraged by his father "to obtain a glimpse of the best things men have done in education, art, agriculture, city building" in Europe even at the expense of missing some of the Harvard semester, Huntington stayed one week in Berlin. He attended the Wagner opera, studied statues, visited zoological gardens, and gave considerably of his time to the New Museum where he especially enjoyed "the Egyptian rooms" and "the collection of Peruvian and Mexican antiquities." A swift visit to Potsdam was followed by a three-day stay with the family of C. F. Lehmann in Hamburg. There at Lehmann's request Huntington edited the letters he had sent to him. Lehmann then translated them into German and had them published by the Berlin Anthropological Society.[29] Two days later Huntington arrived in London, where he visited the British Museum, twice met with Major Maunsell, and as a result wrote in his diary:[30]

> [He] wants me to write up our trip down the Euphrates and the scientific part of what I write about Germany and Russia in Turkey and send it to the Royal Geographical Society. I think

that I shall do so. He took me to call on Mr. Scott–Keltie, the Secretary of the Society.

Huntington purchased a copy of *The Great Ice Age and Its Relation to the Antiquity of Man* by James Geikie, in order "to have something to read on ship-board." That book was his introduction to the study of climatic change, a subject in which he later became one of the world's authorities. With hurried glimpses of Cambridge, Leicester, and Liverpool, he departed England aboard the S.S. *Saxonia* on October 15, and returned to Boston and Harvard University, where fall classes had already started.

On March 23, 1903, Huntington received a letter from J. Scott Keltie, Secretary to the Royal Geographical Society.

It gives me pleasure to inform you that the Council have awarded you the "Gill Memorial" this year for your work on the Euphrates. The value of the Memorial is about £35. This you can have in the form of a cheque, or if you prefer, it may take the form of a watch, or instrument, or piece of plate, with a suitable inscription. Please let me know your wishes in the matter.

Chapter III

Harvard, William Morris Davis, and Raphael Pumpelly

Huntington left Harpoot determined to learn more of science in order to better understand the Asia Minor he had travelled over the past four years. He had enrolled at Harvard and was soon to know the Harvard Yard in its "golden age." Poet-scientist Nathaniel Southgate Shaler, with William Morris Davis, Thomas A. Jaggar, Robert DeC. Ward, Robert T. Jackson, and Jay B. Woodworth, provided some of the finest courses in geology and physical geography in the country. There he came particularly under the influence of Davis.

On landing in the United States Huntington made a hurried visit to his home, but could spend only a little time with his family. Harvard had commenced its fall term. He took a room in the home of Mr. and Mrs. Corney at 54 Concord Avenue, within walking distance of the Harvard Yard. Room and board at the Corneys was provided for seven dollars per week and was financed by the Townsend Scholarship, which had been awarded him for the year 1901–1902. Certainly his savings were not equal to Harvard expenses, for his salary at Harpoot had been nominal.

In his first term at Harvard Huntington took courses toward a Master of Arts degree in the Division of Geology, in geology, mineralogy and palaeontology. Additionally, Harvard required Huntington to complement his Beloit undergraduate studies by taking courses in German and English composition.[1] He was pleased to have his studies guided by men of science rather than by his own inclinations. Harvard accommodated itself to Huntington's interests. Professor J. B. Woodworth encouraged him to pursue studies in the geology of Asia Minor and to complete a map of the geology of eastern Turkey, rather than enroll in "readings in geology," and had him present a talk, "The Geology of Harpoot," at a Harvard geological conference.[2] Accordingly Huntington submitted a notebook to Woodworth entitled, "Asia Minor and the Harpoot Mountains," which included "a sketch of the physiography and geology of Asia Minor as a whole and of the Harpoot Mountains" and "Asia Minor—bibliography and analysis of."[3] In that term Huntington completed his geological map of eastern Turkey, an article "Germany and Russia in Turkey"[4] which he probably commenced in Harpoot, and wrote "Through the Grand Canyon of the Euphrates River" and "The Valley of the Upper Euphrates River and its People." The first of the Euphrates articles was published in *The Geographical Journal*,[5] the journal of England's Royal Geographical Society; the second appeared later in the *Bulletin of the American Geographical Society*.[6] At the age of 26 and while in his first year of graduate study, Huntington had published substantial articles in what were generally recognized as the two leading geographical periodicals in the English speaking world.

Huntington's devotion to study was punctuated by few pleasures;[7] but occasionally he would visit his sister Ruth at Wellesley College and go skating with her, and he regularly gave time to a Tuesday morning mission study group, a Wednesday evening Y.M.C.A. meeting, Sunday school teaching and weekends with his family in Milton. He came to know well fellow students W. S. Tower, J. W. Goldthwait, R. M. Brown, and G. C. Curtis. At the end of the first term Huntington passed his examinations and proceeded on to second-term courses in geology, history, and zoology. He now came markedly under the influence of William Morris Davis, who was perhaps the most important leader in that newly distinctive branch of geology, geomorphology—or "physiography," as Davis called it—the science of the form of the earth surface.

During the early months of 1902 Huntington corresponded with Frederick B. Wright, assistant editor of *Records of the Past*. Huntington had made extensive notes on certain mounds which he had photographed and sketched while in Turkey. Although his publications in the German magazine, *Verhandlungen der Berliner Anthropologischen Gesellschaft*, already contained information on the mounds, F. B. Wright wrote him, "Sometime within the next six months we would like to have a short article on these mounds."[8] Huntington obliged with "Prehistoric Mounds in Eastern Turkey," which was published in *Records of the Past*, June, 1902.[9] The following May the same magazine published another Huntington article "The Hittite Ruins of Hilar, Asia Minor."[10]

On Friday, June 27, Huntington and students C. H. Dour,

J. W. Goldthwait, and A. S. Cobb departed from Boston in the company of Professor Davis. They were taking a summer field trip to the arid West to see "nature in a new and most uncommon dress." The journey was interrupted at Pittsburgh to attend the fifty-first meeting of the American Association for the Advancement of Science, where both Davis and Huntington participated in Section E, "Geology and Geography;" Davis presented a paper on "Systematic Geography," and Huntington "The Great Canyon of the Euphrates River."[11] At that meeting Huntington heard G. Frederick Wright (Professor of the Harmony of Science and Revelation at Oberlin College, Ohio) deliver three papers on the matter of glaciation and land levels with special reference to Asia, a subject in which Huntington was to become much interested within a few months.

The group resumed its journey via Chicago, Salt Lake City, to Provo, where Professor Davis delivered a series of lectures at a summer school for Mormon teachers. They spent the next six weeks on horseback or travelling by wagon in the southern half of the state, "far from railroads and the ordinary routes of travel," and the last week returned north to the delightful farming country of the Wasatch and Uinta Mountains. On his first trip with Davis, Huntington wrote:[12]

> The genial professor who had seen all parts of the world, the graduate who was on his first long journey, and I who had seen just enough of new regions to be flattered when called a traveller, were geologists from Harvard University who had to keep our eyes and our notebooks busy wherever we went. . . . then begins the ride across the desert, full every day of new geological phenomena laid bare with such diagramatic clearness that every cowboy is a semi-geologist.

The group visited the Colorado river at Mount Trumbull, spent two days "sitting for hours and studying the immensity of the details" in an area which was genesis to Davis's interest in physiography, then rode northward for three days to the southwest corner of Utah, where headquarters were established in the Mormon village of Toquerville. While there, Huntington and Goldthwait made a special study of the Hurricane Fault. Later, the two students wrote "The Hurricane Fault in Southwestern Utah" which was published in the *Bulletin of the Geological Society of America*[13] and "The Hurricane Fault in the Toquerville

District, Utah" for the *Bulletin of the Museum of Comparative Zoology*.[14] After its appearance in the latter *Bulletin* months later, Davis wrote Huntington:[15] "Jaggar spoke of it the other day with high appreciation, and said it was just the sort of thing that counts." On leaving the area Davis travelled to Nevada to study some of the ranges of the Great Basin; Goldthwait returned to Salt Lake City; Huntington spent two weeks visiting the Colob plateau, the Grand Wash, and the lower end of the Colorado Canyon, before embarking on a ride across the desert to the Santa Fe railroad in Arizona at Chloride. He then journeyed to Oakland, California, where he visited his Aunt Theresa and cousin Herbert before continuing to Beloit via Cisco, Donner Pass, Lake Winemucca, and Pyramid Lake. At Beloit he renewed many of the friendships made during his undergraduate days, then returned by train to Boston, arriving October 4. Of the summer's field work he noted, "Nature, painfully arid at first, proved grander than I had expected."[16]

Work resumed at Harvard later that month and Huntington found himself studying more geology under Davis. He had acquired a Master of Arts degree and was now preparing for the Doctorate of Philosophy. Davisian physiography proved fascinating to Huntington, who was already sufficiently impressed by Davis's work to have made a collection of his published writings. He was requested to tutor undergraduates who were lagging in their geological courses, and the income supplemented a Thayer Scholarship which was awarded him in his second year at Harvard. For recreation he requested permission to participate in organized sports at Harvard. That meant a "Universal Test for Strength, Speed and Endurance." Extensive measurements and tests were made, the results tabulated in foot pounds and an anthropometric chart was drawn. Sports at Harvard were rigorous! Interestingly Huntington's statistics were recorded as height 63.4 inches; weight 119.8 pounds; length of arm 26½ inches. He did not participate formally in sports events at Harvard, but was very energetic, skating in winter, and walking throughout the rest of the year. Though slight of build, he possessed great stamina and powers of endurance, as his explorations in the next decade were to reveal.

In 1902 wealthy philanthropist Andrew Carnegie established the Carnegie Institution of Washington D.C. Geographer Daniel Coit Gilman was elected President after serving as President of the Johns Hopkins University for a quarter of a century. Alexander Agassiz, an enthusiast for the work of Raphael Pumpelly, was also a trustee of the Carnegie Institution. In December, 1902, the Institution voted Raphael Pumpelly a grant of money,

> for the purpose of making, during the year 1903, a preliminary examination of the Trans–Caspian region, and of collecting and arranging all available existing information necessary in organizing the further investigation of the past and present physico-geographical conditions and archeological remains of the region.[17]

Pumpelly's inspiration for the proposal stemmed partly from his desires to undertake research concerning the origin of the Aryan race, and partly to sate his curiosity as to whether or not the Aral, Caspian, and Black Seas were principal remnants of an Asian Mediterranean.[18] Doubtless, too, Pumpelly's own nature and desire to travel were not insignificant factors in the venture. At short notice he requested his one-time Harvard pupil of 1869–70, W. M. Davis, to assume responsibility for the "physico-geographical part of the preliminary reconnaissance." Davis selected Huntington as his assistant.

Huntington was obliged to make a decision which would determine his career. At this same time Mr. Barnum, now Principal of Euphrates College, Turkey, was hoping that Huntington would return to Harpoot. Barnum and other members of the staff had maintained a correspondence with him since his return to the United States, and James Barton, Secretary of the missionary board, had written in a testimonial to Harvard that he foresaw that Huntington might attain the Presidency of Euphrates College soon after his return from Harvard.[19] Huntington realized that there was a place for him at Euphrates College, and that he was needed there. An even more attractive suggestion had come from Thomas Norton, Huntington's companion of sheepskin days on the Euphrates. On September 30, 1902 Consul Norton had written:[20]

> The Consulate at Erzerum will be vacant next Spring (I have been asked myself to consider it). The salary is $2000. . . . A Consul can move around freely in the district . . . and has 2 months annually vacation outside of his district—Would you like this appointment? I ask the question, first because I am anxious to see some one there thoroughly in touch with the mis-

sion's work; second it is an admirable field for just the kind of
work you wish to undertake especially about Van; third I would
like to see some one with your linguistic equipment, knowledge
of eastern Turkey, scientific acquirements, and Yankee push,
located at that point, for the sake of the service.

But on April 18 Huntington instead opted for another, more
scholarly kind of career, when with W. M. Davis he sailed from
New York on the *Kron Prinz Wilhelm* to Europe. At Vienna
Professor Albrecht Penck met their train and took both men to
his home. The Penck family was delighted to find that geologist
Fred Gulliver was Huntington's cousin, "for he was a great fa-
vourite with them." Penck, archaeologist Hornes, and Professor
Hrobl took Davis and Huntington to Krems "forty or fifty miles
up the Danube to see some loess deposits in which remains of
palaeolithic man have been found." Two days later Davis and
Huntington resumed their journey. At Bucharest Professor Mur-
goci and his assistant met the Harvard pair and were "immensely
pleased to have the honor of entertaining Professor Davis."
Travelling by boat from Constantinople across the Black Sea,
the pair spent some hours ashore at Trebizond with missionary
friends whom Huntington had known in his Harpoot years, then
continued to Batum, where they entered the Russian Empire on
March 8. A journey along the Kur Valley provided them with
geologic conversation and content for their notebooks. After a
two-day stay in Tiflis, capital of Transcaucasia, they resumed
their eastward journey along the valley to enter Baku, a city of
15,000 people and 5,000 oil wells. Huntington did not develop
an affection for the city, but he found fascination there on the
shores of the Caspian.[21]

> The smoke, the smell, the dust, the dryness, and the lack of
> verdure all make Baku an undesirable place to live in . . .
> (Baku) was what might at first sight be taken for a cyclopean
> cemetery. Tall pyramidal towers of rather slender shape were
> scattered in profusion amid pools of oily water.

Here Huntington began the study of Russian from an Armenian. He had been vexed by not being able to converse more
with his companions, and while in Tiflis had declared, "I can
stumble along in excruciating French, German and Turkish, but
it is dreadfully unsatisfactory."

In Baku, Davis and Huntington hired a Tartar and his phaeton to drive them to the southern point of the Apsheron Peninsula where they took a tramp over the hills, and while there Huntington took notes to which he returned again and again in later studies:[22]

> At an elevation of 600 feet above the Caspian we found what we had already found elsewhere south of Baku viz the remnants of a beach formed at an exceedingly recent geological period. The water rose rapidly to this level, or the land sank, there was a brief period of rest, perhaps only some hundreds of years and the land and sea assumed nearly their present altitude. The sea however was somewhat lower than now and has since risen. What it all means we do not know and shall not try to say until we have done a good deal more studying.

By prior arrangement the pair met Raphael Pumpelly and his son, Raphael Pumpelly, Jr., a Harvard junior, who brought with them from St. Petersburg Serge de Brontzvine, a recent graduate of the University of St. Petersburg, who served as interpreter. "He is a pleasant obliging fellow and we like him very much. It is an immense convenience to have him along." At St. Petersburg the Pumpellys had arranged matters for the excursion. The party then crossed the Caspian to Krasnovodsk "after the smoothest sea voyage I ever took." The Governor of Krasnovodsk had received word of the expedition from St. Petersburg and extended a Russian hospitality which included the loan of a horse to Professor Davis and the use of the Governor's own bath house, "so that we enjoyed the great luxury of bathing in the Caspian." When the party left Krasnovodsk they had a special railway car to themselves. "We pay one fare apiece and get a car with six compartments which is absolutely at our disposal to be dropped anywhere for as long as we like. It is very handsome of the government. . . ."[23] The prospect of study in Central Asia with Davis and Pumpelly excited him. His respect for W. M. Davis had been established in Cambridge and on their trip to Arizona and Utah; of Pumpelly, Huntington wrote:[24]

> He is a fine looking tall man with white hair and a long white beard. His eyes have a very kind expression and are full of fun. He has seen lots of the world and enjoys telling about it which he does in a very interesting way.

The party was en rapport. Huntington had a Tekker guide take him to the Amu–Daria before the party reached Ashkhabad. He enjoyed the company of the expedition but found it too large and unwieldy for best results. Frequently he sought the company of Davis and the two would stalk off together to take "scientific walks," usually in the early morning. The midday temperatures of 100°—105° proved uncomfortable for Davis. Ashkhabad was soon reached and the first journey of the expedition was planned—a five-day sortie, or "flying excursion" as Pumpelly called such ventures, to the south across the Persian boundary. The party had so far found no sea beaches on the east of the Caspian, nor evidences of recent subsidence of the land or rise of the water. Here, however, terraces showing "recent interesting change" were found in numbers. Inspired by Davis they journeyed on into the Kopet Dagh, the mountain range along the Russo-Persian frontier. Huntington observed in his diary:[25]

> We are going to the mountains to look for evidences of ancient glaciation. If we find them we shall try to correlate them with the terraces and then those with ancient lakes and lastly all of these with early remains of man. It will take a long time, years, to do the whole thing.

The four Americans made the journey with two Russians, two Persians, two Turkomans and "two others, probably Turkomans," aided by "fifteen or sixteen horses." The Governor had sent his aide-de-camp, Yanchevetzki, to assist the party, while the Persian Consul provided a cook and two assistants. The cook insisted on not less than three dishes per meal, all of which encouraged Huntington to write, "the scale of this expedition is rather large you see, too large for quick work or economy." Huntington had drawn up an outline of things he wished to observe "in order to make a complete ontographic study of this region. You see we want to study not only the country and climate but the relation which these have had to life of every form."[26]

The party returned to Ashkhabad June 4, where they were joined by a Mr. Norton, friend of Raphael Pumpelly, and on June 9 proceeded at the train's regular pace of twenty miles per hour until Merv was reached June 11. Temperatures of 95° prevailed inside the train and upwards of 105° in the sun. Near

Merv the railroad had been washed out by the melting of snows
on Hindu Cush, and the passengers were obliged to walk and
carry their baggage amidst locusts, camels, and naked workers.
In Merv, Davis and Huntington visited Mr. Dubosof, Superin-
tendent of the Imperial Estate of 25,000 acres, to whom they
presented letters of introduction. The result was that the party
was lodged in the "Palace," one of several private estates owned
by the Tsar. The purpose of these estates was to apply methods
of irrigation and agriculture to the oasis tract and thus teach
the natives how to improve their condition. In notes logged faith-
fully in his diary Huntington reconstructed six different Mervs
of the past, and noted that each successive one had been located
farther to the west and south.[27] He found the history of Merv
"so thrilling and at the same time so vague" that he was obliged
to return in May, 1904 to make a much more detailed study of
the area. He did not understand why all around Bairam Ali
(near Merv) there were a great number of isolated and half
ruined mud houses "that look 50 or 100 years old." This perplexed him, because in non-urban areas the Turkomans lived in
circular felt tents called Kibitkas, not mud houses. At Merv
Huntington described the solitude:[28]

> You remember the places in the Bible where it speaks of deso-
> lation razing a city to the ground and ploughing it over, aban-
> doning a city to jackals. . . . I stood all alone in Old Merv and
> saw nothing but four great walls surrounding a level plain. . . .
> I saw no living thing save some lizards and a bat and heard
> nothing but a plaintive wild pigeon. Then I knew what the
> prophets meant by desolation.

The party spent only four days in the vicinity of Merv before
attaching their car to the regular passenger train. Travelling
across sand desert, passing the oasis of Charjui, the Oxus River,
and journeying by way of the Zarafsham Valley, they reached
Samarkand on June 16. Huntington was delighted to find letters
from his family awaiting him and was delighted with Samarkand; "The old town is quite indescribable. It is the most
oriental place that I have ever seen." The next day the party
journeyed to Tashkent, dined with the governor-general in
sumptuous fashion, then prepared to divide. The Pumpellys and
Norton were to travel through the Fergana valley to the Pamir
while Davis, Huntington and interpreter Brovtzin prepared for

a mountain journey to Issik Kul, whence Huntington alone would continue to Kashgar.

Davis and Huntington packed maps, notebooks, and much of their heavier paraphernalia and left it in the military club in Margelan. Equipped with horses, saddles, 100 gaudy bandanas (to give as gifts along the route) and "quite a supply of stores," they visited geologist Tchernachef, Director of the Imperial Geological Survey, then proceeded by train to the city of Andijan, still not recovered from an earthquake which had occurred six months previously. On horseback and drawing four carts, the party proceeded from Andijan June 27 across the plain of Fergana. A Minbashi, guides, and policeman accompanied Davis, Huntington and Brovtzin through the land of the Sarts and Kirghiz. The Minbashi of Kugart showed them every courtesy and presented Huntington with a fine gown of silk and Professor Davis with a rug.[29]

> Professor Davis with much ceremony said that he was going to send the Minbashi his book on physical geography which has many pictures. Later he presented him my old compass which is a very good one worth four or five dollars.

Huntington wrote an article about the journey from Andijan to the Kugart Pass entitled "With a Minbashi in Turkestan" which was later published in *Appalachia*.[30] They reached Son Kul and spent July 8 and 9 studying it, then continued to Issik Kul. They reached Lake Issik on July 14th then proceeded eastward along the northern shore. Both men were much impressed by the size of the lake (120 miles east to west, and 40 miles north to south): They climbed several of the mountains that surrounded the lake in search of moraines and other evidences of glaciations, and then when hot and tired, bathed in the lake's waters. Huntington was learning a great deal from the experiences provided by the journey and at least as much from W. M. Davis:[31]

> Two months ago Issik Kul was a place far away that perhaps I might visit a year or two from now. Khiva and Kashgar were places that I wanted to visit but did not have much hope of seeing until at least two or three years later. Now so to speak we have pocketed Issik Kul, Kashgar is my next station and Khiva is not far beyond. . . . For years I wanted to travel with

someone from whom I could learn how to observe. Now I have
had these two long journeys with Professor Davis. Three years
ago I concocted schemes for visiting central Asia; now I am
there. The beauty of it all is that the things have come just as
fast as I was ready for them.

At Sazanovka, a Russian settlement on the lake's northern
shore, Huntington and Davis agreed to part. Davis and Brovtzin
journeyed via Vyernyi (now Alma Ata), Semipalatinsk, and
Omsk to St. Petersburg where Brovtzin lived. Davis arrived
home in Boston on August 28.

Huntington, meanwhile, journeyed onward to Kashgar and
the Takla Makan Desert. He was by now persuaded that uniform
climatic change through historic time, in the direction of desiccation, accounted for the evidences of dwindling population
which he noted. His notebooks contain a detailed account of
each day's observations and especially reveal his embrace of
Davis's deductive system, cycle of arid erosion, and "ontography." His travel with Davis had constituted a most unusual opportunity to receive a field tutorial while in the saddle. He
counted and studied terraces, found moraines and searched for
other glacial evidences, measured heights, made diagrams, took
numerous photographs, compiled extensive notes of what he
saw, and set some pages of his diary aside for "speculations."
Much of this work was accomplished while on horseback, but
stops were made to enter more complete notes in his diary, pref-
erably during the daylight hours, for at night the light provided
by candles and a dung fire tried and teased his eyes:

> The writing of scientific notes takes so much time that these
> letters get crowded out. The interesting thing here in the moun-
> tains is the glaciers old and new and the determination of how
> many glacial periods there have been and whether man was here
> during the last of them. I have just been stopping to think
> whether a certain set of moraines means a third or a fourth time
> of glaciation. I am becoming more and more convinced that
> during glacial times the climate was relatively much warmer
> here than in America and Europe.[32]

Days more of bread and strong tea, the climbing of long mountain paths in a variety of weather which burned his face so that
"if I laugh or squint my eyes, or try to turn up my nose, I have to

pay for it," and the eating of horseflesh, were all experiences that Huntington endured before he won his way to the plateau top of the Tian Shan at an elevation of 12,500 feet to behold "a sea of mountains . . . the real thing, regular waves, one after another growing higher in the distance, white with snow on the northside, brown on the other."[33]

Then Huntington rode into the great interior basin of the Tarim river system, arrived at Shor Kul August 15 (1903) and there spent six days studying the lake, which he regarded as "most important as an indicator of climatic change." He resumed his journey and approaching Kashgar wrote, "there was little that was beautiful or new in that view, but yet it thrilled me because it was so broad and because it was that great heart of Asia, lifeless and unknown."[34] He spent five days in Kashgar, in the house of the Russian Consul. It gave him constant language training: "Yesterday was one of those fearful days when I talked five tongues and by evening had no idea whether I was talking Hindostani or Esquimaux." In the city of fifteen to twenty thousand people where it was said donkeys outnumbered humans, Huntington visited the bazar, a local school, and much of the city; but he was better introduced to Kashgar by Swedish missionaries Mr. and Mrs. Anderson and a Colonel Miles. It was a world unknown to him, where people wore flowers over their ears "much as a clerk wears or carries his pen," where on the flood plain of the Kuzzil Su, "the stream that vitalizes Kashgar," he counted "twelve dustwhirls rising hundreds of feet into the air all at one time," and where "the great snow mountains of the Pamir rose grandly to heights that have never yet been attained by climbing."

After this brief introduction to the Tarim basin, Huntington turned back toward the Russian border. He journeyed via Ulugkchat to the Russian frontier post of Irkestan high in the Alai Mountains, where he spent an evening "in trying to work up a magazine article on Kashgar."[35] By September 7 he had reached Osh; he rested here two days before hiring two fresh guides, Turdu and Sherif, both of whom had previously travelled with the Swedish explorer, Sven Hedin. Turdu had travelled with Hedin for eighteen months; Sherif only some weeks. (Huntington was familiar with Hedin's work and had read "Die Geographisch—wissenschaftlichen Ergebnisse meiner Reisen in Zentralasien 1894–1897," in *Petermanns Mitteilungen*, 1900.)[36]

The journey from Kashgar to Osh had been extremely hard; Huntington had entered in his diary "that our road is difficult is

shown by the large number of skeletons of horses and donkeys
that lie beside it, more numerous as the way gets steeper and
higher." He had travelled as much as nineteen or twenty hours in
a day on this stretch, yet had found time to maintain his diary,
to observe carefully not only local geology, but also flora and
fauna. Especially was he interested in wild flowers and birds.
After gathering and sending to his father seeds of the dolona,
wild apricot, karateghi, chishekanak, wild rose, yellow poppy,
chrysanthemum, shilbi, and melon, he wrote,[37] "I am sure it
would be delightful when I come home after two or three years,
if I stay so long, to have Papa take me down to the garden and
show me two or three scraggly little Asiatic bushes." And of his
interest in birds he noted in his diary,[38] "If I had worn glasses
when I was younger I should probably have been an ornitholo-
gist. As it was I could only see the bigger facts of nature, so I
became a geographer."

He continued the journey to Margelan where he stayed at the
Military Club and where he had deposited several of his diaries,
maps, and some equipment on the outgoing journey. On the
journey from Kashgar to Margelan he wrote, "It had made me
practically sure that there were five glacial epochs with warm
intervals between." Huntington had used his field glasses frequently, taken many photographs, and had an excellent opportunity to become familiar with Kirghiz life. Later, in his *Principles of Human Geography* the Kirghiz received a chapter to
themselves.[39]

Huntington was rapidly gaining an ability to select the most
significant details from his daily round to record in his notebooks
and diaries. The notebooks were reserved for scientific observations; the diaries were written as letters to his family. Always
he made a carbon copy of these letters and so retained a record
in the event that these homebound letters were lost. The process
of making a carbon copy of writing mystified Asians from Harpoot to Kashgar.

> One of my privileges, now-a-days, is to always have a lot of
> writing to do. I am acquiring quite a literary habit. This journal
> letter takes some time, but the scientific notes take more and
> are the ones that have to be written up every day no matter
> what happens. I have been trying lately, too, to write a report
> on this journey to send to Professor Davis as soon as I can get
> to Ashkhabad.[40]

Huntington left Margelan and reached Ashkhabad, October 1, 1903. There he remained for seven weeks, had half a dozen notebooks made—"One of the absolutely indispensable things on such a journey as this is plenty of notebooks"—and settled to some serious thought and writing. He wrote some popular magazine articles, and more importantly, "A Geological and Physiographic Reconnaissance in Central Turkestan." This 42,000-word report was later sent to Davis for editorial improvement and then published as part of *Explorations in Turkestan with an account of the Basin of Eastern Persia and Sistan*, the official report of the Carnegie-sponsored reconnaissance.[41]

While resident in Ashkhabad Huntington received letters from W. M. Davis in addition to those from his family. Davis was very busy at the time. He was a member of the Committee on Arrangements and Chairman of the Committee on Scientific Program for the Eighth International Geographical Congress to be held later that year in Washington, D.C. He had given thirteen of sixteen lectures on Turkestan at Harvard, had presented lectures on the journey before the Geographical Societies of Boston, New York, Philadelphia, Baltimore, and Washington, D.C. and had written "A Summer in Turkestan" for the *Bulletin of the American Geographical Society*.[42] Davis was "planning to organize . . . an American Geographers Club or Association," and was trying to excite the curiosity of his wealthy one-time student, R. L. Barrett, in the terraces of Issik Kul "in as much as it seems to be out of the Carnegie reach." Davis wrote to Huntington that he hoped it would be possible for him and Barrett to work together "or at least in association, on the many physiographic problems that need to be taken up." Of more immediate importance to Huntington while he was writing in Ashkhabad were the suggestions Davis made on the report fragments that he had already sent his teacher. Davis, a master stylist, urged more diagrams, fewer inverted sentences, a reduction in the use of the terms "former" and "latter," and made many other helpful suggestions.[43]

At the end of the third week in November, having completed his writing, Huntington travelled south and entered Persia. By following the Heri Rud, then traversing the mountains of eastern Persia within viewing distance of the Afghan "Desert of Despair," stopping frequently at Persian military posts, he and his retinue reached Sistan in the southeastern corner of Persia on December 31, 1903, after forty days of hard journeying. During this time he had sought to enter the forbidden land of Afghanistan on five occasions, and had each time been refused permission, though once he had journeyed five miles into the country to a fortress to receive the refusal. He thoroughly enjoyed the exercise of trying to enter Afghanistan, and while still en route to Sistan had begun "A Call on the Afghans," a 6,000-word sally in a popular vein.[44] This was one of several such articles which he sent to his father for criticism, before having them forwarded to popular magazines.

The 800-mile journey from Ashkhabad to Sistan was proceeding earnestly and without mishap until Huntington hired a guide who pretended to a knowledge he did not have. Then the party was led into difficulties. Food, water, and funds ran low. Huntington had already purchased barley so mixed with sand that his horses would not eat it, and had been given a short measure of rice, so that his situation became serious. He recorded in his diary "we have no bread or meat, only rice, and there is almost no barley left for the animals and the place affords no grass for the horses." At one point in the journey Huntington's party held a water hole, demanding bread at a fair price from an Afghan caravan which wanted access to the water.[45]

> We were in command of the spring, so to speak, and said that they should not have any water till the bread question was settled. When they tried to go down to the spring in spite of us, Khiva Klich was ordered to stand guard over the water till the bread question was settled. More Afghans gathered till there were about fifteen among the Klan. Of course we could not use force . . . but it had in it all the elements of something very exciting. My imagination is growing. Think of what it might have been—a fight in the desert! Bread in exchange for water! Afghans against Turkomans! Because of a lying guide. It could not really have come to that, for we had not the slightest idea of fighting. It made me realize though the value of bread and of water.

Huntington reached Sistan on the last day of 1903. He promptly telegraphed Teheran for funds, and wrote to Davis of his plight. Fortunately, early in December Davis had sent $1,000 by cable to Teheran for Huntington's use and had informed the U.S. Minister of that city of his action. The normally imperturbable Davis was greatly concerned for the welfare of his student.[46]

> I have sometimes lain awake nights lately, wondering where in
> the world you might be, and how you were getting along without
> money in those desert basins of Persia. . . . I am now writing
> again to the minister, hoping to learn from him that you have
> connected with him and have money enough for your needs.

Huntington remained in Sistan until February 5, 1904, largely
as the guest of a physician, a "nervous little man," Dr. A. J.
Miller, the Russian Consul. Miller extended aid and advice to
the Huntington party and enabled them to make several valuable
journeys in southeastern Persia that otherwise would not have
been made. While in Sistan Huntington spent a few hours as a
guest of the British officers connected with the Sistan Arbitra-
tion Commission. The British Commissioner, Colonel G. H. Mc-
Mahon, was then making "an enthusiastic study" of the region
and aided Huntington in the compilation of notes for his report
on the basin of eastern Persia and Sistan, later to be published
by the Carnegie Institution.

Huntington had been dispatched to southeastern Persia, there
to study the history of recent physical change. It was supposed
that the study of the physiographic history of basins neighboring
the Caspian would help reveal the truth regarding Pumpelly's
suggested Asiatic Mediterranean. (Huntington had already visited the interior lake basins of Goljeuk and of the Caspian itself.) In addition to lake basins, mountain valley terraces were
also investigated. The terraced character of mountain valleys
noted by the Pumpelly party in the Caspian basin and in Trans-
caspia was thought to reappear in Persia. Huntington developed
great enthusiasm to find and study such phenomena and to interpret the message of climatic change hidden in them. His diary
notes make frequent mention of terraces observed:[47]

> The terraces of Kuh-u-Khoja and of all the regions round the
> lake are of the greatest importance as records of the many
> changes that the lake has gone through in the last hundred
> thousand years more or less. For three months now I have
> been looking forward to the Hamun of Sistan as a critical test
> of the theories that seemed to fit the facts of central Asia. I
> have been trying to keep myself in the true scientific attitude
> of being as ready to have my theories refuted as confirmed. Yet
> I must confess that I feel very happy to find that so far as a
> brief view can be conclusive, they are exactly what I had ex-

pected. I see already that this place is so important that I must
stay in Sistan some weeks.

While in Sistan Huntington wrote much in his diaries, on
which he later based "The Waterless Land of Persia," Chapter
X of his book, *Asia—A Geography Reader*,[48] and "The Depression of Sistan in Eastern Persia"—published in the *Bulletin of
the American Geographical Society*.[49] More importantly he prepared a 60,000-word report which he sent to Davis for editorial
revision, prior to its inclusion in *Explorations in Turkestan*.
Concluding this essay was a statement entitled "Climate and
History." It was Huntington's first published statement concerning the relation of history and physiography. An impressive array
of data was assembled to suggest that:[50]

> At Sistan history and physiography appear to join hands, for
> the change from the conditions of greater water supply during
> antiquity to the desiccation of today is apparently the change
> from the last fluvial epoch to the present interfluvial epoch.

Huntington thus theorized a change of climate within historic
time, a gradual but persistent desiccation. Already he felt called
to philosophize on his Asiatic travels:[51]

> I want to devote ten or fifteen years to the writing of a book
> that shall show the true relation between history and geography
> as exemplified in Asia. . . . In that book I want to so bring out
> the relation of man and his history to his physiographic and
> climatic environment and to changes that have taken place in
> that environment that every future historian shall have to take
> into account the ideas there laid down. That is the sum of my
> scientific ambition.

Huntington began his return to Ashkhabad on February 5,
1904. There he was to meet a second Carnegie-sponsored Pumpelly expedition as soon after March 1 as possible. He reached
Ashkhabad March 13; five days later Mr. and Mrs. Pumpelly,
their son, a German archaeologist, and two young Americans
arrived. During April, May, and June, digs were made at Anau
and Merv. Huntington's task was to supervise the laborers, frequently numbering 100 Turkomen, to insure that the day began
at 5:00 A.M. and continued until 7:00 P.M., with appropriately

spaced intervals for rest and meals, to collect all artifacts excavated and to gather them for appraisal during the evening hours.
The workers variously supposed Huntington was searching for
gold or his ancestral burial ground. To allay suspicion he frequently took camel's milk, bread, and tea with them, eating
with his fingers in a manner he loathed. He succeeded in maintaining good order among the men notwithstanding a locust in-
festation which "filled the dig with swarming creatures"; un-
pleasantly high temperatures and the spread of disease were
largely responsible for terminating the work. Revolutionary unrest the following year in the Russian Empire forbade continu-
ance of the work.

At Merv, Huntington made a special study of the former distribution of population as revealed by the distribution of Kurgans, later published as "Description of the Kurgans of the Merv
Oasis."[52] The digs revealed over 136 feet of successive culture
strata, containing at least four almost uninterrupted culture
stages, extending apparently through the Neolithic and bronze
into the beginning of the iron stage. The undertaking revealed
much of value to the student of archaeology and prehistory, and
it strengthened Huntington's conviction that a gradual desiccation accounted for the desertion of the sites under excavation.

Huntington left Merv on June 15, and travelled via Krasnovodsk, Baku, Batum, and Odessa to Vienna where he spent
four days with Albrecht Penck and some students in the Alps.
Then he continued to New York, arriving September 13. He
travelled immediately to Washington, D.C., to participate in the
Eighth International Geographical Congress. Davis introduced
him to many of the foreign geographers present as "my assistant
in Asia," then insisted that his student share the suite of rooms
in which he and Henry Gannett were resident.

Huntington returned to Milton and settled to the task of
writing up the scientific findings of his Asiatic sojourn. Among
the first of these was a paper concerning evidences of desiccation in Asia for the first meeting of the Association of American
Geographers, held in Philadelphia late in December, 1904. He
also made arrangements with Robert LeMoyne Barrett to revisit
Asia the following year.

CHAPTER IV

"Pulse of Asia" Days

On January 7, 1905, Huntington and Robert LeMoyne Barrett sailed from New York on the S.S. *Ivernia* bound for England en route to Asia. It was destined to become perhaps the most important expedition Huntington undertook. Arising from his Harpoot and Pumpelly days in Asia, he had developed the idea that climate throughout the world in postglacial time was becoming drier—a uniform desiccation. In the seventeen-month journey that took him across the Himalayas to Inner Asia, he found evidences that provided him with the notion of climatic pulsation during historic time. *The Pulse of Asia* (1907) was taken directly from the evidences which he amassed in his diaries of this expedition, financed and led by Barrett.

Barrett had been graduated from Harvard College in 1898, where he had studied physiography under W. M. Davis. A self-styled "naturalist and globe trotter combined"[1] and independently wealthy, Barrett had proposed the trip to Huntington at Davis's suggestion. It was to be financed by Barrett and to be known as the Barrett Expedition. The purpose of the trip was outlined in the *Bulletin of the American Geographical Society*:[2]

> The chief points of study will be the history of the basins of Central Asia during recent geologic times, and the changes which have taken place since the occupation of the country by man. . . . In addition to physiographic studies, in which Mr. Barrett is chiefly interested, Mr. Huntington will undertake investigations of the relation of physiography to life, and especially of human life and history. The expedition is under the auspices of the Association of American Geographers.

On January 20, 1905, Huntington and Barrett arrived in London in a thick fog which Huntington described as "much like a combination of a laundry, a smoking-room, and an engine yard." Here they made rigorous preparations for the journey, visited J. Scott Keltie and Colonel Younghusband at the Royal

Geographical Society, and then departed on the S.S. *China* bound for Aden. Brief stays in Gibraltar, Marseilles and Port Said preceded a passage by searchlight and moonlight through the Suez Canal, which inspired Huntington to write:[3]

> This is the beginning of the East. . . . The pyramids and the Pharoahs lie on one side with Sinai on the other. The interest of the latter grows upon me. I want to study it some day in connection with Palestine and Jewish history. I keep telling myself that this is to be my last long journey, but nevertheless I am continually planning new trips for the far future.

As they continued through the Red Sea south of the Sinaitic Peninsula, the portholes were fitted with ventilators, punkas were hung, tropical wardrobes were amply in evidence, and dress for dinner was the rule. Between tantalizing glimpses of the desert coast, Huntington occupied himself watching deck games, entering notes in his journal, writing letters home, and reading the Bible and John Fiske. The ship docked at Aden and the travellers had six hours ashore before resuming their journey to Bombay across the Arabian Sea on board the S.S. *Arcadia.* From the deck Huntington took especial delight in the jellyfish —"delicate pink, yellow, and blue"—, the flying fish, and the beauty of the night sky.

The *Arcadia* anchored in the roads of Bombay, February 24, 1905. It was Huntington's third visit to the Asian continent. A telegram sent to the Bombay Customs House by the India office averted difficulty since Huntington and Barrett quite by chance had guns of a forbidden bore; they were similar to those used by the Indian army. The pair took rooms in a hotel, then wandered the streets sight-seeing, making visits to the Parsi community, the Tower of Silence, a native market, the Moslem quarter, and the Bombay gardens. Huntington called on Mr. Peacock, agent of the American Board, to whom he delivered a letter of introduction from Dr. Barton. Mr. Peacock showed him one of the Board's missionary schools, a Sunday school, and a boys' orphanage, then "compared the Parsis to the Jews in character and ability" (a comparison which was to reappear in Huntington's later writing on kiths): A swift visit to the caves of Elephanta Island aroused Huntington's enthusiastic interest in Indian art. Then, by train, they ascended the Deccan escarpment to Igatpuri and visited the cave paintings of Ajanta and Jalgaon.

The journey was continued to Agra where visits were made to the Taj Mahal and the Pearl Mosque. Huntington then journeyed to Umballa, arriving March 7, spending two days with a college friend, Mr. McCuskey, and his wife, who were helping to maintain a Presbyterian mission school. Huntington and Barrett again entrained and after a hard jolting ride reached Peshawar, where they met Mark Aurel Stein, the archaeologist who had so far done the most to uncover the story buried in the ruins of the Tarim basin. Huntington described Stein as "a little man with a German accent, very affable and agreeable." Huntington had read much of Stein's work, and in fact had received a copy of the archaeologist's *Sand Buried Ruins of Khotan* from a family friend, Charles R. Lanman, only days prior to his departure from Massachusetts.[4] Stein and Huntington corresponded during the next year while the latter remained in Central Asia, and later exchanged publications and occasional letters until the death of Stein in 1943.

Huntington and Barrett next travelled to the approaches of the Khyber Pass eighteen miles from Peshawar. Military regulations prevented them from ascending the summit, but they enjoyed magnificent views. The journey was resumed by ekka (a two-wheeled vehicle with one horse) via Mausera, Garrhi, Musafirabad, and Uri, where on March 19 they engaged a houseboat on the Jhelum River. Four days later they arrived in Srinagar and began to make arrangements for the journey across the mountains to the Tarim basin of Chinese Turkestan. Huntington sought good snow boots, reliable servants, and ample provisions of all kinds. Impatient to commence the Himalayan climb, Huntington entered in his journal, "we have not done much in Srinagar except shiver, drive off merchants and eat." But, despite the continual bleating of beggars, he found time to develop films, write several journal pages on Kashmir, and work out the notion that while past desiccations had exerted an adverse effect upon "basin Asia," highland Kashmir had benefitted from them, as they had provided the region with a more equable climate. Huntington became attracted to Kashmir and wished to stay longer, but a program of work beckoned him across the Himalayan Mountains to the Tarim basin. Kashmir inspired him to review his notions concerning environmental influences on man:[5]

Naturally I am trying all the time to test my theories as to the influence of geographic environment on habits and character.

Just at present, which I know will please mother, I am more
inclined than formerly to lay stress on racial characteristics and
on religion. A thorough study of Kashmir would throw floods of
light upon the whole question.

From notes and observations made at this time he later wrote
"The Vale of Kashmir," which was published in the *Bulletin of
the American Geographical Society*.[6]

On April 4, Huntington and Barrett resumed their journey,
at first by houseboat on the Jhelum River as far as Gunderbul.
Then, with ponies and servants, they made their way up the Sind
valley. Huntington enjoyed visits to several mission schools en-
route, evaluating each mission's work in his journal. On April
9, they reached Battal, whence they continued on foot for five
days. Thirty-five coolies were paid eight cents a day to carry
loads weighing as much as eighty pounds apiece. Progress was
slow, for even though a start was made each day between 4 and
5 A.M. the coolies could journey but nine to twelve miles a day
under the conditions. Huntington noted in his journal: "Even
with my light load of a nine pound instrument belt I was tired
when the day's march was finished." In places the snow had ac-
cumulated to such depth that the men walked at the level of
the telegraph wire, with "the constant sound of avalanches on
all sides." During the day Huntington and Barrett each proceeded at his own pace, made sketches, took photographs or
notes of whatever interested him, but rejoined each other in the
evening when camp was made. At the end of each day Huntington would complete his journal notes, add to his scientific notes,
drink some salty Himalayan tea, and relax with a book, perhaps
Shakespeare. His father had given him a set of Shakespeare's
complete works, in the smallest of volumes, convenient for journeys of this nature. He carried with him "portable portions of
Shakespeare, Tennyson, Milton, Cowper, Arnold, Goldsmith,
Pope and Wordsworth," also *Songs of Three Centuries*, and certain of the works of Stein, Hedin, and Schimper. It is interesting
to cull from Huntington's journal that while he rested on a green
canvas cape (the distinctive gear of the caravan), in a little
known Himalayan Kingdom at an elevation of 11,000 feet,
burned and bearded, dark glasses combating the sun's glare,
brown puttees and grass sandals on his legs and feet, he could
read and enjoy *As You Like It*. The third week in April was
spent in hard journeying on a route that took the travellers

through Kurgil, Lamayuru, and Nemo to Leh, allowing them several visits to lamaseries.

Barrett remained in Leh while Huntington travelled east over the main range of the Himalayas to the salt lake of Pangong, on the shore of which he camped for five days. He entered in his journal:

> Scientifically the lake is even better than artistically. Together with its companion it forms the largest known example of a valley eroded by a glacier into a long rock trough or basin.

He observed lacustrine deposits and shore lines, which he felt were evidences of climatic change, and made extensive notes upon the subject. (Later his article "Pangong: A Glacial Lake in the Tibetan Plateau" published in the *Journal of Geology*,[7] won commentary in *The Geographical Journal*,[8] where it was noted that Huntington was the first observer to claim for the lake a glacial origin.) He then returned to Leh after struggling across the Chang La, an 18,400 foot pass, under unusually difficult circumstances; the temperatures dropped to 15° below zero; horses broke through the snow crust (some were unable to negotiate the pass at all); and the men needed frequent five-minute halts to regain their breath and relieve their headaches.

On May 14 at Leh Huntington rejoined Barrett, who had formed a new caravan and was ready to continue on to Chinese Turkestan. The caravan retraced Huntington's steps across the Chang La, then followed the Shyok Valley to the Karakoram Pass. Travelling north along the Shyok Valley Huntington recorded:[9]

> We are travelling now like the patriarchs. Our caravan consists of fifteen horses and five mules of our own, eight hired horses, two sheep, one goat and three kids, our six men, three men with the hired horses, one with the sheep and goats, and two Sahibs, in all twelve men, twenty eight baggage and riding animals, and six animals for food.

They stopped for one day, May 27, while Huntington climbed to a height of 20,500 feet, read his instruments, and looked out over the Asia below him. Later he recorded "the chief interest of the view lay in its confirmation of our previous ideas as to the origin of the Himalayas."[10] On June 1 camp was made at the foot of the Karakoram Pass (18,290 feet) in preparation for passage into China. In order to negotiate the pass, the two traveller-scientists and the coolies stopped eating meat and drinking Ladakhi tea with its high butter content, to endure a diet of cold rice, raisins, and cheese. Dead animals from previous caravans were to be counted in the hundreds on these mountains. Spices, bales of tea, and other merchant wares had been discarded by other caravans. The Barrett party won through the Karakoram Pass only to be confronted by ten days of continuous snow. The Hindu Tash Pass, a high-elevation shortcut into the Tarim basin, loomed ahead as an especially formidable adversary under these conditions. Yaks were purchased—"mine seemed to be the biggest of the lot, a great shaggy beast which grunted like a pig and ground his teeth most horribly"—but even these sure-footed creatures had to turn back when within 400 feet of the pass summit. The attempt to win passage through the Hindu Tash Pass was finally abandoned. They retraced their steps, and took the traditional lower route to Sanju, arriving June 18.

Huntington and Barrett made their separate ways to Khotan, escorted by "hangers on" who had learned that Peking had ordered aid for the two American travellers. Officialdom at Khotan now proved to be a hindrance. Preparations for the journey eastward through the desert basins were delayed, and all the while the warmer weather of the summer began to pass. Even so, a thirteen-day stay in Khotan provided a rest for the two travellers, and enabled Huntington to complete his notes and correspondence, read more of Hedin and Stein, experience his first thirty course meal with "eggs from a past generation," and send more seeds to his father, and some to the Office of the Agrostologist, Bureau of Plant Industry, U.S. Department of Agriculture.

From Khotan Huntington and Barrett travelled east, entered the foothills of the Kwen Lun Mountains, then followed the numerous rivers northward into the desert through lower spurs of naked rock, green pastured uplands, foothills covered with fine sand traversed by ribbon valleys, piedmont slopes of naked gravel, set amidst reeds, tamarisk mounds and dissected sand dunes, and finally into the billowing sand which announced the Takla Makan. Numerous transects were made following these south to north flowing rivers. Shrines were visited, manuscripts were read, oral traditions were studied, pottery and wood documents were excavated and gathered, ruined villages and cities were located. Rivers, water courses, and abandoned fields were examined for their salinity, and the tax system was studied providing data on villages which had moved in the recent past. Intellectually excited Huntington wished to make a thorough "investigation of the climate of antiquity." He took photographs, stopped regularly to correct the map, excavated numerous sites, and spent time with indigenes in studying folklore which might advance the study of climatic pulsations. Indeed, he had already begun to plan a program for the months ahead:[11]

> What I should like to do would be to stay in Central Asia till next spring, spend the summer in Persia and Turkey, and the fall in Palestine and the countries south of the Mediterranean. Such a division of time would throw the maximum amount of light upon the problem which I am trying to solve.

He wrote to Davis of his wishes, then applied to the Carnegie Institution for the necessary funds. But Barrett did not share Huntington's enthusiasm for spending so much time in the search for evidences of desiccation; he wished to continue working with his phototheodolite in the mountain border of the Lop basin.[12]

So, on September 18, 1905, they agreed to separate. The men and animals were divided and Huntington continued eastward across the southern margin of the basin. Here he found ruins visited by Hedin and Stein and a few not previously noted by European explorers. He corrected the known map of parts of the Tarim basin, studied several medieval maps, and gathered much folklore. He also had chronicles of Moslem invasions read to him, an intimacy due, in part, to his kindness in paying to help fence a Moslem holy place, an act that Huntington's men appreciated deeply. He was considerate of the men and won them to his cause, and they worked most earnestly for their "Sahib." Indeed, in treating him as a Sahib, in selecting his food, choosing his camel, preparing his bed, removing his boots, leading his mount across rivers, they became annoyingly ever-present; this encouraged Huntington to write "I'm tired of being somebody and long to play nobody." But he had the good sense to let the men work for "a big Sahib." Later, Ghulam Rassul Galwan—one of Huntington's caravan bashi's—reflected on the qualities of Sahib leadership in *Servant of Sahibs*.[13] Huntington ordered his caravan east at a slow rate, stopping at prearranged places while he and two of his men made transects along many of the rivers

that flow from the Kwen Lun mountains north into the Lop
basin. The arrangement was not without its uncertainties, and
occasionally the Huntington party had difficulty in finding its
caravan. But it was in this way that Huntington journeyed from
Khotan to Lop Nor, a distance of 700 miles. He counted seventeen rivers "worthy of notice by reason of their size or because
they support oases." Journeying north into the desert beyond
the point where the rivers sink into the zone of piedmont grav-
els, Huntington noted dead and dying vegetation at places fifty
and sixty miles from the surface-flowing river which had once
kept this vegetation alive. He also observed that the minor
streams which lost themselves in the piedmont gravel "have
old channels never occupied now by running water, and therefore in process of being filled with sand." In support of his con-
tention that the rivers had withered during historic time, on
thirteen of the seventeen rivers he mapped the ruins of towns
"dating usually from the Buddhist era, a thousand or more years
ago." On six of the thirteen rivers the ruins were seen to be of
one age; on five of the rivers they were of two ages; and on two,
of three ages. The older ruins were father downstream than the
the more recent ones and of them Huntington wrote, "it would
be impossible again to locate towns of equal size in the same
places, unless a far better system of irrigation were introduced."

Huntington studied with especial care the Dumuka stream,
the Niya river, and the Endereh river. Mounted on his faithful
"but obstinate" camel, Black Eyes, and aided by his men he
collected wood documents, parchments, stone carvings, and pottery from carefully mapped sites in order that he might later
confirm or dispute Stein's dating of some of these settlements.
After working along the Endereh river for some days Huntington applied his theory of desiccation to the evidences afforded by
that river and the vegetation, topography, and artifacts to be
found in its previous course:[14]

> At Endereh, a hundred miles farther east (of Niya) the result
> was not only depopulation, but the decay of all manner of arts
> and a complete change in the mode of life of the people. At the
> beginning of the Christian era Tuholo, as Endereh was then
> called, was a prosperous oasis with ten or fifteen thousand in-
> habitants as I estimated after traversing the ruins. The houses
> were well-built structures of sun-dried brick, or adobe, sup-
> ported by hewn timbers of fine white poplar, and were admir-

ably adapted to withstand the cold of winter and the heat of
summer. Agriculture flourished, as is evident from the remains
of orchards and fields which apparently surrounded every house.
The people were adept in the art of pottery-making; and their
crude artistic sense displayed itself in the designs with which
they had ornamented their utensils. Other decorative arts such
as painting, wood-carving, and the moulding of clay and plaster
into images and floral designs for temples appear to have been
practised assiduously in all the oases of that time. Wood-turning
was common; writing was apparently so well known an accomplishment that private persons often wrote letters and kept accounts. During the first four or five centuries of the Christian
era, Tuholo appears to have lost much of its former size though
it was still a considerable town with forts, temples, and shrines,
and a golden statue of Buddha as an ancient Chinese pilgrim
reports. Nevertheless the time of its destruction was at hand. By
the end of the sixth century the oasis had caused the water to
become too saline for use in agriculture. When the Chinese pilgrim, Hwen Tsiang passed through Tuholo in A.D. 645 he
found nothing but ruins. After the days of Tuholo, if we may
judge from the scarcity of ruins of that period, the water of the
Endereh river was scarcely used at all except perhaps by shepherds until after the Mohammedan conquest about 1000 A.D.
The next ruins worthy of notice are those of the small and decadent walled village of Bilel Konghan which contains the ruins
of a mosque and of houses sufficient for a population of something less than a thousand souls. Apparently the village dates
from the time of slightly improved climatic conditions of which
there are various indications during the Middle Ages. The fall
of Tuholo and the rise of Bilel Konghan were separated by the
Mohammedanist conquest; but this does not appear to have
been responsible for the difference in the civilization of the two
places. The great changes which took place were exactly such
as would naturally accompany desiccation. In architecture fine
timbers of white poplar, hewn and carved, were replaced by the
knotty, unhewn trunks of the wild poplar, apparently because
the increasing salinity of the soil prevented the growth of good
trees. Reeds and tamarisks replaced adobe bricks, probably because when clay becomes saline it loses its adhesive quality. This
may account for the decay of the art of pottery-making, which
would entail that of the subsidiary decorative arts, although
these were perhaps doomed in any case by the Mohammedan

prohibition of pictures. Mohammedanism may have accelerated the decline in the arts of writing and wood-carving though the latter would in any case inevitably have deteriorated because of the growing scarcity of good wood. Other arts decayed in similar fashion, especially agriculture, the greatest of all. Now, in the decadent present, it is practically extinguished. The simple peasants of Endereh, numbering scarcely a hundred, have reverted to the pastoral life of their remote predecessors long before the days of Tuholo. I found them living in small huts of wild poplars and unplastered reeds, here and there as the seasons dictate. All arts are unknown to them save that of spinning the wool of their sheep. War and the advent of Mohammedanism may explain part of the changes at Endereh. They cannot explain the decay of agriculture, nor the diminution from a population of perhaps ten thousand at the beginning of the Christian era to nothing five or six centuries later, nor the mediaeval recovery of a crude oasis with degenerate arts to a population of less than a thousand, nor the present state of pastoralism and a population of only eighty. At Endereh increasing aridity appears to have caused not only depopulation and change of habits, but the decay of civilization and perhaps a radical change in the character of the people.

Huntington's study of the rivers of Chinese Turkestan had quite convinced him of the validity of his desiccation thesis: "the basin has yielded me some of its best secrets." Before departing the basin he wrote an essay, later revised and published in *The Geographical Journal* as "The Rivers of Chinese Turkestan and the Desiccation of Asia."[15] It attracted the attention of Harvard climatologist Robert DeCourcy Ward, who published a note on it entitled, "The Desiccation of Asia" in the Geographical Record section of the *Bulletin of the American Geographical Society*.[16] Ward could accept the notion of gradual desiccation, but when Huntington developed the pulsatory hypothesis Ward would not endorse his position. Huntington found interest in the physiography of the Tarim basin, and in letters to Davis of July 12 and September 13, 1905, enumerated and described nine physiographic regions. Davis presented this delineation of the Tarim's physiographic provinces before the Association of American Geographers in New York that December[17] and it was later published in the *Bulletin of the American Geographical Society*.[18]

Huntington and the caravan journeyed across the Tarim basin, reaching Lop Nor in late December, then travelled across the salt plain of old Lop Nor between December 25 and January 11. Nights were cold, ranging from $-2°F$ to $-17°F$. Huntington reports "one night I actually ate dinner with my plate in the fire." He was obliged to record his daily notes in pencil for his pen had frozen. Difficulties to be surmounted included a lack of fresh water, a lack of firewood which could provide some warmth for the men, lack of fodder for the camels, and huge salt blocks in the form of pentagonal prisms 5 to 12 feet in diameter heaved into positions resembling a ploughed field. The worst trouble confronted Huntington when his camels were lured away one night by wild camels. Handum Bai, one of the native caravan men, gave pursuit, and after more than a forty mile chase across the Lop basin returned with the animals. The caravan moved with extreme difficulty, but Huntington did not allow physical obstacles to hinder his search for further evidences of desiccation. He travelled seven days in an "abomination of desolation" through an area which old Chinese itineraries and other records showed to be the main trade route to the west at the beginning of the Christian era. The only sign of life was a dead plover and the deeply buried roots of some reeds which must have flourished in the expanded Lop Nor of a previous epoch. He traced two roads around the old salt bed of Lop Nor, which added eight or nine miles to an east-west journey, and which he felt could only be explained by a one time larger lake. This notion placed him in opposition to the conclusion reached by Hedin. Huntington also found five or perhaps six different lacustrine strands and a number of hitherto undiscovered settlement sites at Lulan, quite deserted in 1906, all of which encouraged him to write,[19] "A month ago I thought that in its rivers we had found the best that Chinese Turkestan can offer to the geographer, but I believe Lop-Nor is better."

Later, Huntington published a twenty-one-page article, "Lop-Nor—A Chinese Lake" in the *Bulletin of the American Geographical Society*. Part I was entitled "The Unexplored Salt Desert of Lop,"[20] and Part II "This Historic Lake (Lop Nor)."[21] The article was noticed by Keltie of the Royal Geographical Society, who published, "Prof. Huntington on Lop Nor," a 650-word précis in the Monthly Record of *The Geographical Journal*.[22]

Huntington journeyed on to the Turfan depression via Kuzzil

Singer, Kara Sher, Kumish and Lukchun, where he received a
letter from President Woodward of the Carnegie Institution an-
nouncing that his request for funds to continue his researches
in the lands bordering the Mediterranean had not met with
success. It is doubtful that this letter occasioned Huntington
much disappointment. He had been in the field at a distance of
approximately 10,000 miles from his home for more than a
year; he had journals and diaries filled with notes awaiting more
permanent expression, photographs and artifacts to care for,
and maps in need of correction. His theory concerning climate
and man began to assume detailed form, as he wrote while at
Lukchun:[23]

> The work that I laid out in the beginning as essential is all
> finished and all of it has been successful. Yesterday made a
> fine ending to the main work, for I found the facts, beds of coal
> alternating with lacustrine deposits, which put the second of
> my chief theories on a footing firm enough to command respect.
> It was all the more pleasant to come on the facts, as long ago
> in Persia I had come to the *a priori* conclusion that they must
> exist somewhere.
>
> The first of the two theories to which I refer is the familiar
> one that the climate of the earth as a whole has been changing
> during the last few thousand years and is still changing, thus
> profoundly influencing geography and history. The second
> theory, a gradual growth during the last two years, supposed
> that climate has always been subject at times to times of rapid
> fluctuation like the glacial period, preceded and followed by
> more stable conditions either of aridity or of comparative mois-
> ture; and further it supposes that each kind of climate has left
> its appropriate record in the rocks of the earth's crust, whereby
> we can gather up the history of the earth much more definitely
> than is now possible, and can tell exactly what events in one
> part of the earth were coeval with others elsewhere, and where
> and when first and under what physical conditions animals and
> plants of various kinds developed. And if, as I tentatively be-
> lieve, the climate changes of the earth are due to fluctuations in
> the heat of the sun, a study of their sequence and intensity may
> open to us many secrets as to the nature of the sun and thus of
> the nature, origin and future of the universe. Understanding of
> climate and its influence would advance immeasurably our in-
> sight into astronomy, geology, geography and history, almost as

evolution has advanced biology, botany, zoology, and physiology. Of course I am a crank whose horizon is filled by a single subject; and of course you do not see how from so small a seed as climate I can get so big a tree. I only see it dimly myself, and it will take years of study before even I shall be convinced that it is true. But it keeps growing by logical steps as it did yesterday when I became convinced that the coal theory is at least tenable or today when the astronomical possibilities dawned on me.

Huntington then travelled via Shikho, Kurte, and Omsk to Moscow, arriving in Milton, Massachusetts early in May, 1906. He had been absent from a close-knit family for sixteen months. Not infrequently he expressed the concern that he should be at home sharing domestic duties and economic responsibilities with his aging parents. Yet a force seemed to be urging or even compelling him to investigate his notion of climatic pulsations which he felt held such great possibilities for the interpretation of history and of which he was architect and author. He was committed to this scientific pursuit, not as a hobby, but as a task that demanded his constant and continued attention. During the time he was alone in Central Asia, the scientific urge was dominant, but it was correspondence from his family, W. M. Davis, and J. S. Keltie that sustained in him an inner optimism and outward good spirits. From his family Huntington received numerous letters; his father encouraged him with critical appraisals of the articles and journal notes that he sent home; his mother sent him Bible references and news of a domestic and social nature; his brothers and sisters also wrote to him and after learning that their brother had eaten wild camel and eggs from a past generation, composed a ditty:

> Here sits a man who will not mind
> Devouring food of any kind
> For nightmare cannot phase a man
> Whose braved the wilds of Turkestan.

From Davis—who besides carrying on personal correspondence, published excerpts from Huntington's letters in the *Bulletin of the American Geographical Society*,[24] and read other excerpts before the Association of American Geographers—Huntington received encouragement and a quiet assurance that his work had scientific validity. J. S. Keltie, secretary of the Royal Geographical Society, sent Huntington most encouraging letters[25] and printed excerpts from Huntington's letters in *The Geographical Journal* and in the London *Times*,[26] even printing a note in the Society's *Journal* when Huntington passed through London on his return to the United States.[27] Doubtless too, Keltie's correspondence with Huntington was in part responsible for G. T. Goldie's remarks in the 1906 presidential address to the Royal Geographical Society,[28] "I believe that Mr. Huntington has done much to solve some of the problems connected with the geography, the desiccation, and the archaeology of Central Asia."

With the completion of the Barrett Expedition, Huntington needed to find a source of income and to write an extended report of his recently completed Central Asia journey. He wished to secure a university position. Davis knew of Huntington's desire and had already inquired of his geographer friends if they knew of a vacancy. On April 4, 1906 Davis wrote to Huntington:[29] "Jefferson of Ypsilanti said he thought he had a place where you could work for a year at least and more than cover expenses, but the difficulty there would be a lot of class work and few facilities for your writing."

Within a week of writing this letter, Davis had secured from Harvard University an Edward William Hooper Fellowship for Huntington, tenable during the academic year 1906–1907. It paid $1,000 and left the recipient free to travel or reside where his purpose was best served. Davis urged Huntington to accept the grant, and to inquire of Keltie on his homeward journey whether the Royal Geographical Society would be interested in publishing the findings of the expedition. As to Huntington's position for the following year, Davis wrote:[30]

> It has often occurred to me that such a place as librarian or editor, under the American Geographical Society in New York, would in many ways be more appropriate than a place as a teacher; for I fancy you are cut out to be a studious sort of a geographer all your life; and the A.G.S. is in need of just that kind; but at present they have no vacancy. They are rich, and able to maintain a strong body of workers, with good collections; and I have still hopes that something may come of my idea there.

Map of the Lop Basin and Neighboring Parts of In

By Ellsworth Huntington.

Scale 1:5,643,000.   1 inch = 89 miles

The ovals in the sandy areas indicate that the sand is arranged
in long parallel dunes.

- - - - - - - Routes in 1903 and 1905-6.
┼┼┼┼┼┼ Railroads

Unshaded areas in the Lop Basin
indicate vegetation

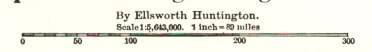

CONTINUATION OF MAP AT LOWER LEFT HAND CORNER SHOWING KASHMIR, LADAKH ETC.

Asia

▦ Piedmont Gravel	○ Inhabited Town or Village
░ Sand	✛ Ruins
〰 Clay	● Spring
▭ Salt Plain	

In Milton, Huntington ensconsed himself in his room, laid out his journals, diaries, artifacts, correspondence and proceeded to write. Numerous papers that he had begun in Chinese Turkestan were completed, typed and sent to the *Bulletin of the American Geographical Society, The Geographical Journal,* and the *Bulletin of the Geological Society of America.* They include: "The Rivers of Chinese Turkestan and the Desiccation of Asia;" "Pangong: A Glacial Lake in the Tibetan Plateau;" "The Vale of Kashmir;" "Lop-Nor—A Chinese Lake;" "The Depression of Turfan, in Central Asia." One article, which necessarily had to await library study, was written in Milton, "Archaeological Discoveries in Chinese Turkestan."[31]

He wrote to Professor John E. Wolff of the Harvard Geology Department on May 21:[32]

> Three years ago I believe that the Department of Geology voted that I had done enough work in residence at Harvard to allow me to become a candidate for the degree of Ph.D. I should like to try for the degree provided there is a fair chance of my passing the required examinations. In the subjects of Mineralogy and Paleontology I have done nothing since I studied them four years ago, and am therefore very rusty. In the press of other work I do not feel that I can take time to study them up again. If, under the circumstances you think that there is any chance of my success, will you kindly inform me when the examinations will be held and in what subjects. For a thesis I offer my reports in No. 26 of the Publications of the Carnegie Institution.

Huntington's application was accepted but his offer of work already published did not satisfy the thesis requirement; so after consultation with Davis he settled to the task of writing a thesis entitled, "The Funtion of Climate in the Determination of Geologic Synchronism." Simultaneously he wrote a manuscript entitled "The Pulse of Asia."[33] Frequent consultations on these subjects were held with Davis in Cambridge, which were both encouraging and helpful to Huntington. In December, 1906, Davis, who was President of the Harvard Travellers Club, invited Huntington to speak on his recent Asian travels. In a letter dated December 23, 1906, Davis wrote:[34]

> What I said at the close of your story at the H.T.C. meeting was in substance this:

"This is the real thing! It brings to mind some verses I used to
hear as a boy—
    The race ain't always to the swift
    Nor him that fastest runs—
    Nor the battle to them people
    That have the longest guns"

Meanwhile, Davis had chatted with Herbert Gregory, Head
of the Department of Geology at Yale, concerning the possible
employment of Huntington in his department. Davis had sent
Bowman to Gregory in 1905, and proposed that Huntington
now join Bowman, his former fellow student at Harvard in
1902–1903. It seems very probable that Huntington and Gregory discussed the matter in New York at the annual meeting of
the Association of American Geographers that Christmas season, where Huntington delivered a paper which had been growing
upon him for some while, "Changes of Climate and History." In
it Huntington presented numerous evidences which he believed
pointed to the probability of climatic change within historic
time. He insisted that these changes were of longer duration than
the Brückner thirty-year plus cycle, and of shorter duration than
a glacial epoch. He insisted that such climatic pulsations were
of enormous consequence in understanding recorded history.
The paper was in fact a vital part of the manuscript he was writing—"The Pulse of Asia." Davis led the discussion of the paper
and was enthusiastic for it.[35] It was the third paper that Huntington had read before the Association in three consecutive
years. (Only four other members of the Association had thus
far made a similar contribution—Cyrus C. Adams, Isaiah Bowman, A. P. Brigham, and Davis himself).

Little research was being done by American geographers with
regard to either Asia or the notion of desiccation. Gregory
needed a geographer to teach an Asia course at Yale and realized that Huntington was one of only a very few men in American geography who could do so. Consequently Gregory offered
him a position as instructor, with a salary of $1,000 for the year.
But, confident of a successful publication with the "Pulse of
Asia," already with considerable travel experience and a substantial bibliography to his credit, Huntington indicated to
Gregory that he had hoped to obtain a higher salary.[36] Upon
learning of these circumstances from Gregory, Davis wrote to
Huntington:[37]

If universities wanted men tested in capacity for desert trips, your book would be of much aid and doubtless it will be of aid in showing your capacity for research and product. But university presidents (when looking for professors and assistant professors) while recognizing the importance of research, want men of proved capacity in the way of teaching, controlling and inspiring young Americans, and in those respects your book must have less value. My own feeling is that you are not likely to get any offer so good as that which Yale presents—the delightful position, chance to grow, fine association, appreciative colleagues.

Since Huntington had great admiration for Davis as a geographer, and respected his judgment, he accepted the appointment, was formally awarded the position by the Prudential Committee of the Yale Corporation February 18, 1907, and remained in association with Yale (with the exception of some months, 1915–1917) until his death in 1947.

Huntington completed a thesis of 25,000 words and 17 pages of diagrams in which he wrote:[38]

I propose merely to present certain facts which, by throwing light on the true nature of glacial periods, seem to indicate that in the case of the Permian glacial period we may perhaps ere long be able to correlate the strata of widely separated regions on a climatic basis. Thus, as it were, we shall pass a horizontal plane through the rock series of all parts of the world; and, in the middle of geological time, shall secure a datum-level by which to test the accuracy of our present paleontologic and stratigraphic methods of determining synchronism.

Some of the thought of this thesis was incorporated into an article, later published as "Some Characteristics of the Glacial Period in Non-Glaciated Regions."[39] As a supplement to this thesis, he submitted to Harvard Secretary Hurlburt, September 19, 1906, a list of articles both published and unpublished which would support his candidacy for a Ph.D. degree:

Himalayan Province of Ladakh
Karakorum Plateau
Physiography of Lop or Tarim
People of Lop or Tarim Basin

Geographic Influence of Loess, per Ellsworth Huntington, Rich-
thofen and Others
Vegetation and Desiccation
Lop Nor, Past and Present including Huntington's Journey
Turfan, a Province due to a Geologic Fault
Relation of Climate to History

By unanimous vote of the division Huntington passed his preliminary examination on February 16, 1907. But later, on May
25th, he failed final examination for the Ph.D. degree. On the
advice of Davis, Huntington submitted as his thesis:

A Geological and Physiographic Reconnaissance in Central
Turkestan
The Basin of Eastern Persia and Sistan
The Function of Climate in the Determination of Geologic
Synchronism

Huntington had been preparing the latter for publication
in the *Bulletin of the Geological Society of America*. Davis
suggested that he submit it as part of his thesis. In hurrying
to complete the study Huntington's work left something to be
desired. The Committee agreed to accept the first two papers
as Huntington's thesis. Examination followed: "Prof. Ward expressed his opinion that the candidate disclosed a deficiency in
his knowledge of climatology, a subject chiefly considered in his
thesis."[40] Professor Robert DeCourcy Ward later wrote to Huntington intimating that he should have taken his course in climatology, though apparently Davis had advised against it.[41]

The knowledge of Climatology which I should expect you to
have, considering that you have made such a specialty of climatic changes, would be about what the men get in my course,
Geology 19. That course requires a pass-mark in Geology B,
which is based upon Davis's Elementary Meteorology, together
with four hours a week of laboratory work, for a half-year. Of
course, I give a good deal that is not in Davis, but if you know
that book, you have the major part of the work. In Geology 19
the text book is Hann's Handbook, and the additional matter
you can, in a few weeks, find in my new book, Climate, to be
published by the Putnams. Those two books practically cover
the course, although there is also laboratory work, and outside

reading. There are parts of Hann which I omit, and many of the tables are omitted, or much cut down, but the text is studied pretty solidly, from beginning to end. I may say that we have lately come pretty strongly to the view that Climatology should be part of the equipment of any geologist. In your case that view is naturally a well-founded conviction, in view of the nature of the work you have done.

That Ward should write in this way is a curiosity. Huntington had already established himself as one of the most travelled and most published men in the history of American geography. He had signed a contract with Houghton Mifflin Company for *The Pulse of Asia*,[42] and had been awarded the Gill Memorial of the Royal Geographical Society. On May 17, 1907, the Harvard Travellers Club awarded him its gold medal "For Explorations in Central Asia," the second medal they had awarded since the inception of the club in 1902. (The first medal had been awarded to W. B. Cabot of Boston "For Explorations in Labrador," May 18, 1906.)

W. M. Davis was deeply disturbed by the outcome of the examination, and the following day wrote to Huntington:[43]

> To me it was a horrid shock—and it still is a torment. It has made me feel as I never did before the difference between individual and departmental action. I had anticipated a great pleasure in this natural culmination of our work together. I cannot yet understand, much less accept the ground of the others who placed so much value on elementary matters (which to be sure have their proper place and time) as compared to proved capacity for large accomplishment in the world's work. I could hardly talk to you connectedly yesterday for anger and grief—and it seemed pretty hard that I, who had advocated and defended your case, should have had the task of explaining how you had not satisfied others. . . . but it is a relief to write to you. I have been reading and writing Italian all day for an anesthetic.
>
> Go on with your work. I will shortly send you my notes on your climate essay.

Upon Davis's advice Huntington wrote to Gregory informing him of the turn of events. Gregory reassured Huntington,[44] "A thing like that should not bother you any. . . . This occurrence does not affect my opinion of you at all and I am expecting good work on your part here next year."

Huntington departed Milton, took a room in New Haven, and had barely commenced his teaching duties at Yale when Houghton Mifflin Company published *The Pulse of Asia*.[45] The volume included a faithful account of his journey from the vale of Kashmir to the Turfan depression, together with two chapters based on previous work, Chapter XVI, "The Ancient Climate of Iran," and Chapter XVII, "The Caspian Sea and Its Neighbours." The introduction and the concluding chapter (XVIII), "The Geographic Basis of History," summarized much of his thought.

In the preface Huntington wrote: "If the book possesses any claim to recognition, it lies in the combination of various hypotheses, hitherto unrelated, into a single consistent geographic theory of history." The theory is revealed throughout the 385 pages of narrative, but receives particular emphasis in the final chapter:[46]

> In studying the geography of Central Asia, we have come to three main conclusions. In the first place, we have seen that not only the habits, but to a large extent the character, of the people of Central Asia appear to have been moulded by physiographic environment. In the second place, we have concluded that, during historic times, climate, the most important factor in that environment, has been subject to notable changes. And finally, it appears that the changes of climate have caused corresponding changes not only in the distribution of man, but in his occupations, habits, and even character. We must now go a step farther, and must see whither we are led if we accept without further question the validity of these three conclusions. If they are true, it appears that geography, especially through its influence upon character, is the basis of history in a way that is not generally recognized; and that climatic changes have been one of the greatest factors in determining the course of human progress.

The study was dedicated

> "To William Morris Davis
> First of Modern Geographers"

Certainly Davis had discussed Huntington's plans for the volume, had read the manuscript, and made significant suggestions to Huntington. After receiving a copy of the book and in reply to Huntington's question whether or not he had overreached himself in the final chapter, Davis replied that he had not completed a reading of the book but that "the whole impression is very favorable."[47] The Geographical Society of Paris immediately awarded Huntington its Charles Maunoir medal in recognition of the book.

Douglas Johnson, formerly of the Massachusetts Institute of Technology, but with Harvard since the death of Shaler in 1906, and a member of Huntington's doctoral committee, endorsed the book in a letter to Huntington:[48]

> Personally, I desire to express to you my very great enjoyment in reading *The Pulse of Asia*, and the very high esteem in which I hold it. You have produced a splendid work, and I wish to join others in extending my heartiest congratulations. I only hope you will devote yourself unreservedly to the prosecution of this same problem in connection with European and other histories. There is a great field in the problems you have opened up, and I earnestly hope you will let me hear more of it.

Reviews of *The Pulse of Asia* appeared in periodicals, magazines, and newspapers throughout the world. It was perhaps one of the most reviewed geography books of the early years of the twentieth century. Certainly it was one of the most reviewed geography books written by an American. The reviews were spendid. It was encouraging for Huntington to see the *New York Times*, the *Times*, and the *India Times*—a sort of literary trilogy on matters of scientific travel—review his book favorably, and to have the *North China Daily News* find value and suggestions in the book relevant for consideration by the Chinese Government. London's conservative *Athenaeum* and *Academy* made room for review and passed remark that the author's "account of his purposeful wanderings leaves nothing to be desired as a storehouse of data for future investigations," and that the author "sees with young, and sometimes with strangely discerning eyes," and is "a close and careful observer of what came under his notice, a skillful delineator of character, and a writer of considerable merit." It is not known how many newspapers reviewed the book, but that accounts appeared in Massachusetts, Florida, and California indicate that reviews were widespread. The geographical periodicals of many countries devoted substantial space to review. Huntington subscribed to The Author's Clipping Bureau, Boston, Massachusetts, in order that he would have ready access to the thought of his reviewers. He retained this service until his death in 1947, a tribute to his prolific hand.

The leading American geographic periodical of the day, the *Bulletin of the American Geographical Society*, offered an unsigned review:[49]

> This is one of the best geographical works of the past year. The journey is used throughout to illustrate significant principles of geography.
>
> This book should have educational influence, because it is a good example of the best geographical exposition of the time. Some readers may be carried along by the entertaining character of the narrative, the striking facts unknown to most of the reading public, and the novel and interesting conclusions adduced from the array of evidence; but at the same time, consciously or unconsciously, they will get some grounding in the principles of scientific geography.

Following the exhaustion of the 1907 edition of the book, the Houghton Mifflin Company reprinted the volume in a slightly revised form in May, 1919.[50] In the revised edition Huntington wrote an introduction on work undertaken in the interim. At the request of Isaiah Bowman he also jotted down some unpublished notes concerning his feelings about *The Pulse of Asia* inside the cover of the copy held by the American Geographical Society. It was the sort of statement that could be thought and put on to paper only after the uncertainties and doubts of a first major publication had been eliminated by a later-won intellectual position.

> After the lapse of 15 years the thoughts that one had before and after a book was completed are inextricably mingled. So far as I can now tell one of my dominant motives in writing The Pulse of Asia was the hope that it would have a profound influence upon the course of human thought. I believed that in "pulsations" of climate I had discovered a key which would unlock some of the great mysteries of history. I also thought that the discovery might have a very practical bearing on the problem of future climatic variations, including not only the great swings whose period is hundreds or thousands of years but the smaller

swings with a period of only a decade or two. Like most young authors I greatly over-rated the importance of my work. This does not mean that I have changed my opinion as to the importance of climate in organic and historical evolution. What I over-rated was the conclusiveness and finality of my own contribution to the subject. One reason for this overestimate was my eagerness to discover something which should be a real help in solving the great problem of how civilization may be made better and mankind made happier. Of course I was ambitious to write a great book, but the desire to help the world along was at least equally strong. Aside from these two motives I wrote with ardor because I had much that I wanted to say. That, after all, is the chief reason why most books are written, if I may judge by my own experience. I had had interesting adventures, I had discovered new facts, and explored new regions: I believed that I had gained a new understanding of how the geographic environment of Central Asia influences its people. Therefore I wrote from sheer love of telling the tale and making others understand the truths and the facts which had appealed to me so strongly.

At first I was pleased with the reviews of the book—except one in The Sun which snubbed the young author who was trying to teach historians who were old enough to be his father. Then I was bitterly disappointed because the world seemed to go on just as before in spite of the wise things I had said. Not till six or seven years had passed and numerous books and articles began to appear with discussions of climatic pulsations did I feel that The Pulse of Asia had been a success.

Chapter V

"Teaching the Sons of Eli Geography"

Huntington was anxious to extend his studies of the climatic hypothesis to continents other than Asia. Ideally he would have passed his time alternately in the field and writing up results. As it was he found it necessary to secure employment. He accepted the teaching post at Yale that H. E. Gregory had offered, and became one of a little band of men helping geography emerge as an academic discipline in the United States. Evidence exists that Yale authorities found Huntington's classroom performance lacking; this notion persists in the oral tradition of the discipline. Yet in corresponding with his one-time students for this same period (1907–1915), and with students of a later date one is obliged to accept the collective memory of Huntington as a little man with very large ideas, not teaching in pedagogic vein, but enthusiastically offering his thought and experiences in inimitable fashion, working on a research frontier himself, and taking his students to that line each class period.

Huntington arrived in New Haven in September, 1907, and was given lodgings in the West Divinity School. Yale's 208th year was about to begin. Straggling students, donkey carts containing battered furniture, competing boardinghouse keepers, and the reopening of book shops characterized the annual pageant in the elm-shaded streets. Doric columns, white spires, Gothic towers, rows of colonial style frame houses and dormitories were all part of the college town which boasted one eighth of a million inhabitants, a population larger than any other city in the state. Six railway lines offered convenient access to Boston and New York, while the "Haven" knew the ships from both Occident and Orient. A substantial industry in guns, clocks, corsets, and rubber goods brought employment and prosperity to a community conscious of a civic responsibility. The citizenry had created four parks and a spacious green, and a "New Haven Civic Improvements Committee" investigated such problems as the damage effected by the canker worm and high winds to the elms that had earned for the town the sobriquet, "City of the Elms." The Yale of President Arthur Twining Hadley could no longer be contained in the city area bounded by Chapel, College, Elm, and High Streets; it began to expand its domain northwest of the green. A female supplement to the Yale student body had been provided in 1893 by the creation of the New Haven Normal School. This was the Yale and New Haven that Huntington knew at the outset of his forty-year academic career with Yale University.

In 1907 Yale did not have a Department of Geography. The geographers formed a minor part of the Geology Department notwithstanding that Daniel Coit Gilman had been appointed to a professorship of physical and political geography in the Sheffield Scientific School in 1863, which he held until called to the presidency of the University of California in 1872. Gilman's work was continued by William H. Brewer who took the classes in physical geography until 1898. The President's Report offers that[1]

> Up to 1898, the science of geography received little attention at Yale and the idea that there is some connection between geography and history was met with great scepticism by many of the faculty. Before Professor William G. Brewer took the classes in physical geography, in the early nineties, there had been no attempt to study the relation and he was the first to consider the topography of the earth as an influence on the tribal movements and habits of man.
>
> In that year (1898) this course was turned over to Professor H. E. Gregory, '96, and altered in its title to "Environmental Influences on Man," which was suggested by Professor William G. Sumner, who, in his work in Anthropology, had felt the need for such a course for some time. This course eventually grew into the one now known as "Physical and Commercial Geography" in which the elements cf physical geography were added to the bearing of physical factors on man's method of doing things. The subjects of physical geography were studied, but only as they influenced man. . . .
>
> As the number of students taking the course increased, there arose the need for more instructors, and those at the head of the department decided to make an attempt to fill these positions with men who were specialists on various countries.

Gregory (chairman of the Geology Department) stated that the acquisition of Isaiah Bowman (1905), Hiram Bingham (1907), and Ellsworth Huntington (1907) were stages in his

program for a geography department. He had also acquired
Angelo Heilprin and Leonard M. Tarr (1903), Avard Bishop
(1904), George Surface (1908) and Theodore H. Boggs
(1908). He sought other geographers.[2]

> It is planned to increase the number of specialists on the re-
> gional geography of the world so that Yale may have men for
> Europe, Polynesia and Africa. . . . To keep the department up
> to date, it demands that those who are engaged in teaching
> should have at least one year out of every three for exploration.
>   When these plans are completed, Yale will have men in all
> parts of the world engaged in exploration.

It was to this galaxy of minds, and in a milieu of intellectual excitement, that Huntington was added when he commenced his
teaching duties on September 26, 1907. Huntington, already acquainted with Bingham and Bowman from his Harvard days,
soon established a good rapport with geologists Barrell, Dana,
Lull, Robinson, and Schuchert. "This group of men reacted intellectually on one another in their daily intercourse," wrote
Charles Schuchert;[3] certainly they were active in both the field
and in the library. Bowman had undertaken the first of three
field trips to South America in 1907 and had written numerous
articles resultant to this trip, prior to the publication of his *Forest Physiography*. Bingham wrote many articles on South America, culminating in *Across South America* (1911), was Yale
delegate to the First Pan American Scientific Congress, Santiago,
Chile, 1908, and uncovered Machu Picchu, lost city of the In-
cas. Avard Bishop wrote on geography in the universities
abroad, on the nature of commercial geography, and was one of
three stalwarts who manned sections of the course "Physical
and Commercial Geography" which essentially formed the back-
bone of the geographic offering. Albert G. Keller, who had been
appointed assistant professor of the Science of Society in 1902,
contributed greatly to the geographic offering. He was a dedicated student and disciple of William Graham Sumner, who
supported the work in geography. Bishop and Keller joined
H.E. Gregory in writing *Physical and Commercial Geography*,[4]
a text for that fundamental course. Two years later Keller and
Bishop wrote *Commercial and Industrial Geography*.[5] Both of
these books were read by Yale geography students, and both
were adopted in classes throughout North America. Huntington

read parts of both texts in manuscript form at the authors' request.

Gregory's stewardship of departmental matters augured well for the cause of geography at Yale, but the ranchman from Nebraska had little faith in a Yale that did not employ his talents as he would have wished: "my influence has gone for little." Gregory much preferred to be "doing things." He took up geological work in Connecticut, was an inspector of Connecticut high schools, and then undertook work for the Federal government in the desert regions of Arizona and Utah in an effort to improve the living conditions of the Navajo and Hopi Indians. On one such mission in 1910 after outfitting "with some pretty mouldy supplies" he came close to losing his life by food-poisoning while helping the Indians locate water sources. He lost thirty pounds in weight, and much of his emotional energy. Withal he was the administrative spokesman for geography at Yale. Under his stewardship the geographers were well served. Between the years 1907 and 1911 Gregory invited into his department five men (other than himself), who at one time or another held the presidency of the Association of American Geographers.[6] He also secured pay increases for the geographers. Huntington's salary was $1,000 in 1907, $1,400 in 1909 and $2,000 in 1913. And when the geographers wished to absent themselves from the campus, Gregory arranged that too. Huntington did not sit on any committees and in fact allowed himself to become something of a recluse. Huntington later realized this and reminisced in 1926:[7]

> . . . the nature of my work, especially in its early phases, kept me by myself a great deal. As a result I failed to cultivate the habit of remembering names and faces and knowing the little details of the lives and careers of the people around me. I failed to do the thing which makes a man a good politician. . . .
>
> A second mistake was of the same kind, and yet I am not sure that it was a mistake. When I began teaching it was with the understanding that I was to be an investigator rather than a teacher. I liked teaching, but I loved research. Therefore, I let the research crowd my teaching to the wall. It might have been wiser if I had devoted a few years primarily to teaching, and then gone back to research. Yet if I had done that and if I had devoted more time to companionship, I am not sure whether I would have done as much as I have in research.

Be it remembered that is was Gregory who maintained the presence of a geographic endeavour within the department of geology. When the University of Chicago geographers invited Bowman to join their department in 1908 he journeyed to Chicago, received their offer, but chose to remain at Yale.[8] It was Gregory who had arranged for Albrecht Penck, Professor of Geography at the University of Berlin, and the Kaiser Wilhelm Professor of Political Science at Columbia 1908–1909, to give the 1908 Silliman lectures at Yale,[9] where his son Walther was studying. And it was Gregory who was largely responsible for bringing the annual meeting of the Association of American Geographers to New Haven in 1912. When Gregory relinquished the chairmanship of the department owing to ill health, ("I'm sailing pretty close to the wind now") and passed the title on to geologist Charles Schuchert, the cause of geography was lost. Heilprin's death in the summer of 1907 hurt the cause of geography at Yale; he had fired imaginative minds and encouraged enrollment in geography courses by being the first scientist to ascend Mount Pelée after the eruption of 1902, and by constantly writing and lecturing to audiences in New Haven and elsewhere of his exploits. Three years later William Graham Sumner died, and although his devoted student A. G. Keller remained for many years to teach "the Science of Society" as offered by his mentor, Keller could never support "Physical and Commercial Geography" in quite the same way as had his intellectual ancestor. Nevertheless Keller did teach with the geographers for several years, and at Sumner's suggestion Keller created a museum to support the introductory geography course (Herrick Hall 1905). Sumner, preaching "Sumnerology" as his peers called it, had been an aid to the geographic cause. President Hadley noticed the support in more than one of his Presidential Reports.[10]

Then, too, a joint Columbia–Yale program established in 1905–1906 pursuant to a suggestion of anthropologist Franz Boas, for the purpose of preparing students for consular or commercial purpose in the Far East, never did attract the numbers of students envisaged. When the Yale curriculum was reformed in 1911, the students electing geography courses further dwindled. Geography had not won its way as a discipline, at least in a fashion firm enough to persuade Yale of its inherent worth.

In this milieu Huntington initially taught "Geography of Asia," shared two sections of "Physical and Commercial Geography" with Gregory and Bowman, offered "Geographic Controls in

History" with Bowman, and shared "Geology with Field and Laboratory Work" with Barrell.[11] He was also listed as one of several faculty members who offered "Selected Studies in Language, Literature, History and the Natural and Social Sciences."[12] In 1909 he offered "Geography of Europe" and in the same year shared "Anthropogeography" with Isaiah Bowman which replaced their jointly offered "Geographic Controls in History." His courses were adequately attended, but he did not develop a sustained student following. This was in part attributable to Huntington's preference for undertaking field work in the spring and summer semesters. When the journeying, exploration, and note-taking had been completed he would write of his findings in essays and books. Frequently he engaged himself in that manner from February until October. His own priorities placed field study and research before his teaching duties, which meant that students had access to him only for a limited period of the year. It did not mean that Huntington attached any less significance to his teaching, or that he thought any less of the rôle of the teacher. Certainly Huntington possessed the necessary attributes for successful teaching. He was kind, patient, knew his subject matter, and always found time to help those in need.

He had previously taught a variety of classes at Euphrates College, 1897–1901. Since that time he had undertaken much field study and it is improbable that he was unsure of his performance. He devoted a great deal of effort to developing the courses which he taught. His "Asia" course was almost certainly the finest of his offerings, for in this area Huntington could impart a vast reading knowledge and firsthand travel experience to students with that talent which he possessed for presenting the complex in a simple manner. He built the course from his own experiences; the heat, the cold, the physiographic grandeur, the dietary deficiencies, and all else that he had beheld in his three Asiatic sojourns became a part of his course. He created a course outline, prepared written notes for each of his lectures, listed required reading for each week—then questioned the students on their reading—and revised the course at the end of each year. As the years passed Huntington himself published much literature concerning Asia which became required reading in the course. There seems to be no record of any other college offering a course in the geography of Asia at that time, although intermittent offerings appeared in the catalogues of the normal schools.[13]

Huntington was a man small in stature, who wore steel-rimmed glasses, and whose dome-shaped head became largely bald at an early age. Hard of hearing, he held a cupped hand to his ear when listening to students; later he adopted a hearing aid. Serious, intent on his subject, he rarely displayed emotion in the classroom. His persistent industry could not but show through and impress his students with the competence of their instructor. And his students learned to appreciate, even if they could not follow his example, the value of hard, sustained intellectual effort. He used slides and photographs which he had taken in far-away lands. His examinations were searching, but his marking was gentle. Of Huntington's classes Edward J. Dimock (Yale class of 1911) reports that "many who elected them were looking for something different from the tough classical and mathematical courses that made up most of the college curricula of those days. Many who came to loaf stayed to work."[14] Huntington was so intensely bound up with what he taught that his students quite sensed his enthusiasm, which proved contagious. Henry Hobson (Yale class of 1914) has written:[15]

> . . . He believed so thoroughly in what he was talking about that he would become quite intense and at times excited . . . there was already a controversy going on as to the validity of Huntington's theory, ideas and deductions. We would run across this in some of the books and magazines assigned for reading. Some of us in his class made rather a game of getting questions which would, we hoped, put him on the spot. These questions might be about some point in the controversy then going on, or perhaps a question about history or man's behavior, which we thought was in conflict with Huntington's position. He had a facile mind which enabled him to answer or parry our questions in a way we admired.

And he must have inspired the student who, more than fifty years later, could write:[16]

> . . . He was a superb teacher, so fitted, so devoted, so "at home" in the field he loved. He imparted his knowledge easily and interestingly, because he lived his work, and he made the instruction most appealing, and I recall excursions to clay pits in North Haven, as well as visits to East Rock and West Rock, to note

similar and corresponding strata in both, but the course itself was truly the man's inspiring personality, and his great inquisitiveness, and would be remembered that way. In later years, having seen the Grand Canyon, Bryce, and Zion, I knew then, as did he, that geology gives us a key to the patience of God. His omnipresence bursting through everywhere, which Shakespeare pictured as "sermons in stones."

Huntington offered his courses to students who desired them. He took them on field trips, escorted them through contemporary developments in the field, and, in an impersonal way, offered the benefits of his own travel and research experiences, revealing to them a world unknown. Courses were ventures in personal knowledge offered in scholarly fashion, and men like Huntington were simultaneously sharing in the establishment and the dissemination of the discipline. The man was both active scholar and teacher. Textbooks were few and frequently not suitable for the courses offered; so Huntington's first three books— *The Pulse of Asia, Palestine and Its Transformation, Asia: A Geography Reader*—which were published while he was at Yale, helped fill a pedagogical need. Geography was not an established discipline in United States higher education at the time; in fact original scholarship was almost a necessary prerequisite for teaching geography in the university. *The Pulse of Asia* was followed by a flurry of books and articles. He gave numerous public addresses and, more significantly, frequently presented papers before the Association of American Geographers. During the period 1907–1915 he offered seven papers to the membership of that Association and was elected first vice president in 1913.[17] Occasionally he delivered a paper before the Geological Society of America.

During these years Huntington formulated, analyzed, and developed two ideas which were destined to become associated with his life's work. The first of these ideas was that of the occurrence of climatic pulsations within historic time. He travelled Eur–Asia (again) and North America in quest of evidence, searched the literature, and presented his case in a heaped correspondence and in article and book form. The second of his very large ideas developed at this time involved the notion that there exists a climatic optimum for the human being, regardless of that being's race. He measured innumerable performances and found that performance was invariably associated with cyclonic variability, and temperatures approximately 38°F for intellectual activity and 64°F for physical labor. These ideas were of great philosophical import. The pulsatory hypothesis did much to place the drama of history upon an environmental stage; his studies of climate in relation to productivity, and therefore civilization, gave cause to peoples beyond the confines of the humid middle latitudes to receive his findings with dissatisfaction. Huntington enjoyed building his thought in the grand manner, linking thought with thought indifferent to the discipline from which he might borrow. The whole attracted much attention; some reviewers acclaimed, others derided; opponents and disciples took their stand; national geographies adopted a posture, historians and social theorists studied the matter. At Yale, scholarship had been careful, perhaps conservative. It was difficult for the Yale presence to accommodate itself to Huntington's themes, smacking of boundless energy, optimism, and estimate. It was an age when thought was not ventured into print until it had been thoroughly examined and found acceptable. Huntington perhaps offended the Yale taste by too bold theorization. At least the administration found it necessary on more than one occasion to query his credentials, and on other occasions referred to him as an "explorer."

His academic and personal relations within the Department of Geology, however, were quite comfortable. At meetings of the Geology Club, invariably attended by the faculty, and compulsory for students after 1909, formal papers were presented by members of the Geology Department. Huntington attended the meetings regularly and contributed "Post Glacial Changes of Climate" (1908–9), "The Yale Expedition to Asia Minor" (1909–10), and "The Place of Climatic Problems in Geology" (1910–11). He also attended meetings of the Dana Club which were devoted to review of the current geological literature. He established lasting companionships with Henry Canby (literature) and Irving Fisher (Economics). He belonged to the Yale Graduates Club where he liked to take lunch. Yale honored him with membership in Sigma Xi, (1909), honorary membership in the Mining Society of the Sheffield Scientific School (1914), and associated membership in the Society of American Foresters (1915). Yet he did not forget the rejection which Harvard had accorded his bid for a Ph.D. degree. In October, 1908 he wrote to W. M. Davis of that and other matters, which elicited from Davis:[18]

As to that Ph.D.—I would not give another thought to it, as far as Harvard is concerned. Even a degree from Yale now will be of no particular avail, for you have got the start already that the degree is useful in giving. . . . I would not turn aside from your regular work in order to prepare for some one else's examinations.

Still, on February 8, 1909, and under the tutelage of H.E. Gregory, Huntington made formal application for the Degree, Doctor of Philosophy, to Yale University.[19] Since his arrival in New Haven in 1907, Huntington had been continuing "research work in geography under the direction of Professor Gregory" in the amount of ten hours a week. Probably the submitted statement formalized an informal relationship which was geographically productive, alhough to no one end. In February, 1909, Huntington submitted a transcript from Harvard University, a certificate of proficiency in Latin, German, and French, and seven of his publications under the title "Changes in Climate of Recent Geological Time."[20] The works submitted included "A Geological and Physiographic Reconnaissance in Central Turkestan," "The Depression of Turfan in Central Asia," "Some Characteristics of the Glacial Period in Non-glaciated Regions," "The Climate of Ancient Palestine," "Description of the Kurgans of the Merv Oasis." Three men from the Department of Geology constituted Huntington's committee; Joseph Barrell, Charles Schuchert, and Herbert E. Gregory. Of Huntington's work Barrell wrote:[21]

I have read all of the articles published by Ellsworth Huntington as they appeared and cannot speak too highly of them. With a broad training in geography, physiographic geology, history, and languages he has combined an indomitable spirit of research; carrying forward investigations on his own slender resources. He has lived for years and travelled alone in the heart of Asia and has pursued the subject of geologic changes within the historic period.

His combination of qualities has made him admirably fitted for the investigation and he has attained results which I regard as highly important from the geological standpoint. They seem to me equally important from the historical standpoint, but regarding that others are better qualified to speak than myself.

He is now pursuing the same problem in Asia Minor and Syria under the auspices of Yale University.

I most heartily recommend the award to him of the degree of Ph.D., his published articles being accepted as a thesis of the very highest order.

Schuchert reported to Andrew Phillips, Dean of the Graduate School:[22]

I have the honor to report that I have read the seven printed papers combined by Mr. Ellsworth Huntington under the title "Change in Climate of Recent Geological Time." These papers bring together a great mass of observations made in the field and study by the candidate. The information is clearly stated in an interesting style, and convinces me that the writer has good powers of observation and research along new lines.

The writer's view-point is that of physiographer and geologist combining his results with those of human history together showing that far reaching climatic changes have come over Euro-Asiatic arid countries since the beginning of the Christian Era. In this study Huntington is now one of the leaders.

It gives me pleasure to recommend the candidate for the degree of Doctor of Philosophy.

Nominally, the Ph.D. degree was conferred upon Huntington in June, 1909. At that time Huntington was continuing his researches in the lands bordering the eastern extremity of the Mediterranean. The following year he was promoted to the rank of assistant professor.

Yet lore and Yale administration correspondence[23] suggest that Huntington did not perform well in the classroom. Perhaps it was the posture of Huntington's thought which made it difficult for his students to appreciate his presentations. In his classroom offering Huntington rather assumed that his students comprehended the meanings and intricacies of climatic pulsation, desiccation, and his particular brand of environmentalism. However he presented these matters, it may have been expecting too much that students would absorb these large ideas at once, and with sufficient command to warrant their employ as tools only a little later in the same course. And perhaps it was not Huntington's environment that discouraged the burgeoning of geography at Yale! Gregory wrote in a letter to the class secretary of 1896:[24]

> The geographical end of geology is something rather new in America, and I have endeavoured with the aid of capable young men to organize courses to cover this wide field too. Yale College is a particularly unfavorable field for the development of geography, for the departments of history and economics seem to be organized on the theory that there is no such thing as Nature, and that Man is the whole show. Sometimes I feel very much discouraged that geographical work is not more highly thought of by my colleagues, but I am cheered by the recollection that pioneers in any line usually get it in the neck, and can hope for little beyond paving the way for energetic men of a later generation."

However, classes of 20 and 30 students were not uncommon in some of the advanced courses in geography, while enrollment in the introductory courses was very substantial. Behavior of the students at times made the course difficult to manage. Canby and Pierson have written of "rough necks" in the classroom, the hazing of instructors, spitballs thrown, dogs present, and seniors reading newspapers with the lecturer waiting to begin.[25] Huntington was young, short in stature, and new to the faculty. While most of his classes proceeded well enough, he experienced at least one rowdy class:[26]

> My hardest problem is a class of sixty in the Sheffield Scientific School which I have to take because of the death of Professor Heilprin last summer. The subject is physical geography. The difficulty lies in the fact that hitherto this has been a snap course with nothing but illustrated lectures and the fellows do not expect to work. Moreover this particular division has the reputation of being the worst in college so far as conduct in recitation is concerned. They have been trying to play horse with me, and we have been having rather a fight of it.

Huntington did not allow the antics of a few students to disturb his performance; Bowman revealed to Huntington that he had experienced a similar classroom management problem with the introductory course but had silenced his adversaries with "will the gentlemen of the class refrain from their ancestral brays." And yet that one rowdy class may have made itself heard beyond the confines of the Sheffield Scientific School. J. Scott Keltie of the Royal Geographical Society inquired of Harvard economist F. W. Taussig and William Morris Davis whether they thought Huntington was qualified to accept the chair of geography at Cambridge University. Both men wrote to Herbert Gregory on the matter; Gregory was obliged to consider the matter of that unruly class. Davis preferred that his former pupil establish himself in the United States before accepting an appointment abroad. Nevertheless, and for whatever reason, the matter was dropped. Huntington mentioned the "Sheff" class to Davis in a letter[27] which drew from the latter one of his few statements on pedagogics:[28]

> I have been wishing to know how you are getting along down there teaching the sons of Eli geography. . . .
>
> Hard luck to have a disorderly section to begin with. But most of us have had that sort of thing at one time or another. Do not forget that every time they make you visibly angry or confused or disturbed, they have gained a victory. The great thing is to hide your feelings; grin at them in class; then the victory is yours. . . .
>
> Thirty years ago I should not have written in this way. I had some very hard times then; disorder, no interest aroused, and all that sort of thing. My place here was very shaky; Shaler told me so directly once. But I stuck to it; and "won out" in the end. This is for your encouragement, for I expect you to do the same thing; and in quicker order than I did. . . . At the same time you must work awfully hard to make your lectures first class; clear, sharp, interesting, never explaining things that the boys knew beforehand; always explaining clearly things that they do not know; bringing in good illustrations; telling appropriate stories, adventures, items of all kinds; do not be too logical; yet avoid irrelevance; and above all things avoid reciting a piece; don't tell the same story in successive sections. I could fill pages with these truisms; but I dare say you will know them, unwritten.

Of Huntington's teaching historian George W. Pierson has written,[29]

. . . while Ellsworth Huntington's desert experiences were fantastic, and his theories about climate and the pulse of progress little short of epoch-making, he lacked the will or the art to present such materials dramatically—and few of the students exercised enough imagination to grasp the spectacular possibilities.

Leonard Bacon, a member of the Yale Class of 1909, wrote:[30]

Ellsworth Huntington, I am certain, hated lecturing (in which after thirteen chequered years of it, I can heartily sympathize with him), but nevertheless he stays in my mind as someone momentous. The ideas derived from the study of geography and climate that seemed to hover around him rather than to come from him, may have been applied to history with premature enthusiasm. But certainly there was excitement in them. And I cannot escape the belief that, however he may have been wrong in detail, the hypotheses he worked on corresponded with the facts in the large. Also it was something to a boy who had never been ten miles from a highway, to visit Asia in thought, with a man who had sat down in the middle of the Gobi Desert to write up his diary, after the stampede of camels, whose more than probable failure to return would make the continuation of that diary wholly impossible.

If Huntington had taught in a school other than Yale, his classroom method might well have been championed as a pedagogic model. As it was, he was at Yale where teaching by men like Sumner, Cook, and Hastings was drama, wit, rhetoric, eloquence, physical exertion, every bit as much as it was education. President Arthur Twining Hadley himself was noted for his pump handle gesture! Amid this congeries of pedagogic entertainment Huntington stood remote. He delivered his classroom presentations quietly, in a monotone voice, not finding it necessary to dramatize any particular part of the geographer's skein, but offering with objectivity what he had read, seen, and thought. He was going stolidly about the business of earning a living, the while pondering evidences and indices of climatic change during historic time. If a more volatile performance was demanded, it is hard to comprehend the earlier demise of William H. Brewer, "a vast shambling man, with the face of an old ram stretched on the drum of a great head," whose imagination

was rarely in the lecture room "but rather on the deck of a sinking ship in the arctic or following the wild camels of Arizona,
or noting the geography of the Sierras, which he explored, and
where there is a great snow based peak that bears his name."[31]
Brewer gave his students evolution, tips on horseracing, tales of
monkeys, the results of mixed marriages, the ancestry of the
bull dog, gave them his vast energies, and collected his notes in
baskets suspended from the ceiling by pulleys. Yet in 1898 the
geography classes were transferred to the Professor of Geology.
If the quiet, gentle, monotone manner of Huntington's geographic presentation was not congratulated, neither was the
drama of Brewer rewarded. Canby has written that this was an
age at Yale when scientists of the Sheffield Scientific School
were viewed as suspect by the classicists and humanists of Yale
College, that gossip and even jealousy were in the air.[32] "Not
only were individuals jealous of each other, but whole departments. The anthropologists told terrible stories of the vagaries
of the geographers. . . ." Little wonder that geography at Yale
dwindled in the teens of the century and for the next quarter of
a century was represented solely by Huntington. The all-
pervasive university milieu just as much as individual manner-
isms must share responsibility for such a history. While Sven
Hedin was touring Europe, receiving medals and citations from
societies and royalty, being chaired by university students, Huntington was invited to lecture before only limited audiences of
the American Geographical Society, the National Geographic
Society, the Philadelphia Geographic Society, and his alma
mater, Beloit College. These were matters noted only in local
newspapers and the *Bulletin of the American Geographical Society*.[33] There was the difference: geography had not won respect
in the universities of the United States as a subject with a distinct identity and worthy of departmental status. Geography was
still an adjunct to geology and physiography.

During these years Huntington travelled often. After each
journey he preferred to return to New Haven, or Milton, there
to formally record his thought and observations. He visited
Western Asia in 1909, the arid Southwest in 1910, 1911, and
1915, the big trees in California in 1911 and 1912, Yucatan in
1912, and Guatemala in 1913. Most of these travels were commenced early in the year; the summer was spent in writing. Only
the autumn semester remained for teaching, which meant that
Huntington was not well known to the students. Perhaps for this

reason his courses were not in substantial demand. Furthermore, his imaginative geographic scheme was beginning to tempt criticism even on the part of the Yale community.

The Yale administration, mindful of a need for austerity, and regarding Huntington perhaps more as an explorer than as a scholar, was not prepared to accede to Huntington's request in April, 1912, for promotion to a professorship. When Huntington inquired further on the matter of his promotion, Professor Dana of the Geology Department sent letters to R. S. Woodward, President of the Carnegie Institution of Washington, Eduard Brückner, Professor of the University of Vienna, and Albrecht Penck, Professor at the University of Berlin. In the letter Dana stated that Huntington had requested a professorship and to that end evaluations of his work were being sought.

Woodward replied to the letter on November 16:[34]

> . . . I beg to state that in general the Institution has held Dr. Huntington in high esteem. My personal opinion of his work in connection with the Pumpelly Expedition, and especially of his "Pulse of Asia" and "The Burial of Olympia" and other semi-popular papers, has been very favorable. It must be admitted, however, that he is here and there in his writings and in his methods of procedure quite naive if not immature. I am entertaining some fear for him also just now by reason of his tendency to jump from one field of investigation to another instead of concentrating his attention on one thing, or a few things, at a time. Except for these tendencies I should predict for him a brilliant future; but I fear he must undergo the discipline of adversity before he will be able to find himself completely.

Both Penck and Brückner replied to Dana's letter on November 26. Brückner wrote:[35]

> Since you have requested an immediate answer I do not have the time to look at Dr. Huntington's papers again, but I read them sometime ago and I also met Dr. Huntington in October of this year. Therefore I believe that I may give an opinion about his work and about himself. I, too, admire Huntington's great energy and wealth of ideas. His investigations in Central Asia as a member of the Carnegie Expedition prove his capacity to deal with morphological and glacial problems. However I must confess that his conclusions in regard to repetition of the

ice ages in Turkestan seem somewhat premature. Even though he has determined several terminal moraines he has not yet proved that they belong to several different ice ages rather than to several different periods of one and the same ice age. I have the impression after having read his descriptions that his conclusions are not entirely correct.

His investigations concerning changes and fluctuations of climate in Asia are valuable. With the diligence of a bee and a tremendous amount of material he has developed an important thesis. But I cannot relinquish the impression that he has not been sufficiently critical of his material. He takes his data from historical works without examining it properly. He is not sufficiently aware to what degree he may use data as facts. In particular the archaeological results are by no means definitive enough as he himself explains in his work *The Pulse of Asia*. The considerable uncertainty of the facts naturally affect the results in regard to changes of climate. He has shown several times the desire to fit the facts to his theory.

During my visit to Yale Dr. Huntington showed me the results of his investigations in respect to the rings of old trees in their relationship to fluctuations of climate. He has collected very interesting material but again I had the impression that he concluded more from his curves than a cautious man ought to conclude. He claimed in several cases that he saw a parallelism in the curve where I could not see one.

If I may summarize I consider Dr. Huntington as I have stated at the beginning of my letter to be a most capable, energetic and brilliant young scholar, but one who still lacks at least a quietly partial detachment. In his enthusiasm he gets carried away and sometimes departs from the facts. Therefore I cannot really disagree with those who accuse Dr. Huntington of a certain immaturity as you have written. Under these circumstances I would consider it entirely proper if he were advanced in due course rather than given a jump in rank. . . .

Penck wrote to Dana:[36]

I value Dr. Huntington as a very able and productive scholar and I shall be glad if he makes further contributions. But I must confess that sometimes his thoughts run ahead of the facts. He works more with a vital scientific imagination than with a critical faculty. That is a fact which is true of many of the young and eager men and in time, this quality will emerge.

Considering this I believe that it would be very advantageous to Huntington's development if his scientific career did not lead him too quickly to the highest goals. That he will achieve these highest goals and therefore fulfill the position of a full professor properly at some time in the future I have no doubt. But I believe that he will best fill such a position if he does not receive it at too young an age. . . .

Dana made translations of the letters by Brückner and Penck, met with the Administrative Committee and wrote to Hanns Oertel, Dean of the Graduate School:[37]

. . . we feel that the three men (Asakawa, Bowman, Huntington) deserve to be retained; if the Administrative Committee of your Faculty think it wise, they can be put upon what is known as the "second grade," say, for three years. Asakawa, I suppose, we would like to keep indefinitely: he seems to be a rare man for an oriental. The other men are more problematical and any advancement for them should be coupled with a definite statement that the University makes no pledge for their future. This is conspicuously true in the case of Huntington, who has brilliancy but is certainly immature, and whether he will settle down to steady, sound work is a problem. In any case, these two explorers are luxuries. Huntington has the disadvantage of an enormous overestimate of his own importance to the University.

On February 3, 1913, Dana wrote to Huntington informing him that his appointment was to be extended for a further two years and that $500 would be provided by the Graduate School as an addition to his salary. The matter of employ had been settled for the following two years but by the autumn of 1914 the matter was reopened. Since President Hadley had shown warmth towards Huntington's work in the past, had thanked him for numerous of his articles, and had offered the encouragement that he hoped Yale would be able to do better by Huntington than in the past, Huntington wrote to President Hadley of his future at Yale.[38]

May I take this opportunity to say a word as to my future relation to the University. . . .

It is true that I should not think of staying in any position under the grade of a professorship. It is also true that I should not accept any position which prevented me from devoting a considerable part of my time to research, for I am convinced that I can be far more useful in that way than in any other. This does not mean, however, that I do not want to teach and to take my share in the work of the University in other ways. One of my chief regrets has been that there has not been more opportunity for me to come into intimate contact with the students.

I think that I understand how this mistaken idea of my attitude has arisen. In the first place, a few years ago my courses shared the general falling off in numbers which came upon the whole geological department. The actual figures show, however, that the decrease in my courses was by no means so large a percentage as in some of the larger courses such as general geology. When the new course of study went into effect and became fully operative my courses fell to practically nothing. This is because as the schedule is now arranged there are not more than about a dozen students in the whole College who can possibly take my courses, and the hours are so arranged that even those few find it much easier to take other geographical courses.

I ought perhaps to have taken more pains to remedy this condition, but here another thing comes in. During these last few years I have been absorbed in research to such a degree that I have sacrificed vacations, general reading, and all sorts of social pleasures in order to achieve as much as possible, and I presume that, although I did not realize it, I also sacrificed my University work to a certain degree. As you well know from your own experience there is a time in a man's life when all his previous study and experience seem suddenly to flower into such a wealth of new ideas that he is almost dazed. He knows that if he does not pin them down when they come, they are lost and he will not have them as the foundation on which to build the rest of his life's work. That is why I have been so absorbed in my work for the last few years. At last I have reached the point where my ideas are becoming well sifted and tested. Some I have rejected because I saw that I had made a mistake. Other lines of work have been given up because I think that other men will carry them on, or because they do not seem sufficiently broad. This leaves two main subjects on which

I intend to concentrate the rest of my life work. One is such studies as are illustrated by the maps that I showed you the other day, that is, studies of how far the character and achievements of people in different parts of the world are dependent upon climate. The other is an attempt to put the human side of geography upon a firm basis which shall be founded on exact statistics and not upon mere impressions as has too much been the case in the past.

Both of these lines of work fit in with teaching much better than does the work that I have been doing during the past few years. What I should like to do would be to have the course of study changed a little so that I might give one good undergraduate course on Europe and Asia as illustrative of geographic principles, making the course of such a kind that entrance to it would not be hampered as is now the case. Then I should like to give as my chief University work a course in anthropogeography which would be directly along the lines upon which I expect to do most writing, and which would be a graduate course open to seniors. Finally I should like to give a third purely graduate course in principles of climatology as applied on the one hand to geological problems and on the other to problems of human life such as the one which I now expect to investigate in the South.

May I add one thing more. This letter is written to you personally and not to the Faculty. Therefore I want to say that I realize that one of the hardest things in your position is that so many men feel that if they are not retained in the University they have the right to feel aggrieved. There was a time when I might have felt so. That is by no means the case now. I recognize that the revolutionary character of some of my hypotheses exposes them to the sharpest criticism, and makes it possible that they may be overthrown. The criticism has certainly been of great help in enabling me to revise my original ideas and discard some unwise ones, but I can see that it may also have the effect of making people doubtful as to my ultimate success. . . . Therefore please understand that if the University does not feel it wise to continue my work, I feel that such action is necessary not because my work is not appreciated, but because the first work of a University must be instruction.

The President appointed a committee to consider the matter of his promotion. After reviewing Huntington's undergraduate

teaching record, and the financial condition of the institution the
committee voted not to support his claim for promotion. Huntington severed his connection with Yale as did Isaiah Bowman
that same year. Bowman departed New Haven to assume the
post of Director of the American Geographical Society. Huntington moved his office possessions to the family home in Milton,
Massachusetts. He was thrown totally upon his own resources.

The real reason for Huntington's departure must remain obscure. Correspondence on the subject clearly indicates that
Yale's financial position was a matter of some importance. Yet
if the matter were solely one of financial concern, one wonders
why Dana found it necessary to request letters of Brückner,
Penck, and Woodward concerning the quality of Huntington's
work and why the Yale Corporation hired geographers Loomis
Havemeyer in 1914, and Charles F. Brooks in 1915. Criticism
of Huntington's work, both national and international, was more
than matched by a surfeit of appreciation expressed in reviews
of his books, invitations to address professional gatherings, the
award of honors, and the frequent use to which his peers put
his studies. It has been suggested that Huntington failed to interest his students. Yet many students testify to the great interest
they derived from Huntington's classes. And of course Huntington's own insistence that he be awarded a full professorship
doubtless precipitated what came to pass. Importantly, and typi-
cally of Huntington's character, he did not allow job insecurity
to interfere with the work before him.

CHAPTER VI

Postglacial Climatic Pulsations: The Quest for Evidence and 'Influence'

The Pulse of Asia was published in 1907. It was more than a first book normally is. It was the product of long reflection on the matter of climatic change, since the first glimmer of wonder at Lake Goljeuk, Turkey in 1899. It was the first time a North American author had proposed a pulsatory climatic regime in historic times for Asia, with all its attendant implications for the historic process. Though Huntington was only thirty-one, his book amounted to a manifesto regarding postglacial changes of climate.

One year later he elaborated his theory, with more attention to causes of climatic cycles, in a 16,000-word article, "The Climate of the Historic Past," which was published in two parts in consecutive issues of the *Monthly Weather Review*.[1] The essay was a careful summary of the essentials of his thought concerning climatic change within historic time. He had published much of the content previously, but this essay was a consolidation of his thought, trim but not skeletal and not complected by adventure of travel or lure of region. Huntington summarized his thesis of climatic pulsations within historic time, marshalling evidence from his diaries and journals maintained in the field while he had studied the Vale of Kashmir, Lake Pangong, the Lop Basin of Chinese Turkestan, the Basin of Turfan, the irrigation canals of Son Kul, Sistan and Persia, the Turkish Lake of Goljeuk, and the Caspian Sea. He had investigated the subject in an area as large as the United States extending from longitude 35°E in Asiatic Turkey to 91°E in Chinese Turkestan, and from latitude 30°N in eastern Persia and northwestern India to 45°N on the border between Siberia and China. He observed that evidence indicating climatic change within historic time was widely distributed and was "by no means limited to the central parts of Asia." In an interesting departure he revealed evidences for similar climatic changes within historic time in the New World. Particular evidence from North America was of-

91

fered from the cliff-dwellings of the Zunis, and the city of Mexico and Lake Texcoco. Evidences introduced from South America included Mark Jefferson's observations in Argentina and
Darwin's observations in Chile, Moreno's observations in Argentina and Bolivia, and Bowman's observations on the old
roads of Lake Huaco.

Bowman indeed provided Huntington with much of his information concerning South America. Bowman had presented a paper before the Association of American Geographers in Chicago
in December, 1907, comparing the observations of Darwin and
Moreno with his own discoveries.[2] (The essentials of that paper
were later published in *The Geographical Journal* as "Man and
Climatic Change in South America.")[3] In the following year,
before the same Association at Baltimore, Huntington philosophized on the nature and cause of his recently discovered pulsations in "The Climate of the Historic Past."[4]

W. M. Davis, sympathetic to Huntington's undertaking, suggested that he incorporate Bowman into his scheme of research:[5]

> . . . The important thing then is to have a strong, serious-
> considered, rather long-lasting scheme; possibly involving alter-
> nate years absent and home; and continuing ten or more years,
> systematically advancing along your belt of deserts. If you
> could get Bowman to take up the S. American part, under your
> scheme, all the better; you cannot do it all; the Old World
> ought to be enough for you. But it would be proper for you
> to have a sight of S. America, so as to compare the scale of
> things.

Huntington placed the matter before his Yale colleague and
personal friend, Isaiah Bowman, but the latter had learned from
Mark Jefferson in his undergraduate days at Ypsilanti to seek
man "where he is, and what he is like." So Huntington's grand
scheme had only an indirect appeal to Bowman, who lent Huntington moral support on Sunday morning walks after chapel in
New Haven, but who did not seek further involvement.

Nevertheless, Huntington decided to undertake further climatic investigation in West Asia, and arranged to travel to Palestine in March, 1909. He studied the historic climate of Palestine
as a prelude to field study, and offered his findings to the *Bulletin of the American Geographical Society*. "The Climate of Ancient Palestine"[6] explained the four climatic hypotheses of uni-

formity, deforestation, progressive change, and pulsatory change, offered a résumé of the Palestinian climate, and advanced an analysis of climatic change within historic time inferred from demographic evidences, deforestation since biblical time, decline in the usage of old routes of invasion, migration and trade, and the existence of waterless ruined cities. Yale University granted Huntington a leave of absence from February to October (1909), and a University appropriation—two years income from the Hadley Publication Fund. He was to be accompanied by an assistant, Clarence F. Graham, a student from the Yale class of 1909.[7] When Thomas Wells, editor of *Harper's Magazine*, agreed to purchase from Huntington four articles relating to the expedition at a total price of $600, adequate funds were assured.[8]

The pair departed for Palestine in March and initially planned two months travel in Palestine and Syria before journeying to Asia Minor where they had planned five months travel and study.[9] But once there Huntington revised his itinerary and spent considerably more time in Palestine than was his original plan. His own knowledge of the Bible, coupled with his father's enthusiasm, inevitably resulted in visits to such biblical sites as the Galilee of Jesus and the place where David slew Goliath. More significantly Huntington found an ancient cave which he considered could have been the place of Lot's retreat, and claimed for Sodom a location at the northern end of the Dead Sea at the town of Cheweir, instead of the traditional location to the south of the Dead Sea.

But the location or discovery of biblical sites was not the essential task of the trip. Huntington had journeyed there to seek evidences which by their presence or absence would confirm or weaken his notion of pulsatory climatic change within historic time. He found evidence of a once extensive empire, wealthy, and densely populated, but now the abode of desolation. He visited the ruined cities of Palmyra, Petra, Philadelphia, Gerasa, Hebron, and Beersheba, studied innumerable villages, and the remains of orchards and vineyards, temples, aqueducts, baths, cisterns, and theatres. A special imperial permit obtained from the Sultan of Turkey permitted him to spend one month taking soundings and studying the strands of the Dead Sea from his fourteen foot canvas boat. From the study of these strands he reasoned that the sea had stood higher some two or three thousand years previously. Using his climatic hypothesis he was ready to explain the rise and decay of Petra and Palmyra, the decline in the use of the trade routes, and the marked decline in Palestine's population.

Early in July Huntington and Graham travelled by way of the Cilician Gate and the city of Adana to Asia Minor. There they studied the lakes of Central Turkey and then spent some time in the forested fringe of Southern Asia Minor where it was found that summer rains were induced by peculiar topographic conditions. The presence of fine forests and barren land in close proximity was explained in "The Fringe of Verdure Around Asia Minor."[10] The pair then journeyed to Greece where they studied the alluvial deposits which had covered the Olympian plain. Huntington divined that in the sixth and seventh century A.D. prolonged drought caused the death of the forests of western Greece. The soil formerly held in place by the trees was swept off the slopes by the winter rains and deposited by the Alpheus River in the Olympian plains, burying the ruins. When Keltie requested "a paper giving the most important results" of his expedition, Huntington sent him "The Burial of Olympia" and an accompanying letter:[11]

> I originally meant to write you on the Syrian Desert, but Greece has interested me more, and therefore I have written it up first. I cannot tell how the article will strike others, but to me the subject matter of it is perhaps the most interesting of all that I have written. It is, so to speak, the logical working out of the theories that I have been elaborating for the last eight years.

Huntington returned from Palestine and Asia Minor in the summer of 1909. In the ensuing months he wrote a manuscript on what he had seen and perceived in Palestine; special attention was given to the matter of climatic change. *Palestine and Its Transformation* was published by Houghton Mifflin Company in April, 1911, to a rally of review applause. The book also inaugurated some of the earliest substantial criticism of Huntington's work.

He determined to journey next to arid North America, search for evidence indicative of climatic change within historic time, and attempt a comparison of climatic change for the Old and New Worlds. He sought a sponsor. He remembered a conversation with Daniel T. Macdougal at the 1907 annual meeting of the Association of American Geographers, of which he had written to his sister Ruth:[12]

... the most important paper so far as I am concerned ... was by a botanist, MacDougal, head of the Carnegie Desert Laboratory in Arizona and one of the foremost scientists in the country. He spoke on desert vegetation. I talked with him afterward, and he said that he had a definite plan for inviting me to come out to Arizona and California some vacation at the expense of the Laboratory to study the Salton Sea.

When Macdougal again invited Huntington to cooperate with the Department of Botanical Research of the Carnegie Institution in a study of the climate of the Southwest of the United States Huntington sought financial aid from President Woodward of the Carnegie Corporation. Huntington had worked under Carnegie auspices in the Pumpelly Expeditions of 1903–4, and since that time W. M. Davis had urged him to bring his work to the attention of Woodward whenever possible. Consequently Woodward had read several of Huntington's publications and was not unfamiliar with the posture of his thought. Robert S. Woodward was interested in geography. He had been "astronomer, geographer and chief geographer U.S. Geological Survey" for the period 1884–1890.[13] Although he gave more of his time to mathematics between 1890 and 1905 than to geographic matters, he held memberships in the Cosmos Club (Washington) and Century Club (New York), where he frequently met men of kindred geographical tastes. After reading *The Pulse of Asia* Woodward had written to Huntington:[14]

It is one of the most interesting books I have read. . . . You have gone very far toward sustaining your thesis as to the role of climatic changes on the course of man's progress. Your "geographic theory of history" is not only very interesting in itself but evidently of prime importance in the interpretation of anthropology. . . . My notion is that a man writes well in proportion as he thinks clearly, and one of the charms of your book lies in the fact that you have not only seen straight but have reflected adequately on what you have seen.

Woodward arranged for Huntington to receive a grant of $1500 from the Carnegie Foundation to prosecute the work with MacDougal and the latter's laboratory staff.[15]

The Carnegie Desert Laboratory had been established in 1902 at Tucson—a city of 12,000 inhabitants. Three years later

With Macdougal's "Camel Corps"

Macdougal was appointed director. The laboratory was well equipped with a library, apparatus, and furniture, and was secluded in its own fenced grounds of 840 acres. Several climatological stations were established on nearby mountains. It was a haven for eremologists. Macdougal's work commanded attention and under his directionship there came to the desert laboratory some fine workers, including Godfrey Sykes, Forrest Shreve, William A. Cannon, Robert H. Forbes and William L. Tower. When the laboratory acquired a large motor car for field work the appellation "camel corps" retained! Macdougal had a commanding knowledge of the desert plant kingdom, used camels for local transport, and was at home with society in the East as much as he was with eremology in the Southwest. Huntington joined this group in Tucson March 5, 1910, and began the first of five seasons in arid America.

During the next three months he cooperated with the Desert Laboratory in a study of the deserts of southern Arizona and northern Mexico. He became well acquainted with laboratory staff and especially D. T. Macdougal. He also met A. E. Douglass, professor of physics and astronomy at the University of Arizona, and a pioneer in dendro-chronology.[16] Huntington and Douglass did much measuring and discussing of tree rings in the two years which followed. For his field work in the Southwest Huntington selected two river systems, each nearly 200 miles long, for comparative study: the Santa Cruz, flowing north of Tucson to the Gila, and the Asuncion, flowing to the southwest to the Gulf of California. He studied with particular care the origin of alluvial terraces found along all the rivers, and the traces of an unexpectedly dense extinct Indian civilization. During May he journeyed via Phoenix and Yuma to the Salton Sea, where he was able to study the abandoned strands of its predecessor, Lake Cahuilla. All the while he wrote letters, kept a diary, took photographs, made notes for potential articles for *Harper's Magazine*, and compared the American desert with Asiatic deserts.

After returning to his home at Milton, Massachusetts, Huntington sent a report of his season's work to Macdougal, which was duly published in the *Carnegie Yearbook*.[17] Further of Huntington's thought was revealed when "The Libyan Oasis of Kharga" appeared in the *Bulletin of the American Geographical Society* for September, 1910.[18] On the basis of an analysis of Llewellyn Beadnell's book, *An Egyptian Oasis* (1909), he deduced changes of climate for the Kharga Oasis and compared them with the historic fluctuations of climate already worked out by him for western Asia. (The article was noticed in *The Geographical Journal* for December, 1910.)[19]

A second season in the Southwest was made possible when Woodward informed Huntington that he had been granted "compensation and expenses of travel for an Associateship with our Department of Botanical Research."[20] Macdougal was delighted with the news. Some weeks earlier he had urged Huntington to return to the Tucson Laboratory, "then go to the Salton, carry the work down the Delta, get into the other sunken basin and cut across to the West Coast."[21] Huntington began to plan work prior to his departure early the next spring. He wrote to Woodward of the scope of his proposed future investigations:[22]

> The investigation of climatic changes, insofar as it must be done by agencies outside the meteorological services of the various governments, divides itself into five heads. First comes exploration of the drier portions of all the continents. Next, comparison of changes in diverse parts of the earth, to see how far they coincide in time and in nature. Third, an examination of the history of selected regions, to see how far historic events agree with climatic changes. Fourth, a study of the prevalence of disease and pestilence at various times and places, with a view to detecting any possible relation to climatic vicissitudes; and Fifth, an investigation of the effect of specific climate or meteorological conditions upon various phases of man's mental activity.

Huntington's plans called for the employ of numerous trained assistants, more than twenty seasons in the field for himself and his assistants, and an annual expenditure of from 25 to 45 thousand dollars. He wrote that perhaps not even half the problems would be solved in ten years but that in that time "enough could be done fully to justify the expenditure of time and money involved in the present plan." Meanwhile as a step toward the accomplishment of his plan he travelled to the Southwest and spent the larger part of March, 1911, in the uninhabited desert of the Otero Basin in southern New Mexico. There he studied and mapped ruins in what had become an uninhabitable desert, observed a series of gypsum sand dunes and old lacustrine strands which suggested climatic fluctuations of some severity since the glacial period. In April, assisted by Kenneth Chapman, curator of the Museum of New Mexico and Secretary of the School of American Archaeology at Santa Fe, Huntington visited some of the noted prehistoric sites in the central, northern, and northwestern parts of New Mexico where archaeologists were active. Late in April he visited a dam in the southwestern corner of the state, at Animas, which he recognized as an old lake strand, though it had been described in literature as the work of humans. Evidences of an earlier large population were studied in localities extending from southern New Mexico to northern Sonora.

From New Mexico Huntington travelled to California, hired a wagon and driver, two technical assistants, and obtained provisions for a field trip to the redwoods in the mountains. The party travelled through the General Grant National Park to a tract belonging to the Hume–Bennett Lumber Company, camped there for two weeks, then visited another "Big Tree" region 60 miles farther south on the Tulare River, east of Porterville. There they counted the rings of more than 200 "Big Trees" (*Sequoia gigantea*) which varied in age from 250 to 3,150 years. Huntington resorted to the measurement of tree rings in order to show that it was not personal prejudice that persuaded him to read more into river terraces, lake strands, ruins, than might seem scientifically justified.

> Manifestly it was necessary to devise some new line of research which should not only furnish dates, but should prove positively the existence or non-existence of changes of climate, and should do it in such a way that the investigator's private opinions, his personal equation, so to speak, should not be able to affect his results.[23]

The tree ring measurements were an attempt to bring objectivity to his attempt to prove climatic change within historic time. Huntington had been inspired by "Weather Cycles in the Growth of Big Trees," an article in the *Monthly Weather Review*, (1909) by A. E. Douglass, who had dated the yellow pine of Arizona back to 1392.[24]

The work was monotonous and demanding:[25]

> When all was ready, two of us lay down on our stomachs on the top of the stump, or it might be on two stumps standing

Counting Tree Rings with Canby

close together, while the third sought the shade, or the sun, or a shelter from the rain, as the weather might dictate. The two who were on the stump were equipped with penknife, ruler, and hand lens. The ruler was placed on the flat surface of the stump with its zero at the edge of the outer ring. Then we counted off the rings in groups of 10, read the ruler and called off the number to the one who sat under shelter with notebook and pencil. Had the lumbermen seen us we should have appeared like crazy creatures as we lay by the hour in the sun and rain calling out "forty-two," and being answered by the recorder, "forty-two"; "sixty-four," "sixty-four"; "seventy-eight," "seventy-eight," and so on, interminably. It was not inspiring work merely to measure, and it was distinctly uncomfortable to lie on one's stomach for hours after a hearty meal. Often it was hard to see the rings without a lens, and in some cases even the lens scarcely showed them all, for the smallest were only two-hundredths of an inch thick, very different from some of the big ones, half an inch thick.

Huntington left California July 5, and returned to spend the summer in Milton writing, planning yet more writing, and organizing a book on the subject of climatic change in North America. When J. Scott Keltie of the Royal Geographical Society asked Huntington for a written expression of some of his experiences in arid America, he wrote "The Fluctuating Climate of North America," which was published in two parts in *The Geographical Journal*.[26] At the request of the Smithsonian Institution, and with Keltie's permission, Huntington abridged the article for *The Annual Report of the Smithsonian Institution for 1912*.[27] That same autumn (1911) he completed his first curve of rainfall derived from measurements that he and his assistants had made of the *Sequoia* trees. When W. M. Davis invited Huntington to join The American Geographical Society's Transcontinental Excursion of 1912, Huntington declined on the grounds that it would interrupt his third season studying the historic climate of North America: "I am just in the hey day of work and it is worth more to me to finish up the task I have begun than to make any number of acquaintances."[28] He informed Davis of the completion of his tree ring curve:[29]

In the main it supports my conclusions in regard to Asia. That is, it shows unquestionably, I think, that there have been important climatic fluctuations in America with a periodicity of hundreds of years, and the main fluctuations seem to synchronize with those of Asia.

In September, 1911, Huntington received a letter from Charles J. Kullmer, Professor of German at Syracuse University, which was to influence his thought profoundly.[30]

> It has now been almost two years since Professor Bigelow of Washington called my attention to your work and advised me to consult with you on a hypothesis of climatic change on which I have been working for several years. . . . I have my material now about as far as I shall be able to get it, and should be glad to send you what I have, if you would care to examine it. My hypothesis deals with the connection between climatic change and civilization and finds a striking echo in your concluding paragraph of "The Pulse of Asia."

Huntington was much impressed with Kullmer's manuscript. He returned it to him with numerous suggestions, one being that he read the work of Henryk Arctowski. From Kullmer's manuscript Huntington derived the notion that a variable climate might stimulate the individual. The Syracuse professor confided that although he had made extensive investigations into the sources of Goethe's popular epic, "Hermann and Dorothea" and had published "Poessneck, the Scene of Hermann and Dorothea" (1910), he had come to regard such labors as "literary chaff."[31] In February, 1911 Kullmer wrote to Huntington:[32]

> The field that seems to me most interesting is to investigate the atmospheric electrical potential of a barometric depression to ascertain if there is a gradient. . . . If there is such a gradient, it would be a fine field to conduct psychological experiments with varying electrical potential of the atmosphere. We already know that vegetation is strongly stimulated by high potential wires strung over the field; perhaps the mental operations are similarly affected.

Kullmer measured the number of nonfiction books taken from libraries and the barometric pressure at such time; "high pressure means more serious books, and low pressure fewer, which is the opposite of that which one would expect." He thought he had discovered that banks lying in the path of the storm track invariably had larger deposits than those banks lying on the margins of the storm track, and proffered the notion to Huntington that there existed a relationship between the storm track and civilization, and that shifts in the storm track accounted for shifts in the location of civilizations. Huntington was intrigued with Kullmer's hypothesis, suggested that he plot the individual storm tracks on a map of the United States and compare them with Dunwoody's maps for 1878–1889, and urged him to present a paper on his findings at the next annual meeting of the Association of American Geographers.[33] Huntington did not wholly subscribe to Kullmer's storm track hypothesis but advanced an oceanic low expansion theory. When asked by Kullmer for an explanation of this theory, he wrote:[34]

> My ideas as to the movement of the storm center are not well formulated as yet. I think however that the *Atlantic* low may possibly have been pushed southward. If you can get hold of a copy of the Bulletin of the American Geographical Society for September of this year (August?) you will find an article by Hobbs upon glaciation in which he gives a summary of the new view as to barometric pressure and continental glaciers. In a word, glaciation on a large scale seems to take place where permanent highs prevail; if such *highs* prevailed over the northeastern United States and northwest Europe they would probably tend to coalesce with the Greenland *highs*, and to push the Atlantic *low* farther south. Later I expect to study the question much more carefully.

Huntington was quite eager for Kullmer to map the frequency of storm tracks for all parts of the world, and to present his results to the trustees of the Carnegie Institution. In any case he had been excited by the idea:[35]

> Your idea has led me into lots of speculation. For instance, I have pondered a greal deal over the Italian Renaissance; and now I am wondering whether by any chance that was associated with some change in storm frequency.

The Kullmer notion concerning the relationship between cyclonic activity and civilization was formally presented for the first time in December, 1911, at the Washington, D.C., meeting of the Association of American Geographers. Huntington introduced Professor Kullmer at the meeting, where the latter offered "Storm Frequency and Civilization: The Shift of the Storm Track."[36] Huntington supplemented Kullmer's paper with "The Effect of Barometric Variations upon Mental Activity."[37] Additionally he offered the membership a résumé of his work with tree rings in a paper entitled "The Big Trees of California as Recorders of Climatic Changes."[38] That December Woodward assured Huntington a third season with the staff of the Desert Laboratory, Botanical Division.

Huntington left New Haven on February 27, 1912, bound for Yucatan, notwithstanding the revolution in Mexico. En route he stopped at the house of William H. Hobbs in Ann Arbor, Michigan, and lectured on Chinese Turkestan and geological processes to one of his classes. The following day he lectured on Palestine at 4:15 P.M. to a public audience at the University of Michigan and at 8:00 P.M. went on to Ypsilanti, eight miles distant, where he met Mark Jefferson, lectured on Palestine to a Normal School audience, and attended a reception extended by Ypsilanti's "Twenty Club." He spent the night in Jefferson's house and visited the latter's "Geography of Europe" class the next morning before returning to Ann Arbor, where he lectured on changes of climate, met suffragette Miss Pankhurst in the evening, and resumed his train journey on the morrow. At San Antonio Huntington spent a day "trying to get statistics of piece work for use in investigating the effect of weather." He tried ten factories and found that two of them had maintained statistics adequate to his purpose—a garment factory and a pecan plant. In Mexico City Huntington offered Franz Boas and Adolf F. Bandelier letters of introduction from the Carnegie Institution, and seemed pleased with results:[39]

> The hole that Professor Boas has dug in the Mexican Plain showed precisely what I wanted, viz: different types of deposits associated with different types of human culture. Mr. Bandelier growled, as is his wont, and said he had no use for me, but inasmuch as I had a good letter of introduction he would take notes on just the things that I wanted.
>
> The Revolution was all around, and the bandits took pains to rob some of the places that I went to visit, but they generally did it the day before I had planned to go, or the day after I had been there.

Huntington journeyed to southern Mexico and found alluvial terraces of mountain valleys and the strands of old lakes which were to him indicative of pulsatory climate change. He found traces of ancient cultures buried beneath alluvium, then placed historic accounts of the Spanish conquest and of the times immediately preceding it alongside his finding. In Yucatan he visited ruins in the midst of dense tropical forests, which encouraged him to write "when Arizona and regions in similar latitudes were moister than now, those which lie farther south on the border of the zone of equatorial rains were drier than at present." The Yucatan trip stimulated him considerably. He wrote to Kullmer:[40]

> I was tremendously impressed by the greatness of the ruins and by the evidences which they present of a people who were full of new ideas and energy to carry these ideas to fruition. Nowhere have I felt this more strongly. To-day the people are a slow, amiable, lazy lot, never changing, never doing anything unless they are absolutely forced.
>
> One of the things that interested me most was ruins in forests so dense that now no one could live there. These seem to point strongly to a pushing southward of the subtropical belt of aridity. If this were pushed southward the northern edge of the great tropical forest would become drier, and hence more habitable. This does not fit in with your theory of the movement of the storm track in accordance with the precessional epoch, but it fits in with the changes of some sort in the storm track. It would agree very well with my idea about the pushing southward of the climatic belts of the earth as a whole.

He wrote Hobbs in support of the latter's theory, as opposed to Kullmer's notion of the shifting of the storm track.[41]

> I find that your theory of high pressure areas as centers of glaciation works in with my results at a great many points. For instance, in Yucatan I found ruins of large size in places where now the climate is so moist and the vegetation so rank that clearings and permanent towns are out of the question. This seems to indicate that the sub-tropical belt of relative aridity once was pushed farther south. It looks as if all the climatic belts of the earth were pushed equatorward and this would seem to demand an expansion of the high pressure area which recent researches seem to show exists about the poles.

Huntington returned from Yucatan via Havana, reaching New Haven April 15. He wrote "The Peninsula of Yucatan" which was published in the November (1912) issue of the *Bulletin of the American Geographical Society*.[42] That December Huntington presented a paper, "The Shifting of Climatic Zones as Illustrated in Mexico," to the membership of the Association of American Geographers, which met that year at Yale.[43] He supplied evidence for his hypothesis of an alternate equatorward and poleward shifting of the earth's climatic zones. At that meeting, the membership present elected him First Vice President of the Association. Days later, a more detailed version of "The Shifting of Climatic Zones as Illustrated in Mexico" appeared in the *Bulletin of the American Geographical Society*,[44] and a summary of the article, "Climatic Changes in Mexico," was published in *The Geographical Journal* for June, 1913.[45] The notion expressed in Hobbs's article, "The Pleistocene Glaciation of North America Viewed in the Light of Our Knowledge of Existing Continental Glaciers,"[46] and further developed in Hobbs's *Characteristics of Existing Glaciers*,[47] was advanced as a tentative yet plausible explanation for the shifting of the climatic zones: "At best the theory here presented is only an approximation to the truth; at worst it is a suggestion which may lead to the evolution of a more satisfactory hypothesis." In a paper entitled "Bearing of Recent Climatic Investigations on Geological Theories," Huntington further elaborated on Hobbs's notion at the twenty-fifth Annual Meeting of the Geological Society of America, which followed immediately upon the meeting of the Association of American Geographers. He asserted that "The phenomena of Yucatan seem to find their best explanation in connection with the theory of the development of glaciers in areas of permanent high pressure."[48] When Lieutenant Colonel H. D. Borup invited Huntington to make suggestions as to what matters his son and D. B. MacMillan should pursue in a forthcoming polar expedition to Crocker Land Huntington urged:[49]

> . . . a minute investigation of ice-covered lands with a view to determining the truth or falsity of Hobbs' interesting theory as to the origin of continental glaciers in areas of high pressure. . . .

Only weeks after his return from the Yucatan Huntington began to plan another visit to the big trees. He designed a tree hole-boring machine using the engine of an Indian motorcycle (which the Griswold Company of New Haven built), and by correspondence hired horses, a wagon, tents, provisions, and some helpers to assist him in California. On June 1 of that same year (1912), accompanied by his Yale colleague of literary bent, Henry Seidel Canby, he journeyed to Sanger, California, where by prior arrangement he met five student assistants. The journey from Sanger in the valley to the new lumbering camp at Hume 5,000 feet above took five days. The mules hauled provisions, camping equipment, and the hole-boring machine up a steep trail to Hume. The group ranged within a ten-mile radius of the lumber camp and measured the rings of 250 more *Sequoia*. In his second season with the "Big Trees," Huntington had his party make two, and sometimes three, or four, readings along different radii of the same stump. Some of the trees measured the previous summer were revisited and a second or third reading taken. Identification of the tree ring measurement was made possible by chiselling a number into the stump and correlating it with the data in Huntington's notebook. The hole-boring machine failed to obtain an uninterrupted core to the center of each tree. After a full day's labor with the machine and many pieces of broken core as the sole reward, Huntington abandoned that part of the work and continued with "the hundred years test." A hundred young *Sequoia* from four to six feet in diameter—to be felled the following year—were selected for their various conditions of soil and moisture, and a hundred-year triangular bite was taken from them with a large two-man saw. The triangular pieces of redwood showed growth rings for the last century. He wrote to J. C. Toumey, (Morris K. Jesup Professor of Botany at Yale) asking if a botanist at the school could determine the type of cell structure for each year's growth of the tree rings.[50] If this were possible, he could equate a particular cell structure with the California meteorological record, then he could proceed with analysis of rings from older trees. Huntington achieved little from his suggested study of cell structure, but the wood pieces he had collected were eagerly sought by the Yale Forestry School. Huntington left the big trees in mid-July. He placed Hiram E. Miller, his chief helper of the previous season, in charge of tree measurements for another month and returned to Boston by August 23.

During the 1911 and 1912 seasons, a total of 900 measurements upon 451 trees had been made, with more than 1,300,000 rings counted. Of these tree stumps seventy-nine were 2,000 years old, three were 3,000 years old, and one was 3,150 years old. Most of these stumps were located on the western slopes of the Sierra Nevada, at an elevation of 6,000 to 7,000 feet. There he found trees which were saplings at the time of the Exodus of Hebrews from Egypt. He designed and had manufactured approximately three dozen notebooks to receive the tree ring measurements. From these figures he established a *Sequoia* curve and placed it over the curve he had published in *Palestine and Its Transformation*. The curves were only tentative, as Huntington realized. "These bits of evidence gathered here and there, have enabled the curves to be drawn, but accuracy is as yet out of the question." Later he attempted to adjust his *Sequoia* chronology by use of the "Caspian correction factor"[51] and Mediterranean rainfall records.[52] He thus attempted to eliminate from his curve some of the error introduced by *Sequoia* age, longevity, flaring buttress of the trunk, and paucity of measured trees providing data for pre-Christian time. Simultaneously he sought to develop a chronology that would be interchangeable for Old and New World alike. The whole was as tenuous as it was ingenious. The man was pioneering, and he knew it. Subsequently he used these curves with caution, and as only one of several indications of climatic change.[53]

Sequoia rings were not the only tree rings counted. H.S. Graves of the U.S. Forest Service had placed at Huntington's disposal several thousand stump analyses gathered from various parts of the country. From these Huntington had a series of sixteen corrected curves of growth prepared, extending from 300 to 1,000 years in duration. Special care was taken since different trees are stimulated by different conditions, some trees responding mainly to warmth, some to abundant moisture. Hence before interpretation of the growth curves could be made it was necessary to compare tree measurements over the last century with local meteorological records. That work had been done for the yellow pine by A. E. Douglass and for *Sequoia gigantea* by Huntington.

Additionally, as part of the Carnegie-sponsored work, Huntington made inquiry into the possible relation of climatic changes to other phenomena. When H. W. Pearson of Duluth revealed an apparent synchronism between changes in the level of the sea and the changes in climate suggested by Huntington, the latter decided to investigate the matter.[54] Yet he found that most of the supposed evidences of changes in sea level were due to uplifts or depressions of the land. Another investigation made that same year under Carnegie auspices sought measurement of the eleven-year cycles which Huntington thought he recognized in climate, sunspots, earthquakes, and volcanoes. A list of all known earthquakes from the beginning of the Christian era was prepared and a curve of seismic activity plotted and compared with the curve of climate derived from the big trees. A relationship was revealed of which Huntington wrote:[55]

> The degree of agreement is such as to afford ground for most interesting speculations as to the possible relation of climatic changes, earthquakes, and volcanoes to one another and the sun.

He concluded his third season in the arid Southwest by summarizing his findings in manuscript form. He sent "The Climatic Factor as Illustrated in Arid America," to Woodward in January, 1913. However, following a meeting at Yale in February, 1913, in which he and Bowman met with Boas, Spinden, and some other anthropologists from New York City, he decided to undertake further fieldwork in Guatemala. He wrote in *The Climatic Factor*,[56]

> When the final revision of this volume was made in January and February, 1913, the author felt that his conclusions as to the torrid zone required further testing. The logical place for such a test was Guatemala, since there the Mayas brought to a culmination the highest civilization of native American origin.

His journey extended from March 4 until April 2 of 1913. Following his return to New Haven, Huntington delivered an address on "Guatemala and the Highest Native American Civilization," April 18, 1913, before the American Philosophical Society, which met in Philadelphia. Five days later he sent the findings of his Guatemala trip to Woodward "in the form of a chapter to be added to my book."

The completed manuscript included contributions from A. E. Douglass, C. J. Kullmer, and Charles Schuchert. Douglass contributed chapter 11, "A Method of Estimating Rainfall by the Growth of Trees;" Kullmer contributed "The Shift of the Storm Track" as chapter 16; and Schuchert wrote chapter 21, "Climates of Geologic Time." Huntington could have written these chapters himself, but felt that a greater measure of objectivity would be brought to his work if these three men, each an authority on the topic contributed, were to collaborate with him. Huntington wrote to Schuchert on this matter:[57]

> It will be necessary there to have a statement of the latest conclusions as to the relation of periods of marked tectonic activity. It is possible for me to prepare such a statement myself, but the danger is that if I prepare it I may be biased by some of my theories, and even if I am not so biased, people are likely to think that I am.
>
> So it would be very much better if someone who can speak with authority and who is not interested in my particular theories could prepare a statement which I could quote. Would you be willing to do this?

The Climatic Factor As Illustrated in Arid America, twenty-one chapters in length, appeared May 15, 1914. Huntington had published several of the chapters elsewhere, but he had improved them and presented them here in greater detail than hitherto.

Early in 1914, and again under Carnegie auspices, Huntington journeyed to the Mohave Desert and made a preliminary reconnaissance of the principal basins with a view to framing a climatic scale extending from the Tertiary to the present time. In particular he studied the origin of terraces and other alluvial deposits. He wished to make sure that terraces, which he asserted evidenced the possibility of climatic change, had not been created by movements in the earth's crust. He studied the stages of development of playas and the curtailment of rivers by desiccation. He correlated botanical, chemical, and physiographic evidences of climatic pulsations at Owens and Pyramid lakes, their strands, and the curve provided by sequoia trees only fifty miles distant.

All the while Kullmer's notion concerning climate, energy, and the stimulation of the human system loitered in Huntington's mind. He sought evidence that barometric pressure did in fact influence people in tangible ways. He had a Yale class of 150 students keep a daily record of "their feelings, energy, etc."; he began to consult factory records in search of a relationship between productivity and weather. After analyzing data offered to him by the Bridgeport Brass Company's management he wrote to a distant cousin, Carroll Alden:[58]

This indicates that our frequent changes of weather are one of the important elements in causing the nervous activity of America. It is the first time, so far as I know that we have had anything more than mere speculation on this matter. Here, you see, we have an absolute numerical measure on the effect of our climate on activity.

He requested experimental data from a variety of persons with regard to human bodily and mental reflexes relating to changes in barometric pressure: notably from Dr. W. B. Lombard[59] and more especially from Dr. Rose[60] of Clark University, concerning the sleep of children; from E. J. Swift, on ball-tossing experiments;[61] from C. Stuart on the activity of white rats in relation to barometric pressure;[62] and from J. McKeen Cattell, data concerning the various performances on different days of Cattell's children in typing three stanzas of Spencer's *The Faerie Queene* in relation to barometric pressure.[63] When W. M. Davis sent Huntington a copy of his recently published *Grundzüge der Physiographie*, Huntington thanked him and simply had to inform him of the Cattell children and *The Faerie Queene*:[64]

By computing averages I have eliminated the differences due to increasing skill and have plotted a curve which shows merely the departure of each day from the mean. The result is truly surprising when compared with the curve of barometric fluctuations. In some cases for a month at a time the curve of a child was practically parallel with that of the barometer. Every fall and every rise is reflected in a corresponding mental depression or stimulation. There seems to be a connection between weather and mental ability far closer than we have hitherto suspected. I am at work just now trying to apply this to Japan.

Huntington's reference to Japan concerned "Geographical Environment and Japanese Character," which he had written for presentation at a conference on Japan sponsored by Clark University.[65] He advanced Kullmer's thesis that areas of high civilization are to be found in areas enjoying frequent cyclonic storm activity, illustrated the storm tracks on a map, and suggested that Japan owned much to this circumstance. The paper was delivered on November 24, published in the January, 1912, issue of the *Journal of Race Development*[66] and reappeared in *Japan and Japanese–American Relations*.[67]

His keen interest in physiological climatology led him to plan his next book, tentatively entitled "The March of Civilization." Huntington surmised that a certain type of climate prevailed where civilization was advanced, and that in the past the same type of climate had prevailed where civilization had been advanced. He had already collected statistics from factories and other places of regular employment which enabled him to measure productivity per worker per day and relate them to prevailing weather conditions. And he had read with enthusiam Edwin G. Dexter's book *Weather Influences; An Empirical Study of the Mental Effects of Definite Meteorological Conditions* (1904). By December of 1913, he had assembled his thought regarding the matter of climate and human efficiency. He wrote to T. B. Wells, editor of *Harper's Magazine*, stating that he planned six articles which were the product of his investigations concerning climate and human efficiency: "Work and Weather"; "The Ideal Climate"; "The Distribution of Civilization"; "The Cause of Changes of Climate"; "The March of Civilization"; and "The Next Campaign Against Nature."[68] These articles constituted the outline of his intended book. He visited the Harper rooms in New York City, talked of the matter with Wells, and agreed to submit the six articles to *Harper's* for a total price of $2,500; *Harper's* was to have first option on "The March of Civilization."[69]

On December 7, 1914 he left Milton and journeyed to New Haven, New York, Annapolis, Washington, D.C., Richmond, Hampton and Norfolk, Virginia, Raleigh and Durham, North Carolina, and Cartersville, Georgia. Then he took a boat to the Bahama Islands. Huntington obtained data from life insurance companies, cotton mills, hosiery mills, cigar factories, furniture factories, a shipping company, the Naval Academy at Annapolis, and Hampton Institute. From the Bahamas Huntington returned with notes of many interviews, all of them to the effect that the Bahamian climate discouraged effort and the desire to work. He returned to Milton in mid-March. Within a few weeks he analyzed the statistical performance of 3,000–4,000 factory operatives from Virginia to Florida, over 1,700 students of the U.S. Military Academy at West Point and the Naval Academy at Annapolis, 22 negro students at Hampton Institute, and over 500 factory operatives from Bridgeport, New Britain, and New Haven, Connecticut. He wrote of his findings:[70]

The results are surprising. Changes in the barometer seem to have little effect. Humidity possesses a considerable degree of importance, but the most important element is clearly temperature. The people here considered are physically most active when the average temperature is from 60 to 65 degrees, that is, when the noon temperatures rise to 70 degrees or even more. This is higher than many of us would expect.

Mental activity reaches a maximum when the outside temperature averages about 38 degrees, that is, when there are mild frosts at night. Another highly important climatic condition is the change of temperature from one day to the next. People do not work well when the temperature remains constant. Great changes are also unfavorable. The ideal conditions are moderate changes, especially a cooling of the air at frequent intervals.

He proceeded to compile a map of "The Distribution of Human Energy on the Basis of Climate," which he wished to compare to a map showing the distribution of civilization. The possibility of this comparison had dawned upon him while reading Mark Jefferson's "The Culture of the Nations."[71] In compiling a map of the distribution of civilization Huntington requested the aid of 213 persons. He sent each of these people a letter containing his statement of purpose, 185 slips representing countries or regions of countries, and small envelopes numbered from one to ten. If a contributor placed a slip into envelope 10, that country or region of a country had been ranked highest in the order of civilization as conceived by Huntington. Of the 213 people solicited, 137 replied and 54 participated fully in Huntington's scheme. Correspondence with each of the 137 contributors ensued. Twenty-six of the participants were Americans, eight were British, eight were "teutons from continental Europe," seven were "Latins (and other Europeans not already classified)," six were Asiatics. Since four of the fifty-four participants had improperly completed the task, Huntington listed the collective opinions of fifty of the participants.[72] From these statistics he was able to compile an isopleth map, "The Distribution of Civilization." Then he compared the map of climatic energy with the map of the distribution of civilization, and pursued the matter through historic time. He traced the shift in the climatic zones, traced the shift in the centres of civilization, and emerged with a tentative hypothesis of civilization.

In May, 1914, Huntington sent Wells the first four articles and furthered the matter of a Harper publication of "The March of Civilization."[73] Although Wells wrote to Huntington in July that he would prefer to publish three and not six of the articles concerning climate and human efficiency, *Harper's* was generous in its financial arrangement.[74] The three articles appeared as "Work and Weather,"[75] "Climate and Civilization,"[76] and "Is Civilization Determined by Climate?"[77] The latter brought letters of anger from southern gentlemen, inquiries from medical men and psychologists, a proposal for civic celebration in Seattle, and commentary entitled "Climate and Genius" in *The Literary Digest*.[78] Meanwhile Huntington was writing "The March of Civilization"; he changed the title to "Civilization and Climate." When *Harper's Magazine* declined an invitation to publish the manuscript, Huntington offered it to the recently established Yale University Press. On May 7, 1915, the Yale Press Council's Committee on Publication agreed to publish *Civilization and Climate*.[79] Two hundred and fifty copies of the chapter entitled "The Distribution of Civilization" were printed separately at Huntington's request and a copy was sent to each of the persons from whom he had requested an evaluation of the world's countries and regions. B. C. Wallis seems to have regarded the chapter as a separate Yale University Press publication for he reviewed "The Distribution of Civilization" in *The Geographical Journal*.[80] J. G. Bartholomew wrote to Huntington inquiring if he had "any objection to my publishing your results on a map in one of my atlases."[81] *Civilization and Climate* was later twice revised, reprinted, and translated into Japanese and Spanish.

Since the appearance of *The Pulse of Asia* Huntington had many articles published in the *Journal of Race Development, Bulletin of the American Geographical Society, Bulletin of the Geological Society of America*, the *Round Table, Records of the Past, National Geographic Magazine, The Geographical Journal*, the *Bulletin of the Geographical Society of Philadelphia*, and the *Yale Review*. Most of these articles derived from his travel experiences in Asia and North America, and many were written for his "lay" audience and not his scientific audience. Of more scientific significance were his completion (1909) and publication (1912) of *Asia: A Geography Reader*, his editorship and revision of the Hanson Bellows Company *New Practical Reference Library* (1913), and "Problems in Exploration—Central Asia," written at the request of J. Scott Keltie and published in *The Geographical Journal*.[82] While engaged in the writing of *Civilization and Climate* he gave a series of lectures on the Holy Lands at a teacher training institute on Sunday school matters during the winter of 1914–1915, delivered "Climatic Changes in Historic Times and Their Influences on Man," before the Pittsburgh Academy of Science and Art, wrote "Terrestrial Temperature and Solar Changes,"[83] and edited a manuscript his father had written, "The Life of Samuel Huntington of Connecticut, President of the Continental Congress."[84] He then tossed off "The Handicap of the Tropics"[85]—an indictment of the high temperatures, high humidity and uniformity of the tropics, though with special reference to Guatemala, and in similar vein "The Adaptability of the White Man to Tropical America,"[86] which pondered the thesis that temperatures considerably above the optimum for humans and a nonvariable climate both inhibited the will to work and therefore civilization in the tropics. The latter article had been presented on the occasion of a four-day conference held at Clark University in November, 1913, and later appeared in *Latin America Clark University Addresses 1913*.

Early in 1914 Huntington wrote to Houghton Mifflin Company, *Harper's Magazine*, and the Hanson Bellows Company requesting part-time editorial work for himself. None was forthcoming. He then turned his attention to textbook writing. Huntington spoke to Bowman, then corresponded with Jefferson on the matter of a proposed series of texts to be used in the high schools and normal schools. Bowman's enthusiasm for the texts had been considerable in the autumn of 1914, but after reaching a "general understanding" with the American Geographical Society on December 8, 1914, concerning a post as Director of the Society to commence the following summer, Bowman did not wish to involve himself too deeply in Huntington's scheme. Jefferson had his own writing program. Even so, had the approached publishing companies encouraged rather than dithered and queried, something might have come of the idea.

Prior to his departure from Yale in the summer of 1915, Huntington again visited the Carnegie Desert Laboratory at Tucson, and with some of the members of the laboratory staff made a preliminary reconnaissance of the principal basins in the Mohave Desert region and northward. His purpose was to determine whether further work would furnish an adequate basis for a climatic scale extending from Tertiary times to the present. Penck had already accomplished this on the basis of glaciation in the Alps. Huntington felt that in the region of his desert researches—which drained to Death Valley—the records of past events would have been subjected to a minimum degree of destruction. The evidence of one period would merely cover the deposits of another period. In the Death Valley drainage area the deposits had been eroded to an unusual depth in many places, and in other places had been upturned by recent faulting, rendering them easy for thorough study. Numerous strands of Owens, Pyramid and Winnemuca lakes, and the thickness of mineral deposits studied indicated pulsatory changes of climate within historic time. This information was included in *Civilization and Climate*. The following year Huntington again visited the Southwest to advance his researches, but then he was no longer associated with Yale.

In the summer of 1915 he gathered his personal belongings and returned to his parents' home—222 Highland Street, Milton, Massachusetts.

CHAPTER VII

The Emergence of Criticism

Almost the oldest of the French Chansons is called the Journey of Charlemagne de Jerusalem, and dates about A.D. 1050–1100. It begins at St. Denis (that is at Paris) by Charles taking his wife by the hand 'desuz un olivier,' under an olive tree.
Did the olive grow at Paris in the 11th century?

So wrote Henry Adams to Huntington in January 1910.[1] Later Madison Grant wrote to Huntington:[2]

I have just received a letter from Mr. Allison V. Armour, Hotel Lotti, Paris, France, in which he says, 'may I ask if you know whether Prof. Huntington has published anything in re: his theory of droughts and race migrations. If so I would like to know where such could be had, as I wish to give them to the German Emperor, who is keenly interested in such matters, and particularly in my account of Huntington's theories. Any information would be greatly appreciated.'

These were two of many inquiries addressed to Huntington on matters including astrophysics, weather, climate, biblical interpretation, zodiac assemblage, prohibition, evolution, geography texts to be selected for instruction and advice on careers. Huntington's work had attracted much attention beyond a circle of professional geographers, but it was among the geographers and other earth scientists that Huntington's work was studied and analyzed. Praise had been accorded his endeavours frequently in articles and book reviews. Criticism was also bestowed upon his notion of climatic change within historic time. Thought on the subject of postglacial climatic change had, by the teens of the twentieth century, become a matter of significance to geographers. Numerous thinkers and writers pondered the matter. Perhaps more than any other of its kind, Prince Peter Kropotkin's paper "The Desiccation of Eur-Asia," delivered before the Royal Geographical Society in 1904 and published in *The Geographi-*

cal Journal,[3] had stimulated anew an interest in a subject whose literature predates Aristotle. Three distinct forms of the desiccation theory were championed by Prince Kropotkin, Rowland Thirlmere, and Huntington, who became principals in a debate whose literature was international. (None of these men inaugurated the modern debate, which had been developed in the late nineteenth century by Russian, German, and other scholars.) Kropotkin advanced the thesis that the world was undergoing a steady march toward drought. Thirlmere championed the idea that climate varied in great cycles, each taking thousands of years to run its course. Prior to publication of *The Pulse of Asia*, Huntington had championed Kropotkin's notion, though he had arrived at his conclusions while on the Pumpelly Expedition and therefore independently of Kropotkin. In *The Pulse of Asia* Huntington announced a profound modification of the desiccation hypothesis which he had earlier advanced. He contended that while the world had been for some time moving in the general direction of greater aridity, climatic pulsations, various in duration, provided more or less moisture at different times. Each of the principals in the ongoing debate was criticized, especially Huntington. The Russian Lev Berg—"productive scholar in geology, soil science, climatology, limnology, paleography, geobotany, zoogeography, ethnography, and the history of geographic discoveries and investigations"[4]—published an article in 1911 entitled "On Changes of Climate During the Historical Period,"[5] which was brought to Huntington's attention by W. L. G. Joerg of the American Geographical Society. Joerg requested Miss H. de Hutorowicz, a Russian lady on the Society's staff, to read the paper by Berg and offer commentary upon it. Joerg sent Miss de Hutorowicz's comments to Huntington.[6]

>   To begin with, Berg does not share your views as to desiccation nor as to climatic oscillation. Your work, it seems, inspired his paper, particularly as such men as Aurel Stein and Julius Hann, although in general not in accord with the desiccation theory, accept it for Central Asia.
>   These are some of the points he brings up. In Russia the expansion of the forest area at the expense of the steppe area speaks for increased humidity. Moreover, the disappearance of lakes does not necessarily make for diminution of moisture (I give these statements in the categorical form in which I received them from second hand). For European Russia Berg does not

admit a change in climate during historic time. European Russia and North America has a moister climate than before.

One criticism of your views on Central Asia is, it seems, that you are supposed to be unfamiliar with the geology of Central Asia and that you depended on the report of natives whose language you did not understand. Another is that you are supposed to have disregarded the fact that the rivers in Central Asia have changed their courses more than in other regions.

Finally Berg argues that other factors can be adduced to explain the changes that have occurred. Historical and economic factors may be determining. Thus the wars of Jenghiz-Khan can account for the destruction of centers of civilization in Central Asia. The abandonment of vine culture in southern Bavaria can be explained on purely economic grounds. Finally, the decline of Greece as compared with antiquity goes back to similar causes and not to a change of climate.

Berg is also of the opinion that his arguments invalidate Passarge's theory of the desiccation of the Kalahari.

H. S. Mandell, an instructor in Russian at Yale University, translated Berg's article for Huntington. The same article with minor amendment was published in German under the title "Das Problem der Klimaanderung in geschichtlicher Zeit," in *Geographische Abhandlungen*.[7]

A fellow Russian, A. Woeikof, read Berg's work and in *Le Turkestan Russe* pronounced without any specific refutation on the "inanity" of Huntington's conclusions[8]

In recent years, a member of two American archaeological expeditions, Mr. Huntington, has expressed the same hypothesis. He has seen the places but he has observed badly, and there is so little logic in his reasoning, that one wonders he has produced any impression at all. Mr. Berg, in a remarkable report, has shown the inanity of Mr. Huntington's conclusions.

The more one studies the question of climate during the historic period the more one should come to the conclusion of oscillations of a more or less long duration but without continued variation in one direction or another. This is what emerges from Mr. Berg's work.

Yet Berg had apparently studied only Huntington's earlier work. . . . the publications resultant to the Pumpelly expeditions.

At that time Huntington had advocated a progressive change toward aridity. With the publication of *The Pulse of Asia* in 1907, Huntington had made clear his advocacy of a pulsatory regime. Later, in the introduction to the second edition of *Civilization and Climate*, Huntington wrote:[9]

> Apparently that Russian author (Woeikof) had not read or had failed to understand *The Pulse of Asia*, but had become thoroughly familiar with a book of his countryman, Berg, written for the express purpose of proving that the present author is wrong as to changes of climate in central Asia. At any rate Woeikof pronounces the conclusions of *The Pulse of Asia* "inane," and then proceeds to prove the very thing that led to the choice of the title of that book, namely, that during historical times the Caspian Sea and other lakes in central Asia indicate alternating periods of more and of less rainfall than at present.

Very probably the slow diffusion of Huntington's work into Russia, coupled with attendant difficulties of translation, were responsible for the Russian criticism of thought which Huntington had earlier held, but which he had supplanted with the pulsatory notion. In a review of Woeikof's *Le Turkestan Russe* published in the *Bulletin of the American Geographical Society*, Huntington offered:[10]

> He (Woeikof) summarily rejects the reviewer's hypothesis of longer pulsatory changes, but the context suggests that he has studied it only through the French or Russian works of its critics, and that he does not realize how slightly it differs from his own position.

In January, 1914, Francois Herbette published "Le Probleme du Dessechement de L'Asie Interieure," in the *Annales de Géographie*."[11] The thirty-page article reviewed the literature concerning the climatic history of central Asia; the nine page part IV of the article, "Le Point De Vue Historique," was particularly critical of Huntington's work. Herbette sent a copy of the paper to Huntington. Huntington wrote to Herbette:[12]

> I feel that in your discussion of progressive changes you have been quite conclusive. No thoughtful person, I think, still holds that view, for as you say the demonstration of post glacial stages

and of relatively warm periods in northern Europe between colder periods throws it beyond the limit of possibility.

I am also interested in your conclusion that the records of Istakhri and the walls of Derbent, etc., show that since 500 A.D. there have been fluctuations more accentuated than those of our time. I regret that you do not take up the preceding period more fully and bring forward some distinct proofs that the climate of that time remained uniform, and was essentially the same as that of our day. I also regret that you did not take up the points which I consider as really vital. In the "Pulse of Asia" I should be quite willing to throw away the whole chapter on the "Geographic Basis of History" for I think that I have there gone much too far. The things which I regard as most important are such matters as the ruins of Niya, which you will find treated in Chapter 9. (You may remember that Hann in "Handbuch der Klimatologie," Vol. 1, p. 352, speaks of this as the most conclusive evidence which has yet been adduced in favor of changes of climate.)

I am a good deal disappointed that you have not taken up this matter. All my critics thus far have talked about historic records and about possible explanations of changes of the regimen of streams or of the warping of lake strands. Not one of them has discussed what seem to me the most convincing lines of evidence, that is, the ruins. I hope in all sincerity that you can take up this subject. It may be that there are some points which I have overlooked. If it is done, however, I would urge upon you the necessity of going into details in several cases, and of spreading your investigation over a large number of ruins. For instance, take such a case as Ilandarin or Palmyra, or some of the other places which I have described in "Palestine and its Transformation." What we need is not suggestions as to other possible explanations, but actual facts and figures.

There is only one point in your whole paper to which I seriously object. That is the way in which you have treated my work in connection with that of Pumpelly. It is true that his results and mine appear in the same volume. It is not in any respect true that his work formed the basis of mine. On the contrary, exactly the reverse is the fact. My results were written up long before Pumpelly's, and without any consultation with him. I agree with you that his method of attempting to prove changes of climate is une *oeuvre d'imagination*. I seriously object to having my results classed with his. Whatever other mistakes I have

made I certainly have not advanced any theory without prolonged field work covering a very wide area. That is exactly
what Pumpelly failed to do, and that practically all of my critics
have failed to do. Not one of them has gone out into the field
and brought back careful measurements of ruins, rivers, and a
host of other things. I hope that if you write further on the subject you can do me the kindness to differentiate as far as you
think right between my work and Pumpelly's.

There is one more point where it seems to me that your paper
might well have been more decided. You seem to assume that
uniformity of climate is the normal condition. You admit, however, that during the glacial period and down to 2,000 B.C. when
the Bronze Age began the climate was not uniform. You further
admit that from 500 A.D. down to our own time uniformity has
not been the rule, for the Caspian Sea shows fluctuations more
accentuated than those of our day. It seems to me that this
shows that the probability of pulsations from 2,000 B.C. to 500
A.D. is exactly as great as the probability of uniformity, yet you
say nothing about this.

Thanking you once more for your kindness, and hoping that
we both may continue our work on this interesting question. . . .

The Swedish explorer, Sven Hedin, had already offered modest
criticism of Huntington's work in his two-volume work *Overland
to India*.[13] Unlike Berg, Woeikof, and Herbette, Hedin acknowledged the researches of Huntington and characterized *The Pulse
of Asia* as a "valuable work." It was with Huntington's research
concerning climatic change in Persia that Hedin took exception.
The Swede confronted Huntington's assertion of increasing aridity in Persia with the opinions expressed by W. Tomaschek in
Zur historischen Topographie von Persien:[14]

> By describing fourteen of the Arabs' desert routes and compar-
> ing them, as far as possible, with the accounts of modern travel-
> lers, Tomaschek shows that the climate has remained unchanged
> during the past thousand years.

Of Huntington's assertion that drought conditions caused the
abandonment of villages at the time of Alexander's march,
Hedin offered,[15]

Such an investigation has been made by Huntington. . . . That all the interior of Asia is passing through a period of desiccation is a well-known fact. But is it credible that this phenomenon proceeds so rapidly that it can be detected within the course of 2000 years?

The commentary suggests Hedin may not have comprehended Huntington's pulsatory notion. And elsewhere in *Overland to India* in similar vein Hedin wrote:[16]

On the whole, I quite agree with Huntington's views. I must differ with him in one point only, pointing out with Brückner that the change of climate has progressed so slowly that its existence within historic times cannot be demonstrated with certainty. When, then, Huntington includes Alexander and Istakri, 300 years before and 900 years after the birth of Christ, within the last period of abundant water-supply, I can follow him no longer.

Perhaps a more substantial criticism from Hedin came in these lines:[17]

The fact to which Huntington refers, and which also attracted my attention, that numerous ruins are situated at Zirre and Shela, does not necessarily prove a constantly progressive decrease of water in Mohammedan times. Here, as in Seistan generally and in many other parts of Persia, the numerous ruins may indicate nothing but a change in the position of rivers and lakes. I have fully described a similar occurrence at old and new Lop-Nor, where the population was forced to abandon its villages and farms when the river and lake moved southwards. But this movement had nothing to do with a change of climate, and did not entail a diminution of the population.

In Germany Albert Herrmann wrote "Die alten Seidenstrassen zwischen China and Syrien: Beiträge zur alten Geographie Asiens."[18] In a section of this work Hermann studied the ancient silk trade, discussed the Tarim River and Lop Nor and severely criticized Huntington's thesis of climatic pulsations.

The evening of December 8, 1913, J. W. Gregory, noted for his researches in East Africa and Australia and the first occupant of the Chair of Geology at Glasgow University, delivered a paper before the Royal Geographical Society entitled, "Is The Earth Drying Up?" It was much discussed by Fellows of the Society later that same evening. The paper was published in *The Geographical Journal*.[19] Correspondence concerning the article was also published in *The Geographical Journal* in the months that followed. Gregory's essay reviewed the literature concerning desiccation in postglacial times in a most thorough manner. He cited and summarized the work of over eighty authors, jousted vigorously with Huntington's published work throughout the essay but denied him his pulsatory hypothesis. In paragraph four, "Palestine—A Test Case," Gregory visited the quick of Huntington's hypothesis, claimed the former population of Palestine had been exaggerated, and denied Huntington's previously "forested Palestine thesis" by supplication to the Hebrew word which had been translated "forest," but which might have been translated "woodland," . . . "and perhaps only copse or jungle." Referring to the Bible and the Talmudic books Gregory supported the notion of an unchanged Palestinian rainfall, and an unchanged climate, arguing strongly from historic evidence adduced by the distribution and fruiting of date palm and vine. In denying Huntington's case Gregory concluded:[20]

> . . . one fact does seem to me to result clearly from the evidence; there have been many widespread climatic changes in late geologic times, while in historic times there has been no world-wide change of climate.
> . . . it may be concluded from the most precise tests now available, from the range of the date palm and the vine, and from the facts recorded by Old Testament writers, that the climate of Palestine is the same today as in the time of Moses.

Huntington offered rejoinder with "Climatic Changes,"[21] an article in which he stated that Gregory had failed to distinguish his earlier affiliation with the progressive desiccation theorists from his pulsatory climatic notion made public with *The Pulse of Asia*. Appended beneath the article was a note by J. W. Gregory acknowledging that he had not discriminated Huntington's climatic pulsations from progressive desiccation, and that he agreed with Huntington in asserting that the pulsations were greater than any accompanying resultant movement. Months later Gregory reviewed Huntington's *The Climatic Factor as il-*

lustrated in Arid America, and "The Solar Hypothesis of Climatic Changes," in appreciative vein.[22]

In the United States historian A. T. Olmstead, (an authority on the ancient Near East) took exception to Huntington's published work. Olmstead, one-time fellow of the American School of Oriental Studies at Jerusalem (1904–1905), the American School of Classical Studies at Athens (1906–1907), and Director of two Cornell expeditions to Asia Minor and the Assyro-Babylonian Orient (1907–1908), was teaching ancient history at the University of Missouri. Following the publication of Huntington's *Palestine and Its Transformation*, Olmstead published "Climate and History" in the January, 1912 issue of the *Journal of Geography*.[23] Olmstead asserted that cultural factors had accounted for much which Huntington thought had been climatologically inspired. Later in the same year Olmstead published a long letter in the "correspondence" section of the *Bulletin of The American Geographical Society*, which further criticized Huntington's *Palestine and Its Transformation*.[24] Olmstead insisted that Huntington had not consulted the most accurate of the ancient texts, and hence Huntington's data concerning ancient trade routes, the source of Gudea's building material, the expedition of Esarhaddon 647 B.C. were incorrect. There was much more criticism based on interpretation of source, language, and meaning. Under the heading "Climatic Changes in the Nearer East: A Reply," which was printed on the pages immediately following Olmstead's criticism, Huntington stated that such criticism hardly detracted from his larger hypothesis.[25] At most it subtracted some evidence from a very large total of evidence. Appropriately Huntington quoted his previous work:[26]

> My attitude toward the whole matter is expressed on page 403 of "Palestine and Its Transformation," where I present a curve entitled, "Approximate Climatic Fluctuations of the Historic Period." The statement is there made that, "The line representing climate—as here given—makes no claim to finality. The researches of a single year may cause the shifting of a curve a century or more, or may smooth out some minor curve and add another. Yet in its main features I believe that it will stand.

Huntington concluded with a résumé of his tree ring researches, and a diagram comparing the curve afforded by the evidence of the big trees and the curve of the approximate climatic fluctuations of western and central Asia already published in *Palestine and Its Transformation.*

In fact Huntington had wished to address the historians on his point of view even before Olmstead's article appeared in the *Journal of Geography.* To that end Huntington wrote "Climatic Changes and History" and offered it to managing editor J. F. Jameson of *The American Historical Review.* Correspondence ensued which led to substantial editorial revision of the paper which was published as "Changes of Climate and History."[27] The original manuscript had not included reference to the work of any one historian; it was a summary of his field work to that time, with special reference to the meaning of climatic change for the historian. The revised and published manuscript included reference to Olmstead's point of view concerning the pulsatory hypothesis, evidences both inferred and clinical for the pulsations of climate which he eschewed, then flowered into a provocative—and at the same time, tentative—interpretation of some major historical events.

In July 1913 Huntington wrote to Secretary Keltie of the Royal Geographical Society. "I am sending you an article representing my latest ideas as to geographical methods and as to changes in my own conception of the subject. I hope that you will find it worth publishing."[28] Keltie read the paper, "The Geographer and History," requested opinions of H. G. Lyons, A. J. Herbertson, and H. J. Mackinder as to whether or not he should publish it in *The Geographical Journal.* Huntington invited the historian to make use of the geographers' insights, and urged the geographer to curb his more deterministic pronouncements. Huntington selected two passages from *The Pulse of Asia* which he stated were "too sweeping" and gave "the impression that geographical influences are more direct than is actually the case." The paper was critical of the posture which he and many other geographers had assumed; namely, that the environment exerted, always and everywhere, pronounced and discernible influences. It was a paper of considerable methodological significance. Keltie wrote to Lyons:[29]

> The fundamental idea of the paper, I think is quite sound. Hitherto we have been more qualitative than quantitative in geographical research, and in the practical application, of the subject. But the point seems to me to be, supposing that Huntington's strictures are well founded, would it be advisable at the

present stage of the evolution of the subject in England to publish such a paper?

When Keltie wrote to Huntington that the paper "might give occasion to the enemies to scoff,"[30] Huntington replied "I feel that perhaps it is just as well for us that the enemy should scoff a little. I do not see how we can be spurred up to our duty, unless there is something to make us realize where we are deficient."[31] Mackinder wrote to Keltie, "The paper is one which I think ought to be printed. I am sorely tempted to write an appreciation and criticism of it. It has stimulated me to shape thoughts which have been gathering in my mind for some time past. . . ."[32] Keltie published the paper.[33]

Huntington's self-criticism did rather little to persuade the historian; neither did his reflection upon disciplinal direction seem to restore the faith of geographers in his pronouncements. In the United States many geographers felt that he arrived at his conclusions prematurely, or even went fact-gathering to fit a theory already established in his mind. One of his most stalwart supporters, Mark Jefferson, had written of the matter in this way:[34]

> I want to make a suggestion. The criticism I hear made of your 'fluctuating humidity' studies is an obvious one; that you 'catch at' evidence, with the insinuation of a fear that you are over-hospitable to favorable arguments rather than critically investigative of the facts. In short that you are biased toward a particular conclusion.
>
> Could not the Big Tree argument be treated to a finish as if any conclusion from all the tree facts was being sought and *now*, quite regardless of agreement or disagreement with your other studies? It is of course not in your mind but in what has yet come into print there is a retaining and seeming deferring of *results*. I probably do not make myself clear, for that reads disagreeably, which I did not mean. You seem interested in the Tree evidence more from the bearing it may have on your general argument, while I wish you could make your study of it show more generous interest in mere 'past rainfall as recorded by tree growth'. No one could have more partiality for your work than I, else I would not have made this suggestion. If measurements are still far from completion the time has not come, for the point is how many trees have been measured for

each century and what do they indicate?—rather than how do they agree with the "Pulse of Asia."

Huntington accepted all such criticism with outward calm and was seemingly able to benefit from some of it. He reviewed Hedin and Woeikof quite affably notwithstanding criticism of himself by both authors.[35] An entry in his diary for January 10, 1915, offers; "Read Woeikof's Turkestan Russe, in which he speaks of the 'inanity' of my conclusions, and wrote a very mild review of it." And in a letter to W. L. G. Joerg, he wrote, "I am getting rather used to having people take a crack at me. . . ."[36] Huntington reviewed the criticism thrust at him and wrote a rebuttal which he sent to R. E. Dodge, Editor of the *Annals of the Association of American Geographers*. "I send it along for you to read over. Personally I regard it as one of the most important pieces of work that I have done."[37] Dodge sent the paper "Pulsatory Climatic Changes" to two censors who both felt the paper should not be published in the *Annals*. Dodge wrote to Huntington:[38]

> One says: "There is a question, I think, as to the value of publishing in the *Annals*, so long a paper in defense of one's position, previously stated in full elsewhere. I fail to see very much new in this paper, except a small shift of position, due to the numerous adverse criticisms of Huntington's opponents. I presume that an author should have a chance to answer his critics, but I am wondering whether this should not be in some other journal, especially the one in which Huntington had previously published the views which had been criticised." The other, at the end of a good deal of detailed criticism, says, in general: "I think the paper should not be accepted for publication in its present form. It is far too personal, its English is far too loose or inexact, and it is too prolix."

"Pulsatory Climatic Changes" was a direct reply to the specific criticisms of the pulsatory hypothesis advanced by Gregory, Hedin, Berg, Herbette, and others. It also dealt with the comparison of present climatic changes with those of the past. Some of the content of the paper appeared in "The Solar Hypothesis of Climatic Changes," published in the *Bulletin of the Geological Society of America*.[39] This paper had been delivered in essence without the benefit of written notes on January 1, 1914, at the

Princeton meeting of the American Geological Society.[40] The 113-page article summarized much of his work to that time, outlined the position of his adversaries on the matter of climatic change within historic time, presented his own defense, then contributed something new and original to thought by advancing a cyclonic solar hypothesis as the cause for climatic pulsations.

The publication of this article seemed to silence Huntington's detractors. Perhaps the silence was attributable to the war into which mankind had plunged itself, or perhaps the magnitude of Huntington's solar cyclonic hypothesis represented such an advance over popular alternatives as the carbon dioxide theory of glaciation that he won himself a respite while others reexamined evidences. And perhaps the principals in the drama of desiccation and climatic pulsation felt that enough had been said on the matter. Substantial criticism of Huntington's work on this matter did not erupt again until 1930, on the occasion of the centennial of the Royal Geographical Society. Although Huntington had won an abundance of plaudits, honorifics, and appreciations, it was somehow an inconclusive criticism which became associated with him in the years that followed.

In July, 1915, Huntington once again took up residence with his parents in Milton. At the age of 39, and perhaps at the height of his creativity, he was without employment. His father was nearly eighty years of age, and living on a meagre pension with his wife in a Boston suburb. Ellsworth Huntington became thoroughly reacquainted with his mother and father, undertook many of the chores in the house and garden, and thought of his future. He quickly determined to write a human geography textbook which might be read in high schools and colleges. There was no textbook in human geography written by an American geographer at that time. Huntington perceived that it was the logical extension of Davisian ontography, that he could make of it a system—perhaps a science, and that with sufficient "adoption" the book could provide him with a meaningful source of income. Huntington invited Sumner Cushing to coauthor the text with him.

Cushing, who lived on the other side of Boston in Salem, had first met Huntington on the Harvard Yard, 1901–1903. Since then Cushing had taught in high schools in Massachusetts, Connecticut, and Rhode Island and had been appointed head of the geography department at the State Normal School in Salem, Massachusetts, 1907. Experienced in the teaching of high school and normal school geography, he had access to grade school teachers, superintendents, and children's classes. Huntington perceived that the sales of a human geography text would be larger there than in the colleges where geography was not well established, and that Cushing could help him gain access to that market. Huntington and Cushing met with a representative of the American Book Company and agreed to write two texts; a human geography and a commercial and industrial geography. The human geography manuscript was commenced in July, 1915. The authors met regularly for "picking bees," "when we pick one another's work to pieces." The two men developed an outline for the book, planned chapter content, and then proceeded

to write. Twenty-seven chapters and many letters were exchanged in the mail, and then discussed at the next "picking
bee." They took turns to make the cross-Boston journey between
Salem and Milton to visit each other's homes, where they sometimes stayed overnight to talk over thoroughly differences in
points of view or presentation. Several chapters were totally rewritten and three were eliminated. The manuscript was completed in August, 1916, and they commenced work on the
"Commercial and Industrial Geography." Huntington could well
have written the books alone, but he felt a need to converse with
an educator familiar with the pupils aimed at. Possibly, too,
Huntington wanted a disciplined helper who would cry
"enough" on his inimitable tendency to fill yet another recepta-
cle with climatological matter.

Cushing was a member of a four-man joint committee which
worked under the staff of the Board of Education of Massachusetts. This committee established a "scope of work by grades"
plan, and so gave definite expression to the type of geography
which students should study from grade III to high school. Huntington accepted an invitation to sit on the committee. *Teachers'
Manual of Geography* for Grades VII and VIII, published by
the Massachusetts Board of Education, summarized much of this
committee's work.[1] The recommendation for grade VII students
included "physical geography and practical problems in general
geography" and for grade VIII pupils "commercial and industrial geography." Cushing was educating teachers at the normal
school and he was a member of the state committee. He drew
several of his lessons from the human geography manuscript;
had his student teachers develop exercises from manuscript
chapters; and in collaboration with Miss Mary E. Sanders, devised questions to follow each chapter. The Massachusetts report was requested by states across the nation. It had been
brought to the attention of geographers when Cushing had published an excerpt from the report "High School Commercial Geography," in the *Journal of Geography*.[2] The arrangement augured well for sales of the Huntington–Cushing books.

"Human Geography," the first such text written in the United
States was received by J. Byers of the American Book Company
on September 6, 1916.[3] Fifteen weeks later Huntington wrote to
G.W. Benton, one of the editors of the company, requesting a
decision on the manuscript, only to experience a portent of what
was yet to come.[4] Benton needed more time to obtain "opinions

that are worth anything on a manuscript so revolutionary and so extensive as this one."[5] Early in March 1917, Huntington and Cushing forwarded "Commercial and Industrial Geography," the second of their manuscripts, to Benton.[6] Huntington soon requested their decision on the manuscripts. The company retained the manuscripts without committing itself to publication, which drew from Huntington in August a request to return the two manuscripts at once.[7] Livengood returned them with a covering letter claiming they were still under review. Huntington was teased into returning the manuscripts, unaware that Livengood was waiting for data concerning the sale of Brigham and McFarlane's *Essentials of Geography*, also published by the American Book Company. Finding this book to be purchased in substantial numbers, Livengood finally declined to publish the Huntington and Cushing texts.[8]

Huntington had unswerving faith in the worth of, and in the need for, a text in human geography. He wrote to Livengood of the manuscript,[9] "It will to a large degree determine the attitude of thousands of teachers toward the subject, and will be the deciding factor in their choice of textbooks. . . ." Other companies were approached, but the war intervened.

In January, 1920, Sumner Cushing was afflicted by headaches and an overall feeling of fatigue. He removed himself to Vermont in search of rest, but on February 28 died from what was later revealed as a tumor on the brain.[10] Huntington wrote a detailed obituary of his friend and co-worker. The two men had published "The Nature and Possibilities of Tropical Agriculture,"[11] 1919, and were writing "The Rivalry Between Sugar Beets and Sugar Cane," when Cushing became ill. Huntington completed that article, published in 1920, as a memorial to his friend.[12]

Frances Cushing was widowed, and Huntington was left with two 'unplaced' manuscripts now in need of revision; "Principles of Human Geography" and "Commercial and Industrial Geography." Huntington wrote and rewrote parts of his "Human Geography," gathered illustrations, had diagrams and maps made, and presented the manuscript to John Wiley and Sons. The book was swiftly printed and available by December, 1920. A second revised edition was printed in 1922 and sold 29,098 copies; a third revision (1924) sold 47,391 copies; a fourth edition (1934) sold 19,160, and a fifth in 1940 sold 32,631 copies. By 1924 geography classes in over 100 normal schools, colleges,

and universities had "adopted" the book.[13] In 1921, Calpe, a
publishing house of Madrid, had requested permission to translate the book; but Wiley's conditions probably deterred translation.[14] A Japanese translation of the *Principles of Human Geography* appeared in 1927 in an edition of over 17,000 copies.[15]
The book was also translated into Chinese and Spanish. On the
appearance of the fifth edition (in English) George Cressey
wrote:[16] "Probably no other volume has had such an influence
upon the teaching of college geography in this country." Curiously it had been initially planned as a high school text, but it
was in the normal school, college, and university that sales were
most pronounced.

The book received enthusiastic reviews. In the *Scottish Geographical Magazine* one reads, "We wish to say at once that
we have found this book extraordinarily stimulating. Every sentence, it might almost be said, demands thought, and every
paragraph sustained thought."[17] *The Geographical Journal* provides,[18] "The book is written throughout with remarkable clear-
ness." Jean Brunhes proclaimed the book the first American text
in the field of human geography, and admirably fitted for pedagogical purposes.[19] George G. Chisholm offered in *Nature*[20] that
it was a good book "which may be welcomed as forming an important contribution to the definition of geography as it is coming more and more to be apprehended in the higher teaching of
the subject." He added—"the tendency to lack of due care in
generalizing cannot be denied, and there are . . . too many evil
consequences thereof."

Soon after Isaiah Bowman had appointed Harlan H. Barrows
(Head of the Department of Geography at The University of
Chicago) to the post, contributing editor of *The Geographical
Review* (1920), thus filling the vacancy created by the death
of William Churchill, he requested from Barrows a review of
Huntington's *Principles of Human Geography*. Bowman felt that
"it would be a great mistake to permit this book to go out as
representing modern human geography," and urged Barrows to
review the work critically.[21] Barrows obliged with a 3,500 word
review which, allowing some good qualities, amounted to a catalogue of criticism, some bordering on the personal:[22]

> Numerous errors of various kinds appear to be due simply to
> carelessness and can be explained only by assuming that Dr.
> Huntington wrote much of the book in more than his usual

haste . . . the book . . . fails in its purpose . . . it is to be hoped
that the book will receive an early and thorough revision. As it
stands, it is unreliable, unscientific, and displays a weak grasp
of *principles*, a serious defect in a book with this title.

And in a letter to Bowman, Barrows opined, "I am beginning
to wish that Ellsworth would write less and think more. He soon
will have H.G. Wells backed off the stage."[23]

W.M. Davis wrote to Huntington after receiving a copy of
Principles of Human Geography:[24]

The object of the book as a whole is excellent; but the method
of reaching the object often jars upon me.

For example: Your first page of Chapter II latitude and longitude: they are explained as if the pupil did not know anything
about them. Yet the rest of the book implies much previously
acquired knowledge of geography; for instance in the free use
of locality names like Denmark, Siam, Issik-Kul, and Tian Shan
in Chapter I. Nevertheless you begin latitude and longitude as
if they were entirely unknown and needed the most elementary
introductory explanation.

Davis suggested numerous other errors, or statements requir-
ing modification, took exception to Huntington's "socialistic
interpretation of our Forest Service," and became quite bitter
concerning Huntington's sentence, "For practical purposes it
makes relatively little difference how a plain or mountain originates." Davis wrote:

Your phrase "for practical purposes" p. 81, suggests a disquisition, but I refrain (but I must intimate that, for your practical
purposes, the explanation of the tides seems a waste of paper
and time; any old tides will do just as well). . . . Rainfall, p. 103;
under actual conditions, a very considerable share of rain comes
from evaporation of previous rains; i.e. from evaporation on
the continents. Of course, for "practical purposes" any old rain
will do; but for intelligent understanding??? p. 104, winds that
blow across oceans in winter are warmed, in summer are cooled.
. . . On page 147, Lake Erie is said to be due to ICE closing
its former or ancient outlet; on the next page, it, as one of the
Great Lakes, is explained as occupying an enormous hollow dug
out by the ice. But why bother about these causes; for your

"practical purposes," any old lakes will do. But by sacrificing the inorganic element, you are greatly endangering the real nature of geography. As long as it is GE-ography, its two sides deserve proper attention. On p. 149, why not bring in the socialist view of water power? . . . Why explain how weather changes are caused? Polar rainfall is only half explained, as to its small amount; but why attempt to explain it? Why introduce pressure, p. 227; why not treat winds without pressure? That is, be consistent with your principle that "for practical purposes," winds are winds, rain is rain, rivers are rivers, plains are plains.

Davis was 71 years of age when he wrote this, had retired from Harvard nine years previously, had "been deeply occupied with a memoir of G. K. Gilbert, which from an expected two months has extended all through the winter and spring and is not done yet." Davis no longer had pupils to whom he could impart his point of view; he had only former students who were themselves now developing their own points of view. Huntington was only one of several students who had studied physiography with Davis only to find in "man on the land" a much more interesting field of study. Davisian physiography had held the stage at the turn of the century, but by 1920 other geographies were replacing it. It was unbearable for Davis to be informed by one of his closest students that, "for practical purposes, it makes little difference how a plain or mountain originates." Davis had invested his life investigating just such matters. Huntington replied to Davis:[25]

Your letter concerning Human Geography has caused me to do a great deal of thinking. . . .

Your main criticism, with its series of questions, seems to me quite different from the others. In essence what you say is this: "Since physiography has ceased to occupy the main place in your new geography, why give it any place whatever?" The answer was formulated by Cushing and myself in numerous discussions in which your name and our respect and admiration for you and your work figured prominently. In effect we said: "Physiography, as worked out by Professor Davis, is an important part of geography, but as he himself often said, it is only a step toward a final and fuller geography. In that fuller geography the two phases of physiography and ontography will both be well developed, but ontography and especially its human phases will play the dominant part. What we must do, then, is to devote our main attention to human geography, but we must give enough of the physiographic background to keep the student constantly in touch with it and constantly mindful that our subject is the relation of man to his geographic environment.

In certain cases we deliberately added material which we might have left out had we not said, "Prof. Davis will like to see that. We must not break too completely with his physiography." Curiously enough a large number of the things you criticise are of that type.

Frankly, your letter disappointed me greatly. Cushing and I thought you would say something like this: "This is the logical result of my teaching. Twenty-five years ago I crystallized one phase of the growing subject of geography. Then while I taught that phase I urged my students to crystallize another. Now two of them, taking my work and the work of their fellow students and many others, have done it. Their work has the imperfections of a first attempt, but I welcome it because like myself they have been pioneers."

Davis's reply was conciliatory, yet he did offer further commentary on the correspondence which had developed twixt himself and Huntington, and so revealed his own thought concerning the nature of geography:[26]

You mistake my main point. You attribute to me the opinion: "Since physiography has ceased to occupy the main place in your new geography, why give it any place whatever?" I would word it, "Since the explanatory treatment of physiography is so generally omitted, why give it any place whatever?" Why not treat it empirically thru out?—As a matter of fact I believe it actually impossible to include *explanatory physiography* and *human geography* in a book like yours. Also, that a patchwork book, partly explanatory, partly empirical, will be *undisciplinary* —and yet *discipline* is what normal schools need. I do not believe that a good human geography can be made by introducing explanatory treatment of those facts of physiography which are usually poorly taught. The correction must come in physiography itself.

I should like to know some of the things which I criticized and regarding which you and Cushing had said—"Prof. Davis will like to see that." Also I should like to understand more fully

your statement: "We must not break too completely with his
physiography"—That seems to me a curious attitude on the part
of those who recognize that in the "fuller geography, the two
phases of physiography and ontography will *both* be well developed"! Personally, I do not believe that in the fuller geography, "ontography and especially its human phases will play the
dominant part." Just in so far as one of two related factors is
subordinated, and the other is made dominant, the relation between (and that is the essence of the fuller geography) becomes
vague and undisciplinary. . . .

Later, Davis wrote to Huntington,[27] "It would be a real satisfaction for me to have a talk with you about your book and my
letter." Certainly the correspondence generated by *Principles of
Human Geography* revealed the posture of Davis and one of his
former pupils. And, too, Huntington benefitted from Barrows's
and Davis's criticism as future editions of *Principles of Human
Geography* reveal.

Meanwhile Huntington had realized that an opportunity existed for a textbook which would appeal to students beyond the
ninth school year who had not reached college or the normal
school. On May 25, 1921 he had written to G. B. Roorbach,
then Professor of Foreign Trade at Harvard, ". . . not till today
have I definitely decided what to do. I have now decided to write
a book entitled 'Business Geography'." Huntington inquired if
Roorbach would care to associate with him in the enterprise that
summer. But Roorbach was otherwise engaged. Huntington then
invited J. Willitz of the University of Pennsylvania to join him.[28]
Willitz was writing on personnel management but he strongly
recommended geographer Frank Williams who had recently come
to the University of Pennsylvania from the University of Wisconsin. Williams had worked with Huntington in Washington,
D.C., 1918–1919, was a member of the Association of American Geographers' "Committee on Commercial Geography in
High Schools," and was a member of the faculty of the Wharton
School of Finance and Commerce. When Huntington invited
Williams to join him as coauthor, Williams accepted, and by late
1922 the Wiley Company had published *Business Geography*.

The Huntington-Cushing "Commercial and Industrial Geography" manuscript had meanwhile begun to show its age; it was
in need of revision before it could be offered for publication. In
any case Huntington had wished to revise much of the manu-

script. He sought a publisher, and in 1924 entered into a contract with World Book Company for "Commercial and Industrial Geography," which was published the following year as *Modern Business Geography*. *Modern Business Geography* was "intended for the seventh, eighth or ninth school year"; *Business Geography* was written for "pupils beyond the ninth school year"; the *Principles of Human Geography* was designed for a college audience. For each of the three books, which formed a series, Huntington was the senior author. In fact the three books were advertised as the "Huntington Geography Series." They encouraged recognition of the emerging interest in varieties of economic and commercial geography. Isaiah Bowman noted the emergence of such a genre of geographical literature in an article, "Commercial Geography as a Science: Reflections on Some Recent Books."[29]

Huntington's original touch was upon the face of each of the three textbooks, containing many thoughts fresh to the time. He wrote them solely for the royalties which they would yield. If Yale University had paid Huntington an initial salary of more than $200 as Research Associate, added to which were only modest and occasional increments, two of the texts would probably not have been written.

Wallace Atwood, who had been appointed President of Clark University in 1921, sought to establish a scholarly periodical treating this newly emerging subject matter. He invited Huntington to become a member of the advisory council to the new magazine which was tentatively entitled "Geography in Trade and Industry."[30] When Huntington replied, "I am very glad to hear of your plan for the publication of a journal of economic geography. . . . I hope you will not call the magazine Geography in Trade and Industry," he aided in the formation and naming of *Economic Geography*.[31] When Atwood sent Ekblaw to wheedle an article from Huntington for the new magazine, Huntington obliged with "The Distribution of Domestic Animals,"[32] and then published a summary of the inaugural issue of *Economic Geography* in *The Geographical Review*.[33]

Textbook writing did demand much of his time following the summer of 1915, but not all of it. There were other books—and parts of books—to be written. There was time for lecturing, research in his own interests, writing articles, occasional honors, political reform, and aid to the U.S. military.

On November 3, 1915, Huntington addressed the Philadelphia Geographical Society on the subject "Weather and Civilization." At that same meeting William E. Lingelbach, President of the Society, bestowed the Elisha Kent Kane medal upon Huntington "in recognition of his long-continued study of climatic conditions in all parts of the globe and his valuable contributions to geographic science."[34] George B. Roorbach of the Society requested a written form of Huntington's lecture for the Society's *Bulletin*. The lecture did not exist in written form so Huntington dictated it to Roorbach's secretary the day following the formal presentation.[35] The article, "Weather and Civilization," appeared in *The Bulletin of the Geographical Society of Philadelphia* for January, 1916.[36]

J. Russell Smith prepared an estimate of Huntington's work at the request of the editors of the Philadelphia *Bulletin*, and opined, "Huntington is doing what I regard as the most important geographical work now being carried on by an individual."[37] He inquired if Huntington could address "The Economic Seminary" of the Wharton School of the University of Pennsylvania at a later date.[38]

> The chief thing I want to do is to evolve from you by questions the history of the development of some of your geographical ideas, showing how things first came to you by the observation of some fact, and then clue by clue how other ideas came, were traced up, and checked. I want the men to see that things happen naturally, not by miracle, although I am afraid it is unfortunately true that they happen only to a very few.

Huntington obliged with "Climate as a Factor in Human Achievement" before the Wharton School audience, January 5, 1916. This presentation followed a series of lectures which he had offered in a tour of the midwest only days earlier. William H. Hobbs had arranged lectures at the University of Michigan, Ann Arbor; Mark Jefferson at the Michigan State Normal College, Ypsilanti; Lawrence Martin at the University of Wisconsin, Madison; and George Collie at Beloit College. Huntington offered two or three illustrated lectures at each of the institutions. He offered "Weather, Work and Human Activity," "The Ideal Climate and the Distribution of Civilization," and "The Past Distribution of Civilization and the Cause of Climatic Changes." In essence these lectures constituted a summary of his book *Civilization and Climate*, which helped win adoptions in some colleges and normal schools.

Huntington then attended the Nineteenth International Congress of Americanists (December 27–31), at Washington, D.C., and by invitation he delivered "Maya Civilization and Climatic Changes."[39] Concurrently, the Association of American Geographers was holding its annual meeting also in Washington. He spent most of December 30 and 31 (1915), and January 1 (1916) attending these meetings, and contributed "Geographic Variables."[40] It was on his return to Milton from Washington that he lectured at the Wharton School. Thus Huntington was constantly engaged, if not at the business of scholarship, then giving popular lectures which financed his serious work. Subsequent to the Wharton lecture, he gave "Changes of Climate in Historic Times" before the Academy of Science and Art of Pittsburgh, and "California Lakes and the Solar Hypothesis of Climatic Changes" before the American Philosophical Society. He then published a summary of the significance of Carl Birkinbine's researches on precipitation as it affected waterworks engineering,[41] delivered "Solar Activity, Cyclonic Storms and Climatic Changes" before the Second Pan-American Scientific Congress,[42] and responded to a request from the Harvard economist and friend of W. M. Davis, Taussig, to write "Climatic Change and Agricultural Exhaustion as Elements in the Fall of Rome."[43] The latter article excerpted much from his book *Civilization and Climate* and also revealed a little known questionnaire which Huntington had sent to a group of "confidants"—Oliver E. Baker, Isaiah Bowman, William M. Davis, Mark Jefferson, and J. Russell Smith. The questionnaire sought scientists' opinions concerning changes of climate within historic time. The group responded favorably to the questionnaire, whereupon Huntington sent it also to the members of the Association of American Geographers, to a list of geologists selected by Joseph Barrell, to the Climatic Committee of the Ecological Society of America, and to selected meteorologists. Of the replies Huntington wrote:[44]

Among those from whom replies have thus far been received only three believe unequivocally in climatic uniformity during historic times. Only one thinks that changes have occurred mainly through human actions, altho a considerable number believe that these have been of subsidiary importance. Three accept the idea of a change which progresses steadily in one direction. The remainder, forty-nine in number, believe that during the past two or three thousand years climatic changes have taken place on a scale greater than during the past century. Practically all of the forty-nine hold that while there have been irregular or pulsatory changes, the general tendency has been toward greater aridity in the Mediterranean countries and other similar regions.

The questionnaire elicited some interesting commentary regarding the esteem which American geographers held for his work. Charles R. Dryer, formerly professor of geology and geography of the Indiana State Normal School, wrote:[45]

> . . . I am not prepared by general training or special knowledge to express any expert opinion upon the viability and chances of survival of your famous offspring, but my attitude toward it is one of unqualified admiration and not a little pride. For magnitude and complexity of the problem attacked, for persistent accumulation of facts from a wide range of sources, and for the skill with which they have been marshaled on one side and the other and their possible meaning evaluated, I place your work in the same class with Chamberlin's in the causes of a glacial period and his development of the planetesimal hypothesis. If your work at this stage seems more like an iridescent dream than his, that may be because you have not yet had time to make it as substantial.

John P. Goode, professor of geography at the University of Chicago, responded:[46]

> I am enclosing your questionnaire, with my signature. I think very highly of your climatic hypotheses as applied to the sequence of climate in the past two or three thousand years, and it seems to me that you are doing a constructive work of a very high order. . . .

and from Oliver E. Baker, agricultural economist with the United States Department of Agriculture:[47]

> . . . Personally, may I state that I have found your publications among the most stimulating, if not the most stimulating of those of any geographer in the United States. It is important that hypotheses be put forward, although they may prove insufficient

in certain features, for only thereby can progress be achieved;
and I for one have no patience with the men who frown upon,
much less who ridicule, the efforts of a man, who so to speak, is
pioneering a new path through an unknown country. It is just
such hypotheses as you have put forward that seem to me most
certain assurance that geography is not a dead science in the
United States, and that the future still holds promise of better
things to come. . . .

He had not forsaken his idea that he should convert the historians to the importance of the theme; when H.E. Bourne
wrote to Huntington and requested him to critique "Climatic
and Geographic Influences upon Ancient Agriculture" by Ellen
Semple at the 1916 meeting of the American Historical Association Huntington replied:[48]

> . . . I have so many things that I want to say to the historians
> that if I went so far as to meet with the historians I should
> not be content with merely taking part in a discussion of some-
> one else's paper. I suppose that I may be over-sanguine, but I
> am persuaded that within the next generation the philosophy of
> history will suffer modification because of a new understanding
> of the effect of physical environment, especially climate, upon
> human energy.

When Isaiah Bowman became Director of the American
Geographical Society in 1915, Huntington found his former colleague sympathetic to his climatological investigations. Bowman
was prepared to publish what Huntington had to offer, and even
suggested that if Huntington did not shave one morning he could
write an article in the time saved and send it to the *Review*!
(Bowman may well have known of Huntington's capacity to
write "finished pot-boilers" in a single morning.) Bowman did
seek contributions from Huntington and did publish reviews,
commentary and articles by him, including more notably "Climatic Variations and Economic Cycles,"[49] "The Water Barriers
of New York City,"[50] and "The Geographical Work of Dr.
M. A. Veeder."[51] Of the work which Huntington provided Bowman always had something kind to say:[52]

> Your article on "Water Barriers" is so good that I took it home
> to read to the family. It is going to make a great hit. I do not

know whether I like the introduction better than the end of the
article or the end better than the beginning! It is splendid of
you to let me have so fine a thing for the *Review*. . . .

Of Huntington's reviews Bowman offered:[53]

We mean to select books which you would naturally want to
read. In fact, knowing our low rate of pay I am a little bit ap-
prehensive each time that I send you a book for I know that
your time is too valuable to spend much of it in reviewing.

And,[54]

I am very glad to have your four reviews. I underscored "Short"
because you are one of the few authors whose work we do not
care to shorten; you can do it better than we can. . . .

More fresh experiences came to Huntington with the creation
of the Ecological Society of America, the creation of the Deno-
yer-Geppert Company, a venture into politics, and participation
in the war effort.

The Ecological Society held its first meeting in December,
1916 at Columbia University. Huntington was a founding member. His enthusiasm for ecological investigation had been stimulated by his association with Macdougal, Shreve, Sykes, and
other members of the Carnegie Desert Laboratory at Tucson.
Yet his own researches were often ecological in nature. His correspondence and association with scientists in many fields at the
time was immense. Thus he was well chosen to represent the
newly emerging group. The society grew swiftly and at the end
of one year could boast a membership of over 300 persons. He
helped found the standing committee on climatic conditions,
urged the publication of a journal, and encouraged geographers
to join the society and represent "human ecology." He was a
pioneer in the use of the term "human ecology," which he first
adopted in 1916 to distinguish geographers' work from that of
zoologists and biologists "who could not see beyond their big
toe." Elected president of the society for its second year he delivered his presidential address—"Climatic change as a Factor in
Organic Evolution"[55]—before the society at Christmas-time,
1917, taking his bride of four days to Pittsburgh for the occasion. He retained an active interest in the Ecological Society
throughout his lifetime.

Another venture in which Huntington took part and which enlarged his circle of acquaintances was the founding of the Denoyer–Geppert Company. L.P. Denoyer and Otto Geppert resigned their posts with the Nystrom Map and Publishing Company in 1916 to form their own company. They wished to compile the strongest possible board of cartographic editors available. Denoyer was able to persuade Frank Carney, Walter S. Tower, Sumner Cushing, Jacques W. Redway, and George B. Roorbach that they should associate themselves with his cartographic venture; he was able to secure the services of an enthusiastic Huntington; but he could not win Davis, Jefferson, or Smith to his position. Much correspondence ensued between Denoyer and Huntington. The latter was persuaded that the Denoyer–Geppert cartographic venture was sound both intellectually and financially, and so, in turn, and over a period of some weeks, Huntington persuaded Davis, Jefferson, and Smith to associate themselves with the company. Conferences of geographic editors were called periodically in the first year of business; Dryer was responsible for North America, Davis and Cushing for Europe, Carney and Tower for Africa, Jefferson for the Western Hemisphere, Smith and Roorbach for the World, and Huntington for Asia. That, at least, was the initial arrangement. Numerous changes were made, but maps began to appear, and at the end of twelve months the Denoyer–Geppert Company showed a profit. Huntington was not surprised; he had invested $1400 in the company very soon after its inception.

As for Huntington's venture into politics, it really began soon after his departure from Yale in the summer of 1915. He urged a fitting memorial on the occasion of The Pilgrim Tercentenary and jointly authored a statement with his brother-in-law, Charles Ziegler, which was sent to many notables in the United States, and which was published in the *Boston Transcript*.[56] His suggestion for the establishment of a permanent visible memorial, to include an auditorium, library, headquarters for the accommodation of experts, and a memorial institution, "an international laboratory of human self government,"[57] was met warmly but received little effective support, though the matter was debated in the Massachusetts legislature. Perhaps this attracted to him a certain amount of attention, for he was approached by citizens of Milton, who requested him to seek political office in the State of Massachusetts on the Prohibition ticket. Huntington was not a prohibitionist, though he rarely consumed alcoholic beverages.

Still, he did not favor the saloon. Since neither the Democratic nor the Republican parties showed any inclination toward temperance in their political platforms, Huntington agreed to represent Prohibition in order that the voter might voice his concern regarding the saloon. On September 26, 1916, he was elected at the primaries as a "candidate for the office of Representative, 4th Norfolk District, under the political designation of Prohibition, to be voted for at the State Election on November 7th. He wrote a brief tract on his stand for prohibition but let his supporters campaign largely in his stead. Numerous letters came to him in these weeks concerning his thought and position on matters including wine and spirits, trade unions, women and labor unions, democracy, and immigration. Always he answered his correspondence in a simple and forthright manner, creating a political stance as he progressed. It was an interesting interlude which ended on November 7th when the people voted no prohibition in Massachusetts.

Huntington also held office in the Milton Historical Society, promoted a church council and forum, and became a charter member of the Massachusetts League to Enforce Peace. When the United States joined the Allies in World War I, he was elected Vice-President of the Milton Committee of the Education Society, which distributed pamphlets concerning food preservation in the home. He helped promote local canning kitchens where the ladies of Boston could preserve summer produce. While working in one of these kitchens he became better acquainted with Rachel Brewer, a lady from a Milton family whom he had known for several years. Rachel Brewer had graduated from Bryn Mawr (1905), then helped found the Little House (a settlement house in South Boston), and had in the teens of the century aided in the soup kitchens of Boston.

Ellsworth Huntington and Rachel Slocum Brewer were married on December 22, 1917, in the Unitarian Church in Milton.

CHAPTER IX

Captain Huntington: Military Intelligence Division, United States Army

Following the sinking of the *Lusitania* in 1917 the United States mobilized its resources and joined the Allies in the War. Fifty-two geographers assumed government service in the months that followed. They worked in the Inquiry, the U.S. War Trade Board, the U.S. Shipping Board, the Council of National Defense, the Weather Bureau, Department of Agriculture, Committee on Public Information, Chemical Warfare Services, American Rights League, Bureau of Soils, Red Cross, Geological Survey, Reserve Officers' Training Corps, Student Army Training Corps, Ordnance Reserve Corps, and the Military Intelligence Division of the National Army.[1] Huntington's contribution was made through the last-named agency.

Numerous European geographers had been writing to Huntington of the terrible effects of the War. George G. Chisholm, in fact, wrote to numerous of the American geographers urging them in his inimitably detached way to commit themselves to the Allied cause. Bartholomew wrote to Huntington that the United States really should stop selling ammunition to the enemy. Bryce mused that civilization was threatened. Huntington was very "eager to do something in connection with the war," and to that end presented a plan to the National Research Council,[2] of which W. M. Davis was an influential figure. Davis had been elected President of the Geology and Geography Division of the Council, had written *A Handbook of Northern France*, and had undertaken to recruit lecturers from the Association of American Geographers to give lectures in the YMCA "huts" located in each of the thirty-two army camps in America. He had specifically requested of Huntington a set of slides and an outline lecture on Palestine that could be given to the soldiers. Resultant to this request was Huntington's article "The Future of Palestine."[3] Davis had also solicited suggestions for action from geographers. Thus it was to Davis that Huntington had offered his suggestion:[4]

As to the part to be taken by the geographers in the war it seems to me that one of the best things we can do is to assist in giving the officers and men of our army and navy a thorough understanding of those regions where there is chance of conflict. We must of course proceed as if we thought the war might last two or three years even though we all hope that it will end in a few months. On that basis it is highly probable that we shall send troops to France and that they may operate also in Belgium and western Germany. Therefore why not bend our efforts to getting together the best possible description of the geography of those regions? The Balkans and Constantinople, too, may see some of our activity, although of course we are not now at war with any power in that part of the world. Nevertheless, it is highly probable that when peace is made our voice may be of particular weight in regard to the final disposal of parts of Turkey. Again our navy is likely to operate frequently along the shores of Great Britain, France, and the North Sea countries as far as Norway. Many men also will have work to do in the West Indies. Therefore we need concise, up-to-date and interesting descriptions of these regions with good maps.

Other places will suggest themselves as important. To my own mind it seems that Mexico is likely to prove most important of all so far as our immediate activities are concerned. I believe the chances are nine out of ten that in spite of ourselves we shall come to war with Mexico, thanks to German intrigue. Then it is altogether probable that after the war with Germany we shall still have on our hands a well developed Mexican war. My own personal belief is that we can never stop until we have conquered Mexico and have set it on its feet once more in the same way that we have set Cuba. Therefore I think it might be highly advisable if some members of the Association of American Geographers went to work with the idea of preparing a brief but thorough-going work on Mexico, the kind of book that officers and soldiers alike could read and that would make them understand what they were coming in contact with. It would not be necessary to say much about this so long as we stay at peace with Mexico. If we should not go to war with that country the work could be published in a slighly different form for the sake of our future peaceful intercourse with the Mexicans.

Independent of this suggestion Huntington had drawn up a nine-page plan entitled "Proposal for the Application of a New

Scientific Method to a Phase of Military Training." Following
his performance-studies of students at Annapolis and West
Point, factory workers the length of the east coast, and students
at Hampton Institute, he was quite sure an optimum temperature
existed for both mental and physical labor. He wished to pursue
similar researches in ten or twelve widely distributed camps.[5]

> . . . The purpose of such measurements should be to fill up the
> serious gap in our knowledge of the effect of food, exercise,
> and climate not only upon physical strength, but still more upon
> the psychological status which determines the rapidity and per-
> fection with which men can be trained.

He had talked of this plan to George E. Hale of the National
Research Council in Washington, D.C., and on his return to
Milton confirmed the substance of his conversation:[6]

> I am eager to volunteer my services to the country at the
> present time. Feeling that I can be far more useful in scientific
> ways than in any other, it seems wise to act through the Na-
> tional Research Council, provided the Council approves my
> plans. I am ready to go to work at any time, and to keep on
> working steadily so long as the war lasts. I wish that my work
> might tend to the advancement of scientific knowledge as well
> as toward the winning of the war. Therefore I submitted the
> plan which we have discussed and which is now before your
> Committee.

> This does not mean, however, that I am wedded to that par-
> ticular plan. If the plan is too large for the present, or if I can
> be of more service in some other way, I am quite ready to go
> at the matter by some different method. I feel certain, however,
> that I can work most effectively along the lines of the relation
> of health and efficiency to climatic conditions both in training
> camps and hospitals. This includes mental and moral health as
> well as physical. Further details are not necessary as they are
> given in the later pages of my more formal plan. If nothing
> more elaborate is possible I think that I could be of use if I
> were somehow attached to the army in such a way that I could
> supervise a series of tests on various companies before and after
> they moved from camps in one part of the country to those in
> another. Even within a few months this would give us new and

valuable information as to where camps and hospitals can best be located at different seasons. I am convinced that one of the most important results of such work would be its moral effect. Already my studies of factory work and of deaths in their relation to climate give a considerable body of facts on which I believe that I can base certain conclusions which will be of immediate value. Thus before the tests on the soldiers are available I should hope that I might be able to offer some suggestions of value . . .

G. E. Hale referred Huntington's proposal to Victor C. Vaughan, Chairman of the Medicine and Hygiene Committee of the National Research Council, who informed Huntington,[7] "I am very deeply interested in your plan. . . . I don't believe the time is as yet ripe for attempting to adopt your suggestions." Three months later Huntington reminded Vaughan of the proposal before him, to which Vaughan replied with a note entitled "Subject: Value of Exercise."[8] He had quite failed to perceive Huntington's intent. Huntington visited Vaughan, and General Gorgas of the War Department in Washington, D.C., to further his plan for investigating efficiency in the military training camps.[9] Although he was able to muster support for his idea from several of the leading minds of Yale, Harvard, Columbia and Princeton, neither the military nor the National Research Council seemed to have an interest.

When Bowman suggested that Huntington visit him at the American Geographical Society to consider a piece of research for the Government, Huntington visited Bowman, discussed the matter and evinced interest in the proposition, "The more I think about the plan for research which we discussed on Saturday, the more keenly I am interested in it. . . ."[10] Bowman was, in effect, head of the Inquiry—a non committal title for a group of experts brought together to prepare information for the forthcoming peace conference. It was Bowman who perceived that Huntington's "greatest usefulness would be along the line of coordinating and abstracting reports." Huntington had been invited to join the House Commission when it was created in November, 1917, but with his marriage to Rachel Slocum Brewer imminent he declined the invitation. Later he reflected "If I had gone I should have had an important position in the Paris delegation."[11]

Perhaps it was Bowman who encouraged Colonel R. H. Van Deman and his own brother-in-law, Captain J. Walter Goldthwait, both of the Military Intelligence Division, Washington, D.C. to write to Huntington in May, 1918. Van Deman requested Huntington to list the countries and parts of countries of which he had a special knowledge. Huntington's reply revealed his extensive travels in Europe and Asia. On May 15 he received a letter from his old friend Goldthwait:

> I am writing to you at this time mainly to ask if you would be interested in the chance to join us here, with a similar commission. . . . there is a fair chance that a man well acquainted with Asia, like yourself, will be wanted, in our Branch. The aim of his work would be to follow daily development of combat in that part of the world, according to secret and public information which is constantly coming in, and to interpret this information as to combat in the light of history, ethnology, and geographic factors.

Huntington travelled to Washington, D.C., was commissioned a captain June 6, and reported for duty June 10 with the Military Monograph Sub-Section, M.I.2., Military Intelligence Division. Major Charles W. Furlong—artist, explorer, lecturer— headed the section. Other men soon to join M.I.2. were John Karmazin, Sumner Cushing, Harold Colton, Montgomery Schuyler, James T. Adams, Charles Johnston, and Frank E. Williams. A team of twenty-six research clerks was maintained. Following a report by D. W. Johnson[12] concerning the establishment of a British geographic bureau headed by H. N. Dickson (University College, Reading) in the Department of Naval Intelligence of the Admiralty, the U.S. National Army reorganized and enlarged its own Military Intelligence Division. In the reorganization Huntington was promoted to chief of a newly created subsection in November, and to chief of the section when, later, the subsection was reconstituted as "M.I.9." Huntington wrote of the work of the section:[13]

> The chief work of the Monograph Section is to gather information as to countries where the United States may be obliged to conduct military operations. This information is incorporated in monographs, handbooks, and maps, which fulfill the functions described below, and are among the most important factors in the equipment of a modern army.

Map work was on every side of the section. Occasionally Huntington, or one of the other officers, was asked to study the possessions of someone held in detention on spying charges and occasionally personnel of the section would study the "fermentation charts" which accompanied the "weekly situation report," dealing with the length and causes of strikes, work stoppages, and material deficiencies.

Huntington wrote, "A Plan for Detaching Turkey and Bulgaria from their German Alliance,"[14] but spent more of his time gathering information on Europe. The Committee on Education and Special Training of the War Department included geography in a curriculum which had been designed for the Students' Army Training Corps. Yet geographic instruction in the schools offering these special military programs was usually poor, and a satisfactory text for course work in the geography of Europe did not exist. Hence the National Research Council sponsored a group of men in government service—fifteen geographers, three geologists and two economists—to compose a book "on the geographic conditions of Europe" for use by American soldiers. Huntington spent considerable time editing and writing *The Geography of Europe*.[15] The book was a compilation by several men, but Huntington and Herbert Gregory assumed the larger part of the task. J. Russell Smith wrote to Huntington,[16] "I have just taken counsel with members of the War Trade Board staff, and they agree with me that the names of yourself and Gregory should be given as Editors." The work was completed by October 10, 1918, and was published later that same year by Yale University Press. The published text did not reveal the vast collection of data, largely statistical in nature, which was retained in the subsection's private files. *The Geography of Europe* was adopted by isolated schools and colleges across the United States; in 1919 the text was adopted in the public schools of Ohio.

Huntington's next large task, and that of the monograph section, was to prepare a series of monographs on Siberia. It was probably the largest undertaking of the section. Information was collected from a variety of sources; many travellers from Siberia and other parts of Russia were interviewed, some by Russian speaking people in the section. Of this undertaking Huntington wrote in May 1919:[17]

> During the War, an admirable system of co-operation among officers and research clerks was developed in the Monograph

Section, and the result was ten good books on Russia and Siberia which were printed, and four more which were not
printed because of the Armistice. The experience gained in writing these gave the Military Monograph Section an efficiency
which is believed to be at least equal if not superior to that of
any similar organization in any part of the world.

Huntington interviewed many Russians, intellectuals with
knowledge of Russia, and American and Canadian businessmen
who had business interests in Russia. Frequently this involved
him in security investigations for which he was temperamentally
unsuited; he was always quick to see the better side of a person's
character, and invariably ready to grant the benefit of any doubt
which had arisen. The investigations were part of what Huntington called "his new education."

The other large undertaking upon which Huntington's section
of M.I.D. embarked was a monograph concerning Mexico, all
the more needed since Pershing's invasion of Mexico in search
of "Pancho" Villa. Of the need for this type of monograph
Huntington wrote:[18]

> In our Mexican expedition of 1916 the officers estimate that one
> week in four could have been saved if the Army had been sup-
> plied with proper handbooks and maps. Contrary to the ordi-
> nary assumption local guides are very hard to procure. Even
> when our forces were operating from our own border at Co-
> lumbus, New Mexico, only one guide could be found who was
> acquainted with the main line of march from Columbus to Casas
> Grandes.

The section had not completed the monograph when peace
was proclaimed. When Lt. Col. Campanole was appointed Chief
of the Military Monograph Section following Huntington's return to Milton on July 18, 1919, he sent eight unfinished chapters of the Mexican monograph to Huntington with a request
that he "correct and edit" them. Additionally Huntington was
asked to write an introductory chapter to the monograph. He
obliged and the monograph was printed. Neither the Russian
studies nor the Mexican monograph were made available to the
public. An intimation of the Mexican research was revealed in
one issue of *The Geographical Review*, in which appeared three
articles by personnel of the Military Intelligence Division: "The

Natural Regions of Mexico"[19] by E. M. Sanders, "The Distribution of Population in Mexico,"[20] by the late Sumner W. Cushing, and "The Relation of Health to Racial Capacity: The Example of Mexico"[21] by Huntington. And in the fall of 1919 Huntington presented "The Factor of Health in Mexican Character" at the seventh Clark University Conference upon International Relations: the essay appeared in *Mexico and The Caribbean*[22] and was reprinted in *The Journal of International Relations*.[23]

When General M. Churchill, Chief of Staff of the Military Intelligence Division, signed Huntington's discharge papers, he noted his "very scholarly work in the Military Monograph Section of M.I.D.," and further observed "that upon the foundation which you have helped to lay there will be built up a continually improving War Department policy with respect to military monographs and handbooks."[24] On November 13, 1919, Huntington was given an intelligence duty commission as Major in the Quartermaster Section of the Army. Later, in his reserve capacity, Huntington did edit the "Terrain Handbooks" manuscript for Military Intelligence.

Huntington had wished to see men of science more closely affiliated with the work of the military, both in war and peace, and to this end he accepted membership in the Geology and Geography Division of the National Research Council.[25] He wrote a "Tentative Draft of Resolution for Submission to the Secretary of War and Chief of Staff and the Military Committee of Congress," recommending "a close relationship between the Army and the scientific men of the country." He authored "Suggestions for M.I.D." and proposed:[26]

> To affiliate the Geographic Section of M.I.D. to the Research Department of Yale University and to the Geographic Department of Columbia University, New York, and to affiliate M.I.2. to the Economic Department of Johns Hopkins University, Baltimore. That the War Department shall make a business arrangement with the Universities so as to have the right to send a member of its staff once every two or three months for criticisms and help.

Early in 1918 Huntington had commenced work on a manuscript entitled "World-Power and Evolution." The manuscript was completed in December, 1918, while he was still with

M.I.D.; it was allowed as part of his assignment, though some of the work was accomplished in his apartment during evenings and weekends. It was, in part, a companion volume to *Civilization and Climate*. That book had dealt with the problem of the effect of physical environment upon human progress with relation to space. He had constructed a contemporary world map of "high," "low," and "intermediate" civilization. In *World-Power and Evolution*[27] stands revealed man's voyage of evolution from Silurian time, how man was fitted with lungs and limbs, how an intelligence emerged under the influence of variable climate and weather, and how selection through migration hastened the advent of superior peoples. Waves of health, inebriety, financial crisis, economic and social progress, and the whole corpus of civilization, are related to variable weather and climatic pulsation.

Huntington's interest in eugenics was already upon him, and although in its later, more developed form it would be mainly concerned with the temperament and intelligence of individual families, at this time it involved what he termed "a rule in history,"—that an energizing climate, health, rigor of body and mind, originality, persistence, high civilization, conquest and dominance of weaker races, lead to a flowering of the higher type of civilization. He compared the desiccated Turkish Anatolian upland with an energized Germany. Detached from the emotion of conflict, he viewed Germany's aggression as the inevitable concomitant of boundless energy derived from her variable climate. The manuscript did not pass military censorship. Colonel of the General Staff, John Dunn, Acting Director of Military Intelligence, wrote to Huntington:[28]

> Referring to your memorandum of December 11, requesting permission to publish your book entitled "World Power and Evolution" we would advise that such permission will be withheld until the manuscript is revised to accord with the following suggestions.
>
> (a) On page 229 the assertion that "in her relations with other belligerents, Germany has acted exactly in accord with what would be expected on the basis of her climate," should be so changed that no sanction of German misdeeds can be read into it;
>
> (b) On page 238, the paragraph "When the war ended France, England, the United States and Germany all emerged

with unimpaired prestige, so far as prestige depends upon energy and determination with which they fought," is questionable both as to accuracy and propriety, and should be deleted, or so modified as not to compare Germany so favorably with the victorious arm of her enemies;

(c) On page 235, the expression "superlative energy" could readily, if separated from the context, be interpreted as a praise of Germans above all others, while we presume your intention was merely to rate them on an equal footing with the French, British and Americans. "Superlative energy" should not be accorded the Germans, since the energy displayed by Germany's armies was not the equal of that displayed by several of her enemies;

(d) On pages 238 and 239, the long passage exculpating the German people from the charge of having been dupes, is, in our opinion, not only incorrect and objectionable to loyal Americans and the nationals of the Allies, but is likely in the present and the future to meet repudiation from a great number of Germans themselves. This passage should be modified to eliminate the objections recited.

The changes were made and the book was "found unobjectionable from the point of view of military censorship."[29] Yale University Press published the book in the following year, 1919. Huntington was quite aware of the extent of a sudden German ambition and revealed this point of view in "Germany's Prospective Loot in Asia."[30]

Huntington received a letter from Francis Allan of the Houghton, Mifflin Company early in 1919 which proposed an austerity printing of *The Pulse of Asia*.[31] He agreed to "reduce the external size of the book and drop out some of the illustrations," and proposed that he write a new introduction, "to show how the theory of 'pulsatory climatic changes' which is what gives the book its permanent value, has changed and grown since the book was first written." By May, 1919, Huntington had written such an introduction revealing the logic of his work in the twelve years which followed the initial publication of *The Pulse of Asia*.[32] Not much attention was accorded this introduction; yet it is a succinct but revealing exposition of his mind's flight through the notion of climatic pulsation and its substantiation in North American terraces, lake basins, tree rings, et al. to the influence of variability, selection and mutation of human stock, and a quest for explanation of mechanistic causation between earth and sun. Again the man revealed his extraordinary capacity to accomplish substantial works simultaneously in different fields; on the one hand he was producing the subsection monographs as part of the war effort and on the other hand he was investigating the forces which impinge on and contribute to the process of civilization. The two undertakings were not incompatible, though his management of that diversity bespoke a strong personal discipline.

He was swift to seize upon opportunity in a facile way: while in M.I.D. he spoke with, or was introduced to, many exiles from Russia. He was very impressed with the "high quality" of these exiles which led to a disquisition on a eugenic drain from Russia, later published in *Scribner's* as "The Suicide of Russia."[33]

When Yale Secretary A.P. Stokes, who was familiar with the scope and nature of Huntington's researches, wrote to him:[34]

> I was at the Coal Administration headquarters in Washington on Wednesday of this week and urged upon them the possibility of making a large saving in coal through getting the people to keep their houses under sixty-five degrees of temperature. Among other facts I quoted some of your own conclusions. The department was very much interested in these and said that it would be a great service to them if you could supply them with the results of your investigations and write them a brief article, which they could use. . . .

Huntington obliged with "Save Coal and Save Health" which was published in *The American Review of Reviews*.[35]

And while in M.I.D. he met with Fridtjof Nansen, Food Commissioner of the Norwegian Special Mission to the United States, who presented him with a copy of a study he had co-authored with Bjorn Helland-Hansen dealing with solar and terrestrial changes of climate.[36] Huntington had sought explanation of climatic change in extraterrestrial phenomena as early as 1908.[37] He had spoken to and corresponded with Henry Clayton, Henryk Arctowski, Frank Bigelow, Charles Abbott, Cleveland Abbe, Charles F. Brooks, and many other men on that matter. He published a theoretical statement of major significance in the *Monthly Weather Review*—"Solar Disturbances and Terrestrial Weather" (1918).[38] Inspired by Veeder's work he had come to the paradoxical conclusion that a warmer sun coincided with a cooler earth, at least in most cyclonic areas. His notion was that increased solar activity resulted in more energy sent to earth which increased atmospheric circulation and storminess, leading locally to greater precipitation and lower average temperature. With the Helland-Hansen–Nansen study before him he summarized the theory of the two conflicting schools of thought which had emerged on the matter of the sun's influence on the earth. "The Sun and the Weather: New Light on Their Relation"[39] clearly revealed the conflict in thought between a number of theoreticians and the U.S. Weather Bureau.

The subject of causes of climatic change so fascinated Huntington that in 1922–23 he expounded his entire corpus of thought concerning climatic change in two books, *Climatic Changes*[40] and *Earth and Sun*.[41] In the wake of those two books he was obliged to declare an inadequacy in higher mathematics which precluded further investigation of the field. He did have a fine appreciation for the uses to which a mathematical training could be put in geographical study: he frequently mused on his own inadequacy and urged his students to take up the subject. Even so, his grasp of mathematics enabled him to extract what he needed from piles of data in the wake of the influenza epidemic which ravaged Washington, D.C., and other parts of the country in the winter of 1918–1919. He seized upon the outbreak to further his insight into the relationships among weather, climate, and health. He wrote on the possibility of similar previous disasters being attributable to influenza rather than plague, then wrote "The Interpretation of the Death Rate by Climographs,"[42] "The Control of Pneumonia and Influenza by the Weather,"[43] "Air Control and The Reduction of The Death Rate After Operations,"[44] "The Purpose and Methods of Air Control in Hospitals,"[45] "Methods of Air Control and Their Results,"[46] and "Minds Work Best at 64 Degrees."[47] These were among the articles which elicited from Bowman a request: "Have you a short article, four or five thousand words long, on your geographical invasion of the field of Medicine that carries concrete results that would be of interest to our readers?"[48] Later, Huntington's work was accorded recognition by the medical profession.[49]

Other books were on his mind. Mrs. Mary Austin (author of sixteen books, three plays, and numerous essays) and D.T. Macdougal wished to collaborate with him in writing a book on the nature of government, nationalism, and political systems, but after exchanging numerous letters, copying them and further circulating them among themselves, that effort came to naught. Huntington wrote to the Yale University Press of his interest in writing a book on Armenia—"I had thought of the book merely as something to do during a month's vacation, for most of the material is already in mind"[50]—but the Press discouraged the idea, and simultaneously urged him to write a book on Europe which would recommend itself to college and normal school audiences. Huntington commenced the task and swiftly completed thirty-three chapters totalling one hundred and thirty-seven thousand words. There the work was shelved until he was invited by Samuel Van Valkenburg to join him as coauthor of a textbook of European geography which Van Valkenburg had written in the early thirties, but with which he was not satisfied. On this task Huntington used some of the material he had written in 1919 and 1920.

A very large part of the reason why such projects were started and not finished at that time was Huntington's intense determination to pursue the relationships of weather to health and sun to earth. He departed Washington in 1919 and returned to Milton for the remainder of the summer. He strongly supported the League of Nations, urged men holding political office to ratify the treaty, wrote political tracts to that end which were circulated by the "Pro-League Independents" of Boston, and composed "Clinching the Nails of Peace," an unpublished article revealing his concern for the selection of well chosen international boundaries.

Huntington began to make preparations for a return to Yale that September as research associate in geography!

CHAPTER X

'Research Associate in Geography' at Yale University

Although Huntington had lost his employment by Yale University in 1915, he did not sever informal connections. He had been most helpful to Charles F. Brooks, who took over his office at Yale; he read and accepted *in absentia* Miss Gladys Wrigley's doctoral dissertation; his reviews and essays tumbled from the pages of *The Yale Review*; and the Yale Press frequently requested a manuscript of him and published whatever he offered them. He contributed a chapter, "Climate and the Evolution of Civilization," to *The Evolution of the Earth and Its Inhabitants*, edited by R. S. Lull, and published by the Yale University Press in 1918. When Allen Johnson, Professor of American History, invited him to prepare a manuscript which would inaugurate The Yale Chronicles of America Series, Huntington obliged with "The Red Man's Continent."

The Secretary of the Yale Corporation, Anson Phelps Stokes, a silent admirer of Huntington's prolificity and intellectual verve, sought ways of effecting his return to the campus. It was probably Stokes who originated the notion of "Research Associate,"[1] and it was Stokes who negotiated the larger part of the correspondence with the president, trustees, deans, geology department, and Huntington. President Hadley, warm to Huntington's cause but somewhat uncertain of his intellectual posture; geologists not much interested in geography; and trustees suspicious of the new position—all were won over by Stokes's persistence. Stokes persuaded Huntington that he should return though all he had to offer was "a nominal compensation, say $200 a year, and a suitable office." In fact, when Huntington accepted the post at Yale he paid his secretary $18 per week, fivefold what the University paid him. Under these circumstances he wrote:[2] "I do not know whether I can afford to take up my residence in New Haven, although I am well aware that I need the stimulus of life in an intellectual community . . . it obliges me to sail pretty close to the wind."

But his return was personally satisfying to him, and in any

case, he could depart if his honorarium was not reasonably increased as Stokes had intimated following the return of a settled peacetime economy. Of his fear he wrote to Barrell,[3] "It is certainly a pleasure to me to think of resuming my old associations at New Haven. My only fear is that under the present arrangement I may feel that I cannot stay."

Huntington could have commanded a much more satisfactory salary elsewhere. William H. Hobbs at the University of Michigan, Mark Jefferson at the Michigan State Normal College, and Lawrence Martin at the University of Wisconsin had each invited Huntington to assume professorships at their respective institutions. When the University of Minnesota offered him an attractive post with courses he could structure himself, he declined the offer; but twenty years later he expressed regret over that decision.

Formally Huntington returned to Yale in the autumn of 1919. His financial circumstances had import for his work. He was obliged to assume a fiscal responsibility unusual to the groves of academe. In the following years he divided his time between writing and lecturing for profit, and authoring both textbooks and scholarly monographs. He also sought to found a geography department within the university. That matter consumed a lot of his time. As early as April, 1920, a committee of the University Council had recommended the establishment of a Department of Geography, but the report was "tabled because of the financial straits of the University."[4] The only courses of a geographical nature offered at that time were Bishop's "Economic Geography," and Huntington's "Climatology"; in the autumn of 1922 Ralph Gabriel of the History Department inaugurated a course entitled "Historical Geography of North America." The matter of creating a geography department was amply discussed at several formal meetings of the geological faculty, and recommendation of the organization of such a department was made to the Graduate School.[5] Following a motion that "Doctor Ellsworth Huntington be recommended to the Graduate School for the full professorship in Geography . . ." he composed a "Memorandum as to the Desirability of Establishing a Geographical Center at Yale University." Richard S. Lull read the memorandum and added suggestions to it. Huntington sent the memorandum to President Rowland Angell.[6] The need for geographic instruction at Yale was postulated, the buildings for the Geographical Center were enumerated, the extent of staff, and the cost of the total undertaking was calculated. Following a conversation with President Angell, Huntington sent him the names of men "worth considering in the formation of a Geographical Faculty at Yale. . . ."[7] Huntington listed Wellington D. Jones, H. Karl W. Kumm, Alan G. Ogilvie, T. Griffith Taylor, and Stephen S. Visher.

> The choice among the five men here mentioned naturally depends upon what kind of a department we are going to build up. If we are going to have merely one man and Geography is to be an adjunct of Geology, Ogilvie, with I believe a geological training, is probably the best. I feel, however, that if he were called first it would prevent Yale from doing any really big things in its Geography Department.
>
> If we are content to have a Geography Department with perhaps two or three men and which acquires merely a reputation for good training, Professor Jones seems best. If he were called first, however, and became the head of the department, I should not look for any developments that would make Yale a central figure in Geography.
>
> From the standpoint of scientific research we could do nothing better, it seems to me, than to call Professor Taylor and then Professor Visher. Neither of them, however, seems adapted to build up a department; although they would be most valuable additions if there were someone else to smooth the edges and form contacts.

Huntington concluded that H. Karl William Kumm was, however, probably best fitted for the job. Kumm, the first white man to traverse the north-central African divide between Congo Shari and the Nile, founder and managing director of the Board for Medical Education and Research in Africa, and founder of the Sudan United Mission, taught geography in the Hartford Theological Seminary, only forty miles from Yale University. Huntington knew of him through his friends in the missionary world. Kumm seemed bent on establishing a geographic center somewhere to aid missions abroad. Meanwhile Huntington wrote to Angell of his own ill-defined position:[8]

> After the end of my Army service I returned to Yale as Research Associate in Geography with a nominal compensation which is now $500. I accepted this on the repeated assurance

of President Hadley and Mr. Stokes that while they could not pledge the Sterling Trustees to anything, they confidently antici- pated that the Trustees would accept the recommendations of the University Administration, in which case I should be pro- vided with an adequate salary and with some facilities for re- search.

On this understanding, since July, 1919, I have devoted more than a year to writing a book on *Climatic Changes* which is now in the hands of the Yale Press. Although I believe that Professor Schuchert, for example, is right in saying that the book is the best I have ever written, its nature is such that if I get back the $1800 which I have spent on it for clerical work, tabulation and so forth I shall do very well. I have spent four or five months on an unfinished book on *Europe* which I am writing at the urgent request of the Yale Press. It is like most such books in being too scientific ever to yield more than a small sum over and above the expenses incurred in writing it.

I have also spent a good deal of time in teaching, two hours a week at present, which is not called for in the terms of my appointment. In addition to this I have done a good deal of speaking and writing of an unremunerative sort. Since last spring I have spent between two and three months on work arising from the fact that I am chairman of the Committee on the Atmosphere and Man of the National Research Council as well as of four sub-committees. In the future this bids fair to take even more time, and I hope that it may be one of the items in increasing Yale's prestige as a scientific center.

The preceding activities, which I regard as my main function in life and in the University, have left only scraps of time for the business of making a living. . . . The result is that although we live very economically, we are steadily exceeding our in- come. . . . the reasons stated above, and others which I should be glad to tell you in conversation, make it necessary that I should speedily have some assurance as to my future financial status.

Hadley had retired in June, 1921. Anson Stokes, contender for the vacated presidential post, retired when the distinguished psychologist James R. Angell was selected from the eighty names advanced. Huntington had enjoyed the confidence and respect of both these retired men. Joseph Barrell had died in 1919, and Herbert Gregory only occasionally offered a geography course at

Yale; he devoted a substantial part of his time directing the Bishop Museum in Hawaii. (In 1919 Gregory went to Hawaii to raise funds from Yale Alumni to direct research relating to the Pacific world. In 1920 Yale formally entered into an agreement with the Bernice Bishop Museum in Honolulu and Gregory became Museum Director. Officially he remained a Yale geographer.) These four men were Huntington's main supporters at the college. Upon their retirement from the scene Huntington was left with some hopes, aspirations, and promises, nearly all unwritten, from a previous administration. Huntington was quite certain that the Hadley intent for geographic expansion would blossom under Angell's direction. But Angell was not as sure of Huntington's genius as Hadley had been. Angell, one-time professor and dean of the University of Chicago, later President of the Carnegie Corporation, wrote to Rollin D Salisbury of Chicago requesting his opinion of the worth of Huntington's work.[9] Salisbury characterized Huntington as "a brilliant, erratic, and rather careless man," and noted that his conclusions were frequently "called into question."[10] It was unfortunate for Huntington that Barrows had only recently shown Salisbury his biting review of Huntington's *Principles of Human Geography*, destined for the pages of *The Geographical Review*. Salisbury mentioned it in his letter and offered, "I believe it represents the general opinion of the man's work." Angell showed no inclination to establish the Geographical Center, or even to hire another geographer. He wrote to his successor, John C. Merriam, President of the Carnegie Institution, of Huntington's anomalous position,[11] ". . . we do not at present . . . see our way to retaining him indefinitely as a research man on any salary satisfactory to him . . . it seems a pity to let the chap get out of the investigatory field. . . ." Angell proposed to Merriam that the Carnegie Institution and Yale each contribute $1,000 and appoint him to a research position which would give him a status in both institutions. Angell and Merriam approved Huntington's proposed work for the following year—"A project for determining the numerical relations between variations in rainfall in different parts of the world at present and in the past,"—then each secured a $1,000 appropriation.

Yet the promise of Stokes and Hadley had not been fulfilled, and Huntington wrote to Angell requesting further clarification of "the position of Geography at Yale and my own position as Research Associate."[12] Angell chatted with Huntington about the matter, but refrained from written commitment. He wrote to Merriam again,[13] persuaded the Carnegie Institution to grant Huntington another $1,000 for the coming year in order that he might continue his work on world rainfall, past and present. The relationship was precarious. Huntington continued to pay for secretarial and clerical assistance. He was not given the benefit of a retirement salary. When Huntington pressed the matter again early in 1925, Angell asked Provost H. S. Graves to investigate the matter of support for Huntington's request for an increase in salary; Graves reported,[14] "Mr. Warren is not at all enthusiastic about any additional compensation at the present time. Mr. Cross is also unenthusiastic but is puzzled to know just how Mr. Huntington stands in the scientific world."

Nothing positive was decided and Huntington still did not receive a written statement concerning his relationship with the University. When Huntington wrote to a distant member of the family, Archer Milton Huntington,[15] with a view to securing financial aid to create the geographical center of which Yale had approved, Treasurer T. W. Farnham wrote to Huntington,[16] "no prospective donors are to be approached for University needs without the knowledge and approval of the President and the Treasurer's Office."

Meanwhile several students, including Quincy Wright, Richard Hartshorne, G. Etzel Pearcy, and W. E. Punt (South Africa) wrote to Huntington concerning the possibility of studying geography at Yale. Other students came from distant places to study geography at Yale, only to find upon arrival that he was the only geographer of the staff. Huntington personally accommodated George B. Cressey, Atsushi Tsuyusaki, and K. C. Huang, by creating programs designed especially for them, then later sending them to Clark or Chicago for further study. Huntington wrote to Dean Wilbur L. Cross,[17] "Every year, because there is no opportunity for preliminary work in geography, I have to turn away students who want to come and study with me." He obtained audience with President Angell, then urged that Yale hire Samuel Van Valkenburg, who had recently arrived in the United States from the Dutch East Indies, together with "one or two other men whom we might once more consider for a position in teaching geography at Yale." He also informed the President[18] that visiting foreign geographers frequently asked to see the "Geographical Institute" and seem "incredulous when I show them a single office, comfortable enough, but housed in one after another dilapidated building which stands close to top among those to be demolished."

President Angell could only express dissatisfaction with conditions, "but our financial difficulties are such that other things must certainly be cared for in advance of our development of the geography work."[19] That seemed to be the first official Presidential intimation of an established list of priorities in which geography did not occupy a happy position. In October, 1927, Huntington again addressed himself to President Angell on the matters of his own ill-defined position, and the future of geography at Yale.[20] President Angell accepted Huntington's letter in the serious vein in which it was written and asked Huntington what salary he required.[21] When Huntington requested a professor's salary, Angell consulted the administrative officers who advised and recommended changes in position and salary. In a letter to Charles H. Warren, mineralogist and Dean of the Sheffield Scientific School, President Angell opined that "our relations to Mr. Huntington are needlessly anomalous,"[22] and recognized that while much of Huntington's work was of a "semi-popular character," Huntington was obliged to write for an income. Warren made reply to President Angell in a letter that unalterably opposed university advancement for Huntington.[23] Warren found it necessary to recall Harvard's rejection of Huntington for a doctorate, branded him as "a prolific and interesting writer of pseudo-scientific books and papers for which the public apparently has a large appetite," "a good deal of a propagandist, an unsuccessful teacher. . . ." "His present position as Research Associate seems to me the only one possible if it is felt desirable to have him here at all." Dean Cross regarded Huntington's published works as "excellent reading but . . . loose, . . in their scholarship." Cross did offer that he would like to see Huntington remain as a Research Associate, with some increase in salary, and suggested to the President that the Geology Department be consulted.[24] Another letter from Huntington requesting a decision was written the following March.[25] Angell was obliged to reveal,[26] "I do not find the department, or the departments whose work is related to your own, or the schools concerned, at all inclined to recommend a full professorial salary in your own case." Angell offered to recommend a salary of $2,000 for Huntington, and added, "If, under the circumstances, you feel it impracticable, or inadvisable, to continue your relations with Yale, I shall quite understand this, although I shall personally regret it." But Dean Warren would recommend only $1500 to begin July 1, 1929. The President's suggestion for a $2,000 salary had been denied.[27]

Huntington decided to remain at Yale and abridge his relationship with the institution, and concentrate more on "the paramount necessity of supporting my family." He urged the administration to secure Van Valkenburg, who had meanwhile joined the ranks of Clark geographers; and he informed President Angell that Chicago had secured the services of Griffith Taylor, and that Harvard had employed Derwent Whittlesey. Only months later President Angell wrote to Dean Cross,[28] "I am persuaded that it will now be possible in the near future to develop a Department of Geography along lines or on a scale which will secure Mr. Huntington's approval." But no such development emerged.

Geographers whose names Huntington had advanced to teach undergraduate geography courses at Yale, and with whom he had either corresponded or dined included Stephen S. Visher, Alan G. Ogilvie, Derwent S. Whittlesey, Marcel Aurousseau, Roderick Peattie, and Samuel Van Valkenburg. The first four had been lost to the cause while Angell was trying to generate sufficient endowment to finance additional staff in geography. When it had seemed that Angell was prepared to advance the cause of geography, and first Peattie, then Van Valkenburg, had visited Yale for discussion of their careers, Warren had remarked of Peattie:[29]

> I was not at all favorably impressed by the man from Ohio State. He seemed to me just the type of man we want to avoid. He would have all our students studying grammar school stuff inside of two weeks and be making an outrageous noise about it all the time.

Of Van Valkenburg Warren queried,[30] "The only question I would have is as to how one so obviously foreign would fit into our scheme of things here."

Huntington contributed much to Yale in the twenties, despite the loneliness which he suffered as the only geographer in a geology department. Time and time again he had sought to establish a geography department as Yale had promised was its intent. When in March, 1928, Van Valkenburg visited Yale to discuss his joining the faculty as a geographer, one of the administrative staff informed him "that nothing was to be done

about geography at Yale."[31] Huntington discussed the matter
with Angell, and discovered that the President was not a party
to the incident. But· Huntington had been alerted to an intent
which, while present, had not previously manifested itself in
such an explicit form. In September of 1928, prior to departure
for South America, Huntington sent a memorandum to President
Angell and the deans "to remind you that the subject of Geography is still under consideration."[32] Upon his return in February, 1929, he found that nothing had been done: he wrote to
the President racapitulating the institutional promise and commitment made in 1919, and reaffirmed several times since then,
then tendered his resignation.[33]

It was quite the most effective step Huntington had taken.
President Angell met the very next morning with Provost
Charles Seymour and Dean Cross. Seymour returned Huntington's letter of resignation requesting him to hold it in abeyance,
invited Huntington to suggest a program for geography, and
made it clear that Dean Warren had not been invited to share
the dialogue.[34] "Mr. Angell of course recognizes as I do the
character of the factors which have stood in the way of developing the program."

A committee of faculty, including Huntington, Gabriel, Keller, Flint, and Buck was established to supervise the direction
of geography. In the Yale catalogue for 1930–1931 there appeared a program of courses entitled HUMAN GEOGRAPHY:

Geology 140.   Geomorphology   Flint
Geology 141b.   Geomorphology of the United States   Flint
Geography 100   Climatology   Huntington
Geography 101   Problems in Geography   Huntington
Anthropology 110   Science of Society—omitted 1930–1931
Anthropology 114   Ethnology   Murdock
Anthropology 124   American Society   Davis
Anthropology 125   Frontier Institutions   Leyburn
Government 155b   Research Problems in Political Science
                            omitted in 1930–1931
History 200   Aspects of the Civilization of the United States
                    Gabriel
Zoology 133   Geographical Distribution of Animals   Ball

This concatenation of existing courses drawn from various
departments had been brought together and termed a "minor
concentration." The arrangement was terminal. Huntington re-

tained his enthusiasm for the establishment of a geography department, but prepared to absent himself more from the campus and his office.

During these years Huntington had done much more than seek departmental status for his subject. He had offered two courses each year. From 1920–22 he offered "Geology 113, Climatology" and "Geology 115, Major in Geography;" from 1923–29 he offered "Geology 173, Climatology," and "Geology 175, Problems in Geography." That was more than half the official load of a full professor; yet Huntington's salary ranged from 5 to 20% that of his professorial colleagues throughout the decade. These courses were beyond the terms of agreement which Huntington had made with Anson Phelps Stokes. During the thirties he taught no undergraduate courses at Yale; he offered "Climatology" in the graduate school on five occasions, "Problems in Geography" twice, and shared in the teaching of "Problems in Culture Contacts and Race Relations" three times. In "Climatology" and "Problems of Geography" enrollment averaged only three or four students. Sometimes the course met irregularly and became more nearly a private tutorial. Yet be it said for Huntington that his students sincerely appreciated his efforts.

Huntington also read several dissertations early in the 1920s, some at the request of students, others at the request of administration, always with the approval of Schuchert. Dissertations which Huntington read, or for which he made suggestions, included "Geology, physiography, and water resources of the Papago Country, Arizona" (1920) by Kirk Bryan, "Land Tenure in Latin America" (1921) by George McCutchen McBride, "The Climate and Weather of the Russian Far East" (1921) by Stanislaus Novakovsky, "The Triassic Area of the New Cumberland Quadrangle, Pennsylvania" (1921) by Malcolm H. Bissell, "Correlation of weather and mortality as shown by the mortality statistics of New York City for the years 1883–1888," (1923) by Margaret M. Justin, and "Factors conditioning the religious education of later childhood" (1923) by Hilrie S. Smith. Later he rendered criticism of "The Eskimos: a study in adaptation to environment" by Edward M. Weyer, Jr. (1930), "Climatic and Socio-Economic Factors in Mortality from certain causes" by Iwao M. Moriyama (1937), and "The Evolution of Human Geography in Teacher Education" by Edna Arundel (1942). When two of the readers of McBride's dissertation felt there was insufficient discipline to his work, Huntington made suggestions to McBride, and brought the committee of readers into agreement. He edited S. Novakovsky's dissertation, helped place him at Clark, then encouraged him to assemble an American Yearbook of Geography. Such an undertaking was of much interest to both Novakovsky and President Atwood; but funds for the undertaking, which involved considerable travel, could not be sustained. Huntington urged Novakovsky to undertake a book on Siberia. Following correspondence on the plan to be followed Novakovsky wrote "The Economic Power of Siberia" during March, April, and May, of 1923. Huntington revised it for him and brought the manuscript to the attention of the Yale University Press. Huntington encouraged Novakovsky to select a part of his dissertation, to hone it rigorously, and offer it to *The Geographical Review*. "Climatic provinces of the Russian Far East in relation to human activities" appeared in that periodical[35] and received commentary in "The Monthly Record" of *The Geographical Journal*.[36] In 1924 Novakovsky left the United States to accept a position with the University at Poznan, and while Huntington wrote to him further encouraging his work on the Siberia book, no correspondence ensued. He introduced M. H. Bissell to the Association of American Geographers in 1927 when the latter delivered "Geographic Aspects of the Pennsylvania State Highway System" before the membership. Huntington aided George B. Cressey obtain a post teaching geology and founding a geology department in Shanghai College (Shanghai, China), 1924; read the occasional papers which Cressey sent him concerning "desert physiography and climatic changes;" then supported Cressey's application to the Guggenheim Foundation after brigands had beaten him and taken his cash and instruments during the summer of 1926.

Huntington was kind and helpful to those research students with whom he had contact. He did not have many students during his years as a research associate, but he left an impression that belies the unsettled claim that he was not a success in the classroom. C. H. Crickmay recalls:[37]

> I was a student at Yale in 1922–23. . . . Professor Charles Schuchert sent two of us, Waldo Glock and myself, over to Hopkins Hall to establish ourselves as Huntington's student burden for that session. . . .
> He gave us no lectures. Nevertheless, our round-the-table dis-

cussions that year were quite the most brilliant scientific stimulation I had had so far in my life.

Geoffrey Crickmay, who entered Yale as a "freshman" in 1927
has written:[38]

> Before going to Yale I was told to make every effort to take
> Huntington's course in Climatology. I did; became his only
> student for one semester; and it was an experience.
>
> He introduced me to practical statistics, to Government
> weather reports, to the U.S. Census. A lot of the work he had
> me dig into was not closely related to the course title. For ex-
> ample, I remember preparing a whole sheaf of charts and maps
> on the Dakotas, showing in addition to climate, such things as
> land values, mortgages, crops, etc. . . . No professor taught me
> more about writing a technical paper.

Charles A. Connaughton remembers[39]

> I took a course from him in climatology. This course was one
> of the most interesting experiences I had as a student. There
> were three of us in it. We would sit down around the table with
> Huntington and he would proceed to discuss with us what ap-
> peared to be a matter which he felt of significance to himself
> currently—only to find that as the threads developed they would
> hang together into a real story of climate in relation to some-
> thing or other varying all the way from man to the development
> of continents. . . .
>
> . . . it was a great experience to participate as a student. He
> was a good teacher and one of the real personalities, both in
> and out of the educational field.

Edward S. Deevey, Jr., one time Killam Professor of Biology
of Dalhousie University in Halifax, Nova Scotia, recalls writing
a paper "Climate and Life of the Pleistocene" in a Huntington
seminar:[40]

> Years later I was still mining that term paper for the work en-
> titled "Biogeography of the Pleistocene," a review published
> along with others from an N.R.C. committee in the *Bulletin* of
> the Geographical Society of America 1949, volume 40, pages
> 514–15.

Although the only geographer in a geology department which expanded from six to ten geologists between 1920 and 1929, Huntington met regularly with the geologists in biweekly staff meetings and participated in some of the administrative processes attaching to a department. When faculty and students of the Department held their evening meetings which began with papers and discussion and ended with a social hour,

> Professor Huntington was a regular attendant, sometimes with his wife. . . . Although in a sense a peripheral member of the Department he was never an outsider at these meetings. He was treated by his colleagues as a fully participating member who enjoyed their respect and esteem. He contributed his share to the discussion. My most vivid recollection of him is of his enormous and infectious enthusiasm for his subject.[41]

He is also remembered as one member of the formidable trio (the other two being Richard S. Lull of Yale and William N. Rice of Wesleyan) that regularly sat in the front row at Dana Club meetings, each directing the little black boxes of their hearing aids at the unfortunate speaker.

Conscientious students had little to fear from Huntington, who always sought to be helpful and to see the best that was in them. He occasionally invited students to his home and dinner with his family which now included three children; Charles Ellsworth (1919), Anna Slocum (1922), and George Herbert (1925). The family home reverberated with the laughter of games, and was the scene of much energetic conversation. Mrs. Huntington made all welcome at the home, and is remembered as the perfect hostess. She was an informed and valuable contributor to her husband's work, over the years offering substantial numbers of ideas and suggestions—winning her way into the "acknowledgements" of several of her husband's books, some of which were to bear a title of her choosing. Ward C. Smith, a graduate student in geology (Yale 1932–1936) recalls a visit made to the Huntington home.[42]

> The children, in their teens and younger, were lively participants in table talk, and as often as not vigorously competitive in it—Since EH was deaf, they gained a share of his attention with loud "Father!" "Father!"—Father being definitely the head of the family, while Rachel quietly surveyed everything with an

amused eye, and saw to it that young graduate students were at ease and involved, too, and not overwhelmed by the cross tides of vigorous talk.

The house "a new Englandish place, with old things well cared for, with books, pictures, and objects that showed taste and intellectual curiosity encouraged," had been built in 1922. Three miles north of Yale University, it was surrounded by treed fields, a reservoir named after Eli Whitney and East Rock, a red sandstone bluff; the occupants were presented with as pleasing a prospect as southern Connecticut had to offer.

Another student, Edward M. Weyer, who shared the Huntington table has written:[43]

> One day Huntington told me that a man he knew only by correspondence was coming from Long Island for Sunday dinner at his house, and asked me to come also. I had recently returned from an expedition to Bering Strait, and this man, Fenley Hunter, who was actually a moderately well-to-do manufacturer, had just discovered Virginia Falls (twice as high as Niagara) on the Nahanni River in northwest Canada. This was an important meeting in the sense that the three of us kept more or less in touch from then on. Ellsworth Huntington was an inspiration to Fenley Hunter, as he was to me. Fenley became more and more interested in science and was, in fact, the man who discovered the Tule Springs (Nevada) site, one of the oldest, if not *the* oldest Early Man site in the Western Hemisphere. That was back in 1933, if I recall correctly, but the age was not ascertainable until about two decades later when the C-14 method was discovered. Fortunately the American Museum still had the ancient charcoal Fenley had been careful enough to save. If Ellsworth Huntington had not had the patience in the midst of a very busy life to invite an amateur to dinner, Fenley Hunter would never have discovered the Tule Spring site.

Huntington's lively curiosity about a variety of matters led some of his colleagues to seek information from him, others to request that he lecture to one of their classes (he obliged in sociology, anthropology, history, geology and forestry) while yet others suggested he contribute a chapter for an intended anthology. Numerous were the requests for Huntington to speak to Yale groups which included the Palaeontology Club, Sigma Xi,

Oriental Club, Foreign Relations Group, and Questioners. He arranged an occasional "smoker" for the Zoology Club, arranged for visiting scientists to address Yale audiences and frequently took journalists—who had come for a story—to the Graduate's Club for lunch.

Huntington maintained a steady exchange of notes with Andrew Keogh of the Sterling Library, informing and urging him to buy geographic volumes which were of importance, and advising him on the establishment of a map room. To the library Huntington gave ancient manuscripts and his own publications. He wrote occasional pieces for *The Yale Daily News* and *The Yale Scientific Magazine*. At the request of Wilbur Cross, editor of *The Yale Review*, Huntington contributed several review articles and "Our Biological Future" which was noticed in newspapers across the country. As Research Associate he offered several manuscripts to the Yale University Press which were published: *World Power and Evolution* (1919); *The Red Man's Continent* (1919); *Climatic Changes* (with S. S. Visher) (1922); *Earth and Sun* (1923). He rewrote a chapter "Climate and the Evolution of Civilization," earlier published in *The Evolution of the Earth and Its Inhabitants*, which was published in *The Evolution of Earth and Man* edited by G. A. Baitsell, 1929. He wrote a chapter, "Environment and Racial Character," which appeared in *Organic Adaptation to Environment*, edited by M. W. Thorpe and published by Yale University Press, 1924. He revised *Civilization and Climate* in 1922 and rewrote large parts of the same book for a definitive third edition which appeared in 1924.

Doubtless Huntington could have given more manuscripts to the Yale University Press if it had been able to offer him the terms that the commercial houses could offer. When R. V. Coleman of the press requested the privilege of publishing *The Pulse of Progress*, Huntington wrote that he had made arrangements with Scribner's,[44] "by doing so I insured the publication of several chapters as magazine articles. That, of course, makes quite a difference in the financial return from such a book."

Huntington read and evaluated manuscripts offered to the press, occasionally supplied it with information relating to the author's standing in the field of scholarship, aided it with statements which advertised the finished work, which encouraged Coleman to write, "We lean pretty hard on you for advice." When the idea of "an American Magazine of the Sciences" was conceived, the press staff and other faculty members urged Huntington to become its editor. He agreed to accept the position for three years provided that he was not obliged to spend more than half of his time at the task. But lack of funds prevented the inauguration of the magazine.

In addition to the geologists, Huntington came to know several other members of the faculty well. He exchanged criticism of manuscripts with economist Irving Fisher, co-labored with Charles-Edward Amory Winslow of the Public Health Department, especially on matters relating to ventilation; when the John B. Pierce Foundation Laboratory of Hygiene was established in New Haven (1932) Huntington frequently visited Winslow and his co-worker Lovic P. Herrington. Experimental work at the laboratory seemed to confirm the validity of Huntington's earlier work on climatic optima. Huntington discussed feudalism with Asakawa, climatic change with Rostovtzeff, and read manuscript for oriental historian Kenneth S. Latourette. He showed the documents and artifacts he had unearthed in Chinese Turkestan to C. C. Torrey, who published commentary on them in *Revue Biblique*. Huntington collaborated with the young sociologist Jerome Davis, and wrote two chapters, "Society and Its Physical Environment" and "The Geographic Background of the Revolution" for *Introduction to Sociology* and *The New Russia Between the First and Second Five Year Plans*, both edited by Davis. With the President, J. R. Angell, Huntington engaged in exchange on the subject of eugenics particularly with regard to the manuscript "The Builders of America," and an insurance plan designed to encourage more children among the "better families."

Many were the renowned scientists who visited the house in these years. Included were Vilhjalmur Stefansson, Roald Amundsen, Stephen S. Visher, Ernst Antevs, T. Griffith Taylor, Bertram Thomas, Helmut de Terra, Andrew E. Douglass, S. Colum Gilfillan, and A. Grenfell Price. When the last named came to New Haven, Huntington aided him in the preparation of an outline to "White Settlers in the Tropics." Price recalls:[45]

> Ellsworth was a real inspiration. He would loll back in a sofa after dinner and literally erupt new and challenging ideas. Many would be impossible to put into practice but there was always something of great value worth deep consideration. To him I owe an immense debt even when we differed, for his ideas always demanded the closest attention and thought.

His office was always open to accomplished scholar and beginning student alike. It was invariably a hive of industry. Huntington hired a secretary of his own choosing, frequently the wife of a graduate student, and other times a woman proficient in typing, bibliography, and scientific procedure. Occasionally he would share his office with a fellow scientist as with Visher (1920), Antevs (1923), and Price (1935). Antevs recollects[46] "Some mornings he would rush into his office and fluently without a stutter dictate a whole chapter or article. To me as a listener it sounded perfect and his secretary told me that few editorial changes were needed." His voluminous mail was sorted each morning, and replies to urgent or interesting letters were dictated at once. Less interesting mail might be relegated to a desk drawer if he were engaged upon a large and complex task. Afternoons were the occasions when outlines, designs, and notes of books and articles were composed, and it was usually that time of the day when they were completed. Both at mid-morning and mid-afternoon, regardless of the weather outside, he opened the windows wide, and left them open long enough to bring a complete change of air into the office. All shared the benefits; the secretary might have to don her coat, or in time of heavy snow retreat from the room. A three-mile walk home was followed by dinner and often conversation with guests. In the summer he loved to retreat to the garden of an evening to ply the trowel.

In the spring of 1941 an informal committee was called by Professor A. E. Parr to investigate the position of the geographical sciences in Yale University. A mimeographed statement resulting from the committee's deliberations offered "that the lack of adequate instruction in the various fields of natural geography, or those sciences that treat of events with reference to their occurrence on the surface of the earth, is a very serious defect in the programme of instruction of Yale University." And in the 1948–1949 Yale Catalogue one recognizes the fruit of the labor:

> There is no program leading to a degree in this field. Instruction is under the supervision of the Geography Committee of the University and is oriented toward the curricula in Chinese, Japanese and Southeast Asian Studies and International Relations. Courses in geography are open to qualified students in any department of the Graduate School, with the consent of the student's director of graduate studies and the instructor in the course.

The unifying goal in Huntington's life work became increasingly clear as years passed; it was a deep-seated concern to comprehend the course of civilization throughout history. It was as a student of civilization rather than as a student of geography that he sought to parse the fluctuating fortunes of empire. He developed an avid curiosity about philosophy of history; read Spengler, Wells and Toynbee; and developed a philosophy of his own which might have been rendered more explicit had he written a book concerning a plan for the governance of the world—an idea with which he toyed in the 1940s.

Quite early in his studies he sought to interpret recorded history as the creation of an aristocracy of intellect and ability (later, he added temperament), and the erection and maintenance of the quality and quantity of such elites. It was in the quest to comprehend the forces fostering or inhibiting those elites that Huntington revealed his purpose most clearly. His studies of the environment, and his concern to understand the rôle of biological inheritance in the affairs of man (which increasingly encouraged him to participate in and contribute to the field of eugenics), more and more became parts of an extended inquiry into the condition fostering or denying the emergence of such elites. Early expression of his fascination with the quality of people, quite aside from any influence which might be exerted upon them by environment, reveals itself in his article on the Japanese character.[1]

After the commencement of the First World War Huntington became more concerned with conditions in his own country. He had grown up in a United States more conscious of its own genetic composition than at any previous time. The Mendelian laws of heredity were being rediscovered, the American Breeders Association established a committee on human heredity (1907), the Eugenics Record Office was established with biologist Charles B. Davenport as its head, and the first National Conference on Race Betterment was held in 1914. The decline of the old established New England families was viewed with suspicion. The entry of large numbers of South Europeans into the United States spurred demands for immigration restriction. The movement of the American Negro to the northern cities in the United States encouraged ghetto formation, racial tension, and riot.

Huntington was concerned that the changing composition of the United States population might reduce the quality of its civilization. He was quite persuaded that advance or degeneracy of a nation was intimately related to its biological stock. During the war years he studied the matter of United States immigration policy, and in "Our Immigrant Problem; A Discussion and Review,"[2] opined that a strictly enforced policy admitting only those "whose inherent capacities make them fit to share our citizenship" should be designed; and proposed that a permanent agency should be established to study "the mental and moral characteristics with which various types of immigrants are permanently endowed by heredity." His interest in immigration revealed itself in frequent visits to Washington, D.C., to testify before Immigration Committees, in correspondence with Congressmen, and in discussions with Madison Grant. He felt the Negroes and Porto Ricans living in the United States were less competent than the Caucasians. He wrote "something ought to be done about permitting such free migration to this country from Porto Rico. I do not believe the 100,000 Porto Ricans in New York are of any advantage to the United States."[3]

He agreed with Madison Grant that immigration from Latin America should be subject to the same kind of restrictions as other kinds of immigration:[4] "by rigid restriction of immigration and the application of the best eugenic practices America will not only benefit itself enormously, but will do infinitely more good for the world than it can do in any other way." Reviewing *A Critique of the Theory of Evolution* by T. H. Morgan, *Heredity and Environment* by E. G. Conklin, and *The Passing of the Great Race* by Madison Grant, in "Heredity and Human Responsibility," he warned the reader concerning the quality of American people:[5]

> The whole lesson of biology is that America is seriously endangering her future by making fetishes of equality, democracy, and universal education. They are of great value, but only when they have good hereditary material upon which to work. The books of Morgan, Conklin and Grant all show that we must

drastically revise our immigration policy and must strive even
more diligently to perpetuate the rapidly diminishing type of
strong-willed idealists who have been the country's chief leaders.

In "The Science of Citizenship," published in *The Yale Review*, 1918,[6] Huntington urged that more study should be given
to heredity and eugenics. And in the preface to *World Power
and Evolution* he stated, "the human race must be bred as carefully as race horses." He had studied the work of the biologists,
revisited Mendelian thought, corresponded extensively with men
engaged in livestock experiments, and through fellow members
of the American Ecological Society was well versed on experiments with moths and the fruit fly. He looked back upon the
dynasties of Pharaonic Egypt and could believe in conservation
of hereditary strength exemplified through the practice of consanguineous marriage. He looked to the future and suggested that
"carefully controlled cross breeding perhaps be possible among
mankind after hundreds or thousands of years." Huntington's
work was variously studied, applauded, and cited by contemporaries Madison Grant, Lothrop Stoddard, Roland Dixon, and
Griffith Taylor. The inquiry into racial capacity was perhaps in
its heyday.

Huntington had been led to the study of heredity and the
quality of people, not owing to fears of miscegenation, a rising
tide of color or the like, but because he quested for the causation back of the changing patterns of civilization. That was why
he could write to James H. Breasted,[7] "The main value of history
lies in its answer to well nigh the greatest of all questions: what
is the cause of the rise and fall of civilization? What can we do
to prevent the fall of our own civilization?" He firmly believed
that "every possible measure should be taken to change the relative birth rates of our old Nordic population as compared with
our new Mediterranean and Alpine population."[8] Yet he was
emphatically not a "Nordic booster."[9]

> My attitude toward immigration is that we ought to exclude
> no one on account of race, but that we should admit only those
> persons whatever their race who show a degree of capacity and
> will power greater than that of the average of our own people.

In an explicit repudiation of a Nordic booster posture he
wrote to H. F. Perkins:[10]

We ought to make it clear to all the world that we are just as much interested in a high-grade Italian or a high-grade Chinese as in a high-grade Anglo-Saxon. The thing we are interested in is the high-grade. While Burch would undoubtedly subscribe to this, the practical effect of getting tied up with the American Legion or some of the patriotic societies might be to make people think that we belong to the Nordic boosters.

In September, 1921, The Second International Congress of Eugenics was held in New York City. Expressions of eugenic interest were manifested by exhibitors. Huntington provided one such exhibit of ten maps illustrating the relation of climate to health, energy and civilization, and charts of climatic change revealing such effects on natural selection and the mixture of races. The Membership of that Eugenic Congress appointed Yale economist Irving Fisher Chairman of a Committee to Develop an American Organization for Eugenics. Huntington and Fisher were Yale colleagues: not surprisingly, in 1923, Chairman Fisher appointed Huntington to the Advisory Council of the Eugenics Committee of the United States of America. For Huntington it was the beginning of a twenty-four year participation in the cause of eugenics. Numerous committees were established, and Huntington was appointed to the "committee on organization" of the Conference on Immigration Policy. The Conference met monthly in New York City. Huntington frequently attended the meetings, and occasionally presented the address of the evening. The work of this Committee did influence U.S. immigration policy considerably in the twenties.[11]

Huntington became an avid reader of books dealing with race and eugenics, and began to review books dealing with such matters. Upon receipt of a copy of William McDougall's book, *Is America Ready for Democracy*, he wrote at once to the publishers,[12] "I believe that Professor McDougall is absolutely right in asserting that the declining birth rate of the intellectual classes is the gravest of all the dangers that confronts the world today." He became filled with the idea that in the United States the better families were limiting their size while the less able families continued large. He attributed the decline of standards—religious, economic, political, and social—to this circumstance. When George Vaughan wrote to Huntington inquiring if he thought there had been in this century a decline in religious faith, Huntington replied[13]

> It may seem like begging the question; but I am convinced that
> our greatest trouble is that the biological foundation of moral
> progress has been so terrifically sapped. . . . It seems to me that
> such a decline in human stock of the highest type, who give
> their children the best biological inheritance and the best train-
> ing, is the real fundamental cause of the present difficulties. . . .

Since absorbing Kullmer's thesis of variability Huntington had
been acutely aware of the differences in performance between
workers due to differences in physical environment. He was quite
convinced that the American Negro, living as he had for millenia
in Africa's humid tropics, was possessed of a good sense of humor, patience, and loyalty but lacked versatility, inventiveness,
and power of leadership. He retained an open mind on Boas's
notion of racial adaptation and change following migrant arrival
to the eastern seaboard and decided to investigate the effect of
natural selection working through migration on racial stock.

His presidential address before the Association of American
Geographers delivered at Cincinnati was essentially the theme of
The Character of Races. The results of natural selection, both
past and present, were investigated and particular attention was
given to the racial character of Iceland, China and the United
States. The following year (1925) he published *West of the Pacific*, a work which revealed much of what he had seen and
heard on the occasion of his visit to the Second Pan Pacific Science Congress; Huntington considered the chief importance of
the book to lie in its study of racial temperament and geographic
environment as factors in social organisation and progress."[14]
The Character of Races immediately attracted the attention of
Madison Grant, Lothrop Stoddard, Oliver E. Baker, J. Russell
Smith, T. Griffith Taylor, George G. Chisholm, among other
thinkers. Taylor was delighted that in *The Character of Races*
Huntington had adopted his "Migration-Zone theory of Race
Evolution,"[15] and in turn Huntington was particularly pleased
with a letter he received from Chisholm:[16]

> What has greatly interested me in your book from the first is that
> it is another illustration of your world-wide outlook, an outlook
> for which there is ever greater need among thinkers. As to the
> content of the book I am in essential agreement with you as to
> the fact of natural selection in its infinite variety of modes of oper-
> ation being the fundamental explanation of human evolution. But

I may add that I am also in essential agreement with you in looking to the necessity of deliberate artificial selection for the progress of man in the future. . . . And I am also in agreement with you in considering that one essential requirement for that progress is to have institutions that will favor the multiplication of the better sections of any community and repress that of the worst. The problem is overwhelmingly difficult, but I will never consent to believe that it is insoluble.

Huntington summarized his own book as follows:[17]

I think my theory as given in *The Character of Races* can best be summed up by the statement that up to a certain point races are plastic. We do not know yet about mutations except that they occur. But it seems to me quite clear that by selection and segregation for any race on earth you could produce highly diverse types, some high, some low, provided the selective process worked long enough.

In his book *West of the Pacific* Huntington proffered his realization of the fundamental part played by temperament in determining the status of a people.[18]

Between 1915 and 1923 I made no long journeys. Previously my attention had been focused on physical environment and its direct effects on human occupations, health, activity, habits, and character. During the eight years when I stayed at home I gradually acquired a new conception of the importance of temperament. Without abandoning my old ideas as to environment, I was led to see these ideas in a new perspective. I saw how both physical and social environment often act as selective agencies which pick out special types of people for preservation or elimination in any given occupation or region. In *The Character of Races* I have set forth this line of reasoning in orderly fashion. Here I merely recount some of my observations, and explain what they suggested.

Nearly a third of the book was given to a study of Australia and Australians. In particular Huntington developed the thesis that continuous white settlement in northern Queensland was developing a new race in the tropics; he asserted that this racial selection must be maintained if tropical Australia were to succeed. An even more detailed analysis of the matter appeared in the third edition of *Civilization and Climate*, 1924.[19] This interested A. Grenfell Price, who later consulted Huntington in New Haven, where the two developed the outline for *White Settlers in the Tropics*:[20] it also encouraged C. H. Wickens[21] (statistician of the Australian Commonwealth) and H. W. Cilento[22] (Director of the Division of Tropical Hygiene in the Commonwealth Department of Health of Queensland) to make contradictory retort. Huntington thereupon elaborated his position in "Natural Selection and Climate in Northern Australia."[23] The published exchange, though obscurely placed, constitutes an interesting and valuable addition to the literature on natural selection. In the years that followed Huntington came to feel that neither Frederick J. Turner[24] nor Halford J. Mackinder[25] had taken sufficiently into account the effects of natural selection on biological inheritance and the quality of people.

Huntington's association with the eugenic movement brought him into contact with Leon Whitney, the Executive Secretary of the American Eugenics Society. The latter, deeply concerned with the lack of understanding which the American people displayed toward eugenic principles, wrote a manuscript which he felt would help people better understand the matter. He submitted the manuscript to Huntington, who became so interested in the work that he proceeded to revise it, then to rewrite it. "The Builders of America" had become much different from the original monograph Whitney had authored.[26] The book attempted to reveal the dangers of racial deterioration from undirected reproduction. The "Builders"—leaders in industry, science, the professions, the arts—it was stated, were restricting the size of their families, while the "unintelligent, the degenerate, the weak," were multiplying rapidly. The authors claimed that misguided philanthropy was rendering the problem more acute by thwarting nature's purpose to prune away the unfit. . . . "As things now are the saving of the wrecks is almost certain to cause still further wrecks, for the bad timber is straightway put into new ships."

Newspaper reviewers had a field day with the publication. Review headings included: "Woe, Woe, all is Woe," "Going to the bow-wows," "Birth Control Robbing Beauty," "A bookfull of dire warnings." Exclamations of "bogus," "bushwa," and "Nordic pushers" abounded in hordes of derogatory reviews. Some papers offered large size pictures of "Follies" girls with headings as "Follies girls are utterly failing to reproduce themselves." The latter was in reference to the fact that Huntington and Whitney had deplored the fact that actresses, "feminists," and women college graduates infrequently married and bore children. All this Huntington took in his stride but when an unfavorable and careless review appeared in the *New York Times* he offered rejoinder.[27] Other papers and pamphlets used statistics from the book to demonstrate the cost of crime, and the charitable upkeep of folks unable to support themselves due to lack of ability. Such information was used to support stricter immigration laws. The book did not enjoy wide circulation. Huntington later opined[28]

> I have come very strongly to the conclusion that in the *Builders of America* Mr. Whitney and I made a grave mistake. We ought to have left out practically all the old material and the propaganda. The result would have been a little book no more than a third as large as the present book. It would, however, have been a book crammed with really important material. I am convinced that it would have had far more influence than the *Builders of America* is ever likely to have.

Interestingly, Huntington only once used the word eugenics in the book!

He published several articles which were the product of research undertaken with regard to *The Builders of America*: "Why the American Woman is Unique,"[29] "Religion and Who's Who,"[30] "The Descendants of Who's Who"[31] (with L. Whitney), "The Thing in Families"[32] (with L. Whitney), "Our Biological Future,"[33] "The Next Revolution,"[34] and "A Test for Eugenics."[35] When Margaret Sanger invited Huntington to speak at the "Sixth International Neo-Malthusian and Birth Control Conference," Huntington obliged with "The Effect of Overpopulation on Chinese Character." Huntington again used his experiences of the 1923 trip to advantage: "My main topic will be the effect of overpopulation and poverty as illustrated by the contrast between Australia and China."[36] Considerably more than a thousand participants, representing sixteen countries attended the conference in New York. Huntington spoke extemporaneously, then later edited what the conference stenographer had recorded for his address.[37] Huntington's eugenic message in the twenties was summed up in "Our Biological Future." He felt that one of America's greatest needs was to reduce the large number of children among the less competent half of the population and build up a corresponding number of large families among the more competent members of society. "When that is done we shall have a population which is biologically sound, and which is able to maintain a civilization that constantly makes greater demands upon the human intellect and upon man's moral nature."[38]

During 1929 and 1930 he travelled through parts of the southern United States, Latin America, Europe, and Africa, preparatory to writing some elementary geography. Subsequent to those travels Huntington's approach toward eugenics changed. Upon his return from nearly two years gypsying across four continents he began to de-emphasize the matter of biological inheritance and the field of genetics—though retaining membership in "The American Genetic Association" which he had joined in 1926. (In 1929 he could write[39] "I have done enough work in respect to inheritance to feel not only extremely interested, but more akin to the professional geneticist than to such far-away people as the geologists, among whom I began life.") He began to feel that the best way to improve the quality of people was to work through ever increasing numbers of social agencies, and to permeate the social structure with the principles of eugenics advanced in the simplest language. He helped found the Population Association of America in 1931 and was promptly elected to its executive committee. One year later he became treasurer of the American Eugenics Society, and in 1934 he assumed the presidency (until 1938) and remained a director of the Society until 1947. In 1937 he became a consulting editor to the *Birth Control Review* and frequently extended advice to the editors of the *Journal of Contraception.*

Undoubtedly Huntington's most intense work for the cause of eugenics came in the thirties when he was treasurer and president of the American Eugenics Society. As president he urged the selection of able and energetic officers; he met with these officers frequently and corresponded with them continuously. When the Society found itself in financial difficulty (especially evident after the death of a generous supporter, George Eastman),[40] Huntington sent many dozens of letters to friends, acquaintances, and people who he thought might contribute. In the thirties alone, Huntington exchanged over 5,000 pieces of correspondence on eugenics, euthenics, and cacogenics. When he received an invitation in 1938 to take tea with Mrs. Franklin D. Roosevelt to discuss the American Eugenics Society, he accepted. Later he wrote to the First Lady requesting support for the Society, only to receive a letter from her secretary (26 February 1940):

> Mrs. Roosevelt asks me to acknowledge your letter and to tell you that she cannot join The American Eugenics Society or take any part in its activities as long as she is in the White House. There are many things she cannot do as the wife of the President which she would be glad to consider in private life.

He interested Yale President J. R. Angell in his eugenic activities, then moved the headquarters of the Society into his Yale office. He did enlarge the membership of the Society.

Commencing early in the thirties he de-emphasized efforts to reduce the size of the larger family with poor biological inheritance, and began to urge larger families among the "better" folk. Studies of the performance of selected Yale and Harvard students,[41] investigations of the Huntington family over a period of three hundred years, and an analysis of Puritan names involving dates of arrival in North America and the performance of their descendants, had convinced him that the better families were not reproducing themselves, and in fact were being overwhelmed by the progeny of the less able. He reasoned that by urging more offspring for the better families ("average or above") the balance between children of "better" and "poorer" families could be restored. His studies had convinced him that eugenically less able people were in the ascendant. The prospect bothered him greatly. He began to wonder whether democracy itself would be able to survive. He planned a "eugenics insurance scheme," whereby mothers of the "better families" who restricted the number of children they bore due to financial reasons would be reimbursed certain costs. But the financial condition of the Society, coupled with the tone of "eugenics" abroad, prevented adoption of any such plan.

In an attempt to spread the ideas of the Eugenics Society, Huntington proposed a revision of "A Eugenics Catechism" prepared in 1923 by L. F. Whitney.[42] The revision was to have been distributed to schools, church groups, civic agencies, and the like. Huntington undertook the revision himself; the manuscript soon reached book proportion. The Directors of the Society discussed the content of the manuscript with Huntington, wrote him many letters suggesting improvements and additions, and made numerous criticisms of the several drafts. In 1935 the Society agreed with Wiley to publish the book, retaining the question and answer form of Whitney's earlier work. Huntington requested twenty-five sets of galley-proofs from publisher Wiley which he distributed to eugenists and other students of civilization, including Charles Beard and Will Durant. The book, in its finished form, fairly represented the views of the American Eugenics Society. *Tomorrow's Children: The Goal of Eugenics* was probably the simplest and clearest exposition of eugenic principles then available; in it Huntington wrote "eugenics appears to be one of the five most momentous human discoveries. . . . Now, for the first time, through the scientific use of genetic principles and social processes man is able consciously and purposefully to select the types of human beings that will survive. Thus at long last he became master of himself. . . . we are beginning to thrill with the feeling that we stand on the brink of an evolutionary epoch whose limits no man can possibly foretell."[43] In the preface to the book Huntington had written, "The Directors of The American Eugenics Society urgently request the readers of *Tomorrow's Children* to send suggestions for its improvement to the author at Yale University. . . ." and many readers did correspond. Many of the letters assured Huntington that the book was helpful, needed, and a particularly clear exposition of the meaning of eugenics; other letters offered criticism and scorn. Catholic opposition was substantial. Other letters suggested it was a pity that the author did not "take a job;" one suggested it was a pity Huntington's own mother had not practiced birth control. The writers of a large number of letters railed against the idea of "better" and "poorer" families. In that same year, 1935, he suggested and helped compose parts of *A Eugenics Program for the United States*.[44] Both studies were distributed widely. He encouraged, and helped establish branches of the Eugenics Society in other parts of the country—especially successful was the branch in Northern California. He arranged conferences of eugenists (he urged this form of the word upon the Society) on birth control, the church, housing, medicine, recreation and the use of leisure time, and the social system. He wished to work through as many social agencies as possible. He had become convinced that to be of value, the eugenics movement had to permeate the whole of society. The "better" families had to understand the essentials of the case, and be influenced by it. He helped establish an education committee of the Society (1937) which sought to develop eugenic courses in high schools, normal schools, colleges and universities. In the same vein he urged an essay contest for undergraduate college students, circulated the event to hundreds of institutions of higher learning, and corresponded both with students and faculty regarding the matter. Fifty-seven essays were forthcoming—most of them very ably presented. His Presidential addresses before the Society reveal something of his eugenic philosophy. He was persuaded that those people who were permanently on relief should restrict the size of their families. He wanted the Society to become intimately familiar with the leaders of social organizations and at one with them in regard to the Society's aim:[45]

> . . . the Society proposes to improve the biological character of mankind and thereby to greatly reduce crime, poverty, and dependency, and at the same time to make a great increase in human happiness.

He labored incessantly on the theme that eugenics is primarily a social movement based on biological facts, and that to be effective it must be practical and gradual.[46]

> The essential point to which the earnest and even heated discussions of the past five years have led us is the conviction that the final practical program of eugenics must be of very gradual growth, and can emerge only when the eugenic spirit permeates our entire social structure.

He proposed that the better families (to be recognized empirically) should be persuaded to extend their numbers. The parents of less able families, he insisted, should be educated in birth control techniques. He developed an address, "The Ultimate Goal of Birth Control," and delivered this to many groups in New York, Connecticut, and Massachusetts during the thirties. One major change in Huntington's thought which had implication for his philosophy of history was expressed in his farewell address to the Society delivered May 5, 1938:[47]

> Galton lived under an aristocratic regime, and was firmly imbued with the idea that certain classes of society were of great

eugenic value, and certain others of very little value. The new
view to which we have come during the last decade is different.
In it the idea of race as a criterion of eugenic merit is eliminated. The thing that counts is the biological quality of the individual and of his immediate ancestors. The new view still
retains the idea that there are important hereditary differences
between individuals, and less important differences between
classes.

The modern eugenist, however, believes that we must look
farther than to mere intellect. The great inventor is not necessarily a good parent. He may inherit a weak physical constitution, or unstable nerves. Or perhaps he inherits traits which tend
to make him selfish or anti-social, although we know very little
as to how far such tendencies are really inherited. Again, although his own inheritance may be desirable, his wife may pos-
sess undesirable hereditary traits which will nullify the good
traits derived from the father. . . .

It is obvious therefore that good eugenic material is scattered
throughout the whole range of social classes. . . .

Meanwhile in 1924 Huntington was appointed Chairman of
the Committee on Biologic Genealogy, of the American Eugenics Society, a post which he developed in importance. He felt
that genealogical records could reveal much of value in formu-
lating the laws of inheritance and the biological changes taking
place in the United States population. He set to work measuring
and comparing the performance of long-established American
families and investigating their numerical rate of growth or decline. He studied the families of selected classes at Yale University, and persuaded J. C. Phillips to make similar studies of the
families of Harvard students. More important, however, was a
piece of work whose origins dated back to the 1922 Norwich
meeting of the Huntington Family Association. On that occasion that Family Association voted to undertake some pioneer
work in gathering family records. For the sake of scientific accuracy, the Family Association requested the advice of The National Research Council. Vernon Kellogg, Chairman of the biological division of The National Research Council appointed an
advisory committee which included Ellsworth Huntington and
suggested the appointment of a trained scientist who would
gather data concerning the physical, social, and economic characteristics of several thousand Huntingtons.[48] Huntington sup-

ported the financial drive. He wanted to secure pledges totalling $5,000 per year for five years. By 1928 he had secured a pledged sum of $3,000. At the 1927 meeting of the Huntington Family Association he had agreed to undertake the study. Annette Fallows and Martha Ragland (née Ragsdale) undertook much of the field work. *After Three Centuries* appeared in 1935[49] and Huntington said of it before the Family Association, "It is an attempt to find out what has happened to us physically, mentally, socially, and economically during the last three centuries."

After Three Centuries: A Typical New England Family (1935) was, in part, a return to his interest in natural selection. He opined that any racial group which has undergone a process of selection and segregation will prove superior to its congeners which have not. He chose as examples the Maori of New Zealand, the Parsees of India, the Norse of Iceland, and the Puritans of whom the Huntingtons were a sample. His ingenious analysis of the recorded superiority of Puritan stock was among the first of its kind.

Two years later he offered, "Once More: What's in a Name,"[50] before a reunion meeting of the Huntington Family Association, held in Norwich, Connecticut (September 3). He was fascinated to discover that the descendants of Puritans who came to southern New England between 1620 and 1635 produced at least eighteen percent more leaders in proportion to their numbers than did the descendants of Puritans who came to America between 1636 and 1643. He attributed the difference in Puritan performance to the hypothesis that "unconscious selection on the basis of intelligence, religious fervor, bravery, love of adventure, and physical strength caused the first comers to be unusually strong in both mind and body."[51] Simon Huntington, the first Huntington to leave England for America, died at sea of smallpox in 1633: hours later his widow landed at Dorchester with four sons and a daughter. The Huntingtons were thus descended from the "earlier" and better performing Puritans. Huntington was well aware that the Huntingtons in North America were an exceptional family. He could trace his descent from Simon and his wife through Simon and Sarah Clark, Simon and Lydia Gager, Joshua and Hannah Perkins, Jabez and Elizabeth Backus, Andrew and Lydia Coit, Joseph and Eunice Carew to Oliver Ellsworth and Mary Ann Strong who were his grandparents.

A Huntington Family Association had been formed in 1857 replete with family constitution, hymn, prayer, coat of arms, and genealogy.[52] He had been elected by the Family Association Assistant Secretary (1911), Second Vice President 1912–1927, member of the "Committee of the Huntington Family" 1922, and President 1937. Speaking at the sixth reunion of the Huntington Family in 1937 he talked of the superior inheritance of the Huntingtons:[53]

> The greatest problem raised by all this is the question of how rapidly we shall permit this inheritance to die out. . . . The degree to which it is passed on to future generations depends on the degree to which we can make it feasible for people who possess this high inheritance of germ plasm and culture to have good-sized families . . . If the individual families are to be large enough to maintain and increase the advantages which obviously arise from certain types of ancestry, family groups like this which is gathered here must take a hand in remaking our social system.

He persisted with the study of Puritans and in October, 1940, wrote to William Mather[54]

> A much more elaborate study of all families which belong primarily to colonial New England and to each of the other main sections of colonial America is now nearing completion. The net result is an overwhelming mass of evidence that descendants of the Puritans who came during the earliest years, not only stand remarkably high, but are distinctly different from the descendants of Puritans who came a little later.

Immediately following this extended piece of research Huntington entered with determination upon his long planned book on civilization. He had already written to Lorrin Sheppard, "I am spending more time on it (eugenics) than I really ought in justice to my other work. I believe, however, that the introduction of a genuine system is the most important reform that now confronts us." He was quite dissatisfied with the American social, economic and political system—"barbarous affairs"—and insisted that any system was only as good as the human stock operating it. He joined the New Haven cooperative society and the local branch of a powerful trade union to further spread eugenic ideas. His studies of human selection and segregation, and particularly knowledge he derived from the study of Puritans bulked large in *Mainsprings of Civilization* (1945) and encouraged him to adopt the term "kith."[55] This was the book which had been hovering on the margins of his mind for approximately a quarter of a century. The nine chapters constituting part two of the book, entitled "Heredity," were in large measure a summation of his work in eugenics.

CHAPTER XII

The Productive Twenties

During the twenties Huntington wrote (or coauthored) ten books, seventy-five articles or chapters of books, and many more pieces that never were published. The year 1927 was perhaps the most prolific of his life. It was a creative decade for him. With lots of ideas, a vigorous constitution, and access to the fine Yale library, he wrote scientific pieces, popular articles and textbooks. He did this to supplement a Yale salary which still did not equal the salary he paid his own secretary. These were halcyon years. He had delivered and refined the climatic hypothesis, had grappled with climatic causation, and did not yet feel compelled to write the volume on civilization. He was free to roam intellectually and wrote on matters ranging from sugar to the "new astrology." He became particularly interested in the subjects of race, eugenics, natural selection and long-range weather forecasting. And he began to correspond as never before.

There were letters to write and letters to receive. Letters were the source of many an idea. Frequently Huntington would write ten letters in a day, and in his life probably exchanged 50,000 letters with correspondents. He derived many an idea and helped many a questioner, but it was with a few keen intellects that he enjoyed the most meaningful correspondence. Correspondence with such minds frequently produced a large idea that would find its way into one of his books. Such correspondence in the twenties had been exchanged with Griffith Taylor, Stephen Visher, L. Gentil Tippenhauer, Charles-Edward A. Winslow, S. C. GilFillan, and with numerous men from the medical profession. With Taylor it was the isopleth and race, with Visher the causes of climatic change, with Tippenhauer long-range weather forecasting, with Winslow the effect of temperature, humidity, and air movement on human sensitivity.

Rarely did these men present Huntington with a finished idea with which he had previously been unfamiliar. Enter Columb GilFillan, a young New York student, already a practising champion of spelling reform and a widely read person, especially in prediction, later on, invention. It was he who gave Huntington the idea of the "Coldward Course of Progress."[1] Huntington at first resisted but presently accepted this idea, which had occurred to GilFillan on reading a review of Huntington's *Civilization and Climate*. Huntington had explained the northward movement of civilization's leadership only through the northward movement of the storm belt, but GilFillan most stressed man's progressive learning to cope with cold but not with heat, and added Huntington's idea that mental work, which has become increasingly important, needs a cooler climate than physical labor. Later, in one of GilFillan's many suggestive letters to Huntington he stated that in checking "a few dozen birthdays in *The Encyclopedia Americana*" he had verified a statement by his mother "that almost all the world's greatest men were born between December and April."[2] From that suggestion Huntington derived the notion which fourteen years later emerged as the dominating theme in his book *Season of Birth*. Still anticipating that he would complete a geography textbook on Europe, he invited GilFillan to write the chapter on boundaries. Huntington paid him for the work, then encouraged GilFillan to publish the essay,[3] as his own schedule did not seem to permit completion of the Europe text. GilFillan also prepared the exhibit "Epochs of History Related to Climatic Changes as Recorded by the Big Trees,"[4] on display at The Second International Congress of Eugenics in the American Museum of Natural History, 1921. Huntington wrote letters of recommendation on behalf of GilFillan's applications for a college position, and so helped place him in Grinnell College in 1925. Huntington kept all letters exchanged with him, as with other scholars, forming a repository of ideas and information. Huntington was full of original ideas and lines of thought which he wished to pursue for the satisfaction and science service of it.

Prior to his marriage much of his income was invested in his scientific work. Following marriage he felt an economic responsibility which encouraged him to write more for income than hitherto; hence an increased number of textbooks in the years that followed:[5]

> . . . until I was married at the age of 41 I saved relatively little because I put all my surplus into scientific research.
> After I was married and had children I felt the need of sav-

ing more and of earning more, but even now a large fraction of
my time, at least 50 per cent during a good many years, goes
into work for which I receive no financial return. It is partly
public service and still more scientific investigation. I do the one
from a sense of duty, the other from the sheer love of it.

Two books solely the product of Huntington's scientific enthusiasm were *Climatic Changes* and *Earth and Sun*. They had been
written as parts of a single manuscript which the Yale Press declared to be unwieldy. Huntington agreed to divide the 1,100
page manuscript into two companion volumes. While *Earth and
Sun* logically precedes *Climatic Changes* it was published as the
second of the two works. With the manuscript "Climatic
Changes" in the hands of the Yale University Press, Huntington
rewrote sections of "Earth and Sun," so delaying its publication.
These exciting volumes probably reveal Huntington at the height
of his ingenuity. Working with him was Stephen S. Visher.

Visher and Huntington had first corresponded in 1909, and
since that time had become personally acquainted. During 1920,
correspondence between the two geographers became substantial and Visher demonstrated perceptive insight into many of the
problems upon which Huntington was working. Visher adopted
Huntington's books for his classes at Indiana University, and
even had parts of them read aloud. When Visher wrote "I have
decided to specialize upon weather and climate and their influences as a life work," and followed it with the assertion that he
wished to come to Yale to work under Huntington's direction,[6]
the latter suggested that he apply for the $500 fellowship which
his brother had made available. Huntington's brother, Henry
Strong Huntington, Jr., had donated $500 to the cause of geog-
raphy at Yale in 1919, provided that the research associate in
geography, (namely, Ellsworth Huntington) should determine
the expenditure of such money. Visher successfully applied for
the fellowship,[7] secured a leave of absence for the first semester
of the school year 1920–1921, and made preparation for his
stay at Yale. Visher had planned to travel to Europe in that semester but revised his schedule, and made the trip to Europe in
the summer of 1920. Following Huntington's suggestion he made
detailed studies of Spain and the Netherlands which, when written, could be utilized as chapters in his intended Europe text.
Visher arrived at Yale in September, 1920, and proceeded to
assist Huntington with the climatic researches which had been

commenced in the spring of 1920. Of this research Huntington wrote to his live-wire friend, J. Russell Smith:[8]

> I am pegging away on a book on Climatic Changes, their Solar and Terrestrial Causes. I am writing it almost by accident but I believe it is going to be the best book, that is, the most important, that I have ever written. About a year ago I was going to talk to our Geological Club. I said I had nothing new but would put together some of my old stuff about climatic changes. When I did it I found that my ideas had crystallized into quite a new and complete form. I set out to write them down in the form of an article of perhaps 5,000 words. It grew to ten and then to twenty thousand last spring. Then from June to the end of September I put it aside and in October I said I would revise the article and get it off my hands. Then I found that I had to make a book of it and I have been at work on it ever since. I suppose it is going to be tremendously criticized for it contains more new ideas than anything else I have yet done.

The companion volumes *Climatic Changes* and *Earth and Sun*, published by the Yale University Press in 1922 and 1923 respectively, offered the conclusion that both biological and physical evolution is a function of the exchange of electromagnetic radiation or influence among the heavenly bodies, sun, planets, and stars and is controlled by the relative positions of those bodies. *Earth and Sun* offers explanation of the causation of sunspots by planetary influence, the influence of electrical radiation upon climate, and sunspots as an indication of solar activity. In *Climatic Changes* uniformity and variability of climate in both geological and historical times are examined. The cause of changes in the sun's and earth's atmospheres are explored and a stellar-solar hypothesis of climatic change is advanced. Visher's contribution to the whole was to write substantial parts of five chapters in *Climatic Changes*: "Some Problems of Glacial Periods," "The Origin of Loess," "Terrestrial Causes of Climatic Changes," and "The Changing Composition of Oceans and Atmosphere."

The scope of the undertaking was formidable, and Huntington found it necessary to obtain help from established scientists in numerous fields: Charles Schuchert (Geology), Leigh Page (Physics), Frank Schlesinger (Astronomy), Ernest W. Brown (Mathematics), Harry W. Foote (Chemistry)—all of the Yale faculty; T. C. Chamberlin, Harlow Shapley, H. H. Clayton, J. Kullmer, C. F. Brooks, and Andrew E. Douglass, were the other major contributors. In having such a variety of noted authorities read and criticize component chapters, and the completed manuscript, Huntington did much to summarize and integrate thoughts and findings along a common front of inquiry from many different fields.

Withal the books had impact, not the least of which was occasioned from published reviews which ran the gamut from praise to William J. Humphreys's pejorative, "it's broader conceptions are mere fantasies, while its details show little regard for facts and none for physics."[9] Elsewhere Humphreys (professor of meteorological physics, U.S. Weather Bureau) managed "I have read the whole of that book and have no hesitation to say, and others agree with me, that it is as far from being scientific as *Alice in Wonderland*. Scientifically it is wilder than any dream of Jules Verne."[10] But Sir Napier Shaw blessed it: "These are such magnificent sweeps of the magic wand of science that it is not at all clear with which of the sciences ancillary to geography the subject should be especially associated."[11] Reviewers for and against the undertaking recorded themselves on the pages of numerous scientific periodicals and newspapers on these speculative and controversial works. Huntington's own scientific posture added complexity to an already complex subject matter. He believed that intellectual excursus for the sake of discovery—of truths or falsehoods—was inseparable from the way in which science made its advance. He wrote to Visher regarding the dedication of *Earth and Sun* to T. C. Chamberlin:[12]

> To my mind the fact that some of a man's theories are wrong is no criticism at all of him. A wrong theory is like one of the stairs in a stairway. Nobody wants to stay there, but it is true that its loss would make the attainment of the goal impossible. Some people may go up two stairs at a time, but even though, they get into lots of trouble if the other stairs were missing. So I take my hat off to Chamberlin, as a great stair maker. Perhaps I am too ready to do this because I realize that whatever steps I, myself, am making are soon bound to have others above them.

The two books made of Huntington a celebrity. Publishers and magazine editors clamored for whatever he would write them; institutions begged his lectures; newspapermen sent him telegrams requesting matter for Sunday editorials and visited him at Yale for interviews; individuals asked him if salvation were fact, clerics inquired if he felt there was unity twixt science and religion, the incumbent of a Mellon Institute Fellowship wished to know what Huntington ate for breakfast (and enclosed a questionnaire for the geographer to return), others wished to know where they should retire for longevity, and an inmate of San Quentin requested an author copy of one of Huntington's books dealing with "race conditions."

This recognition seemed to emancipate Huntington from any disciplinal constraint which he might have felt as a geographer. He proceeded to read and write on matters which interested him and which he felt to be significant. As for Visher, Huntington was instrumental in assuring the award of a Bishop Museum fellowship to the Indiana geographer, who travelled the Pacific from California to Australia, and who then wrote considerably on the ecology and meteorology of tropical storms.

In May, 1923, Huntington entrained for Vancouver, British Columbia. He was travelling to Australia to attend the Second Pan Pacific Science Congress, at the invitation of the Australian National Research Council, which also contributed one hundred pounds toward his expenses.[13] He had been nominated a delegate of Yale University, the Association of American Geographers, and The National Research Council, to attend the Congress to be held in Melbourne, August 13–22, and Sydney, August 23–September 3. Huntington had arranged a seven-month excursion for himself in order that he might see parts of the world which he had not previously visited—

> a month in Japan, a week in Chosen, three weeks in sailing to Australia, with brief stops in the Philippines, seven weeks in Australia, two weeks in Java, and five weeks in travelling along the Chinese coast from Canton to Shanghai and thence by rail to Peking and Mukden.

Huntington witnessed Japan both before and after the devastating earthquake of that year. He busied himself taking notes and photographs along the route, talking with local people with the use of hired guides, and made especially sure that he visited people to whom he had been given letters of introduction. He used chopsticks and sat cross-legged in a kimono in Japan, was pulled in jinrikishas in China, and enjoyed native cuisine on board boat for Australia. On landing in Australia at Townsville, he made his way across tropical Queensland to the arid west, then journeyed to the southeastern cities of Sydney and Melbourne. And before his Australian departure seven weeks later he travelled from Sydney via Cobar to Broken Hill and Adelaide.

While in Australia he met Griffith Taylor, with whom he had first corresponded in 1915. He enjoyed Taylor's work, and Taylor felt the need for Huntington's support. In 1921 Huntington had written to Taylor that his climographs, his study of white settlement of Australia, isopleths, and maps of head form "have set me to thinking as have those of few other geographers."[14] He also cautioned Taylor to distinguish fact from opinion and suggested that Taylor come to Yale where the two could work on a common problem. Taylor, busy founding the geography department at the University of Sydney, declared there were few scientists to whom he could turn in Australia for criticism. He opined that residence at Yale as co-worker with Huntington would have been beneficial to him, but financial difficulties prevented the arrangement. Taylor was genuinely pleased to have Huntington think so well of his work, for Australian "boomers," anxious to crowd the continent, lambasted Taylor's notion of the optimum population for Australia. Poor Taylor—"Yesterday the *SUN* suggested I leave my job and devote myself to *ARID* Australia and Anti-Nordic Theories—where I could not do harm!! It was a whole leader. It's not all beer and skittles being a minor (or minimus) latter-day Prophet!!" he wrote Huntington.[15] The two men did seem to share an unusually large point of view. Huntington expressed it well:[16] "Long before I saw you the similarity of our work and the resemblances in the way our minds attacked the problem of science made me feel that you and I are unusually near together." When Huntington adopted Taylor's "Migration–Zone Theory of Race Evolution," Taylor took new heart, "I do not know when I felt more pleased."[17] And when Huntington made public his point of view concerning the optimum population for Australia—not more than 20,000,-000—Taylor had a field day! He seized the opportunity to have Congress reporters record the fact in their columns. Twenty-four years later, after Huntington's death, Taylor wrote to Visher:[18]

The Government gave each scientific group the opportunity to invite some distinguished foreigner, and we geographers naturally invited Huntington. He spoke very freely at the meetings, stressing the difficulties of tropical settlement. Especially important were his comments on our tropical populations, where he was struck by the 'picked' character of the settlers. Few old women, many men, and an undue proportion of young women (compared with temperate Australia); thereby demanding a rather higher birth rate. This had never been ventilated before, and I am sure led to a more balanced attitude toward tropical problems.

He accompanied our major excursion to Broken Hill. I have a vivid recollection of a trip to the Frome Plain in the desert. Here he pointed out the varying character of the rubble-deltas on the slopes, and showed that they were indicative of changing rainfall in the desert. You may see the actual photo I took in my book "Australia," while another of the few photos in that book shows Huntington at Harrington's Tank (the preceding plate).

Following the Australian tour Huntington visited Java with several of the Congress delegates. There, "amid tea plantations and within viewing distance of an active crater smoking in the distance," Huntington met the thirty-two-year-old Samuel Van Valkenburg, cartographer for the Dutch government, working in the Topographical Service at Batavia. Van Valkenburg's wife and children suffered from the climate, and Van Valkenburg wished respite for them. On his return to the United States Huntington edited and rewrote parts of a Van Valkenburg article, "Java: The Economic Geography of a Tropical Island," which he persuaded editor Gladys Wrigley to publish in *The Geographical Review*.[19] He wrote letters to eight departments of geography urging Van Valkenburg's employ, eventually bringing about his permanent affiliation with Clark University. A friendship was commenced in Java that lasted a lifetime. And to complete a triptych of friendships which had import for the geographic world Huntington returned to Japan, where both before and after the earthquake he was escorted by Atsushi Tsuyusaki. This geographer, the epitome of Japanese courtesy, showed Huntington a very great deal of Japan. Altogether he quite persuaded

Huntington that Japan had no designs beyond her own boundaries. Eighteen years later Huntington was stunned when the Japanese attacked Pearl Harbor. Tsuyusaki had first written to Huntington in September, 1920, introducing himself. He had read several of Huntington's works, and stated that he wished to read the remainder. An intense correspondence resulted. Tsuyusaki requested and received Huntington's permission to translate both *Asia: A Geography Reader* and *Civilization and Climate* into Japanese. Tsuyusaki completed both translations. The translation of *Asia: A Geography Reader* was at the printers when the earthquake of 1923 struck Japan. Both translations were lost. Tsuyusaki rendered another translation of *Asia: A Geography Reader*, which was published in 1927.[20] He also translated *Civilization and Climate* again, had Naomasa Yamasaki read it, then compared the translation with yet another translation by Hideyo Tanakadate. Both translations were published informally (in 1938 Masato Masaki rendered another translation in paperback).[21]

When Huntington travelled through Japan in 1923, many of the educators knew of his work, for they had read it in English. Huntington was requested to write for Japanese newspapers while he was there. He gave the proceeds to Tsuyusaki's family following the earthquake. When Tsuyusaki's wife died some months later, he wished to travel to the United States and study geography under Huntington's tutelage. Huntington arranged matters for his visit but was obliged to inform him that there was little opportunity to study geography at Yale. Tsuyusaki visited Yale, then Clark University and the University of Chicago, before returning to Japan—quite bewildered by the lack of a geography department at Yale. In fact Huntington was, in part, responsible for helping these three men visit North America—Van Valkenburg permanently, Taylor for more than twenty years, and Tsuyusaki for some weeks.

Huntington addressed the Pan Pacific Science Congress twice and found himself the subject of newspaper headlines when he pronounced that natural selection rather than climate was responsible for the favorable health record of Australia, and again following an address in which he had urged Australia to invest less money in immigration schemes and more money on accurate long-range weather forecasts. He learned so much from his extended travels west of the Pacific that he decided to recount his thoughts and experiences in manuscript form. Most of the manuscript—later published as *West of the Pacific*—had been completed before his ship landed at Vancouver, December 19, 1923.

His head buzzing with thoughts concerning natural selection, racial character, and temperament, Huntington made his way to Cincinnati where he was to deliver the presidential address to the Association of American Geographers. He probably owed his election to the presidency of the Association in 1923 to the unwitting Harlan Barrows. The unnecessarily harsh review which Barrows had accorded Huntington's book, *Principles of Human Geography*, had been written while Barrows was president of the Association. It had been at a time when one of Barrows's books was competing with Huntington's for adoption in the state of Indiana. Such an "adoption" meant sales of several thousand books a year; salesmen scoured the state in droves wining and dining people who had influence. Barrows's review was used to denigrate Huntington's book. The circumstance was unpleasant. Huntington wrote a "letter to the editor" of *The Geographical Review* entitled "The Ethics of Book Reviewing," but he did not send it.[22] He suffered the situation in silence. Yet there were geographers who did not like what had taken place; and *voilà*, Huntington was soon elected president of the A.A.G. Lawrence Martin was one of the men behind the scenes who brought about Huntington's election. When Huntington asked Martin in a letter[23] if his election had been related to the unfortunate Barrows review, Martin had replied,[24] "There is, of course, a relation between the two things, but I did not realize that you knew it. And, in any event, you should have been made President about that time anyway."

Huntington delivered "Geography and Natural Selection, a Preliminary Study of the Origin and Development of Racial Character," as his presidential address before the Association. The address, published in the *Annals of the Association of American Geographers*[25] and summarized under the heading "Work of Natural Selection seen here and in Australia" in the *New York Times*,[26] constituted a résumé of parts of a book he had been writing concerning race character. *The Character of Races* appeared in October, 1924, and by the end of the year over 1600 copies were sold. A chapter summarizing parts of Huntington's thought from that book appeared that same month in *Organic Adaptation to Environment*, edited by M. W. Thorpe and published by the Yale University Press. The following month Yale University Press released the third, and very much revised, edition of *Civilization and Climate*. (The second edition of the book, little altered except for a new 43-page introduction, had been published in 1922.) Now, two years later, came the definitive third edition much revised and expanded. Of it Huntington wrote:[27]

> The most interesting feature of it has been the spirit in which it has been reviewed. When the edition appeared in 1915, it was violently criticized from some quarters. The third edition, on the other hand, seems to be almost universally accepted as an authoritative statement of a point of view which has found its place as a part of the world's large equipment of knowledge.

This edition contained an almost wholly new introductory chapter emphasizing the importance of heredity, three chapters resulting from his investigation into human health (based on his work with the life insurance companies of New York City in the wake of the influenza outbreak of 1918), elaboration of the hypothesis of pulsatory climatic changes, an extended statement concerning "the pulsatory hypothesis and its critics," and "the case of the white man in Australia." Unknown is Huntington's 48-page introduction to what could have been a fourth edition of the book in 1939, which the Yale University Press declined on the grounds that *"Civilization and Climate* as it now stands is something of a classic. . . . to attempt to bring the book up to date with an introduction and changes in a chapter would not permit reviewers to treat it as a new book." Additional to the Japanese translations of 1928, 1929, and 1938 was yet another by Hideo Nishioka (1950); a Spanish translation was accomplished by Luis Perriaux (1942). A German translation was planned by physician Carl Haeberlin (1936), but events leading to the war prevented completion of the work.

The intense writing program which Huntington established for himself obliged him to decline an invitation by geographer R. N. Rudmose Brown of Sheffield University,[28] to address Section E of The British Association at Toronto in August, 1924. Huntington had tentatively offered the title "Human Migration and Racial Transformation," but in August found himself wrestling with three new books, rewriting a fourth, and preparing numerous articles. Yet he did find time to show Percy M. Roxby some of Boston on his return from the Toronto meeting.

Both *West of the Pacific* and *The Character of Races* displayed a very marked concern with racial inheritance not present in his earlier work. Of this matter Huntington wrote:[29]

> . . . Although I am primarily a student of environment I am gradually coming to the conclusion that at any given moment inheritance is more important than environment. But of course inheritance owes much to past environment through the selective action of that environment and perhaps through its direct effect in causing mutations. About ten years ago I came to the conclusion that I was growing one-sided. I started life as a firm believer in the idea that the world's salvation was to be attained through education, religion, good government, and social reform. Then I studied physical environment and health, and was switched from cultural to physical environment. At that stage I began to study genetics and the results of recent biological research. The result is a book now in press called *The Character of Races*, and a firm conviction that any man who asserts that either inheritance, physical environment including food, bacteria, climate, etc., or social environment including all the cultural elements is more important than the others is talking through his hat. Each is essential just as air, drink, and food are essential to human life. Thus from my point of view the man who ignores or minimizes the importance of race and inheritance weakens my confidence in his judgement just as does the man who ignores the importance of health, or of social organization.

In fact Huntington became intensely interested in the matter of eugenics in the twenties, and sustained this interest for the remainder of his life. His scientific work in the twenties included investigation of all manner of cycles, their periodicities and relationships to other phenomena; advanced speculation concerning long-range weather forecasting based on a comparison of his own studies and those of Charles F. Brooks, Henry H. Clayton, L. Gentil Tippenhauer, W. T. Foster's Weather Bureau (Washington, D.C.) and Guillermo Hoxmark; and study on the relationship of atmosphere and man from the point of view of health. The latter investigation was accomplished over the period of a decade (1920–1930) while he was a member of the Committee on Atmosphere and Man of the National Research Council. The report was based on a study of daily deaths in New York City and was published as a Bulletin of the National Research Council in 1930 as *Weather and Health: A Study of Daily Mortality in New York City.*[30]

But as it became increasingly clear to him that Yale was not willing or able to provide him with a professorial salary, he wrote numerous pieces for the more popular magazines relating to eugenics and the impact of weather upon people. He began to plan his life's *summa*: a comprehensive work on civilization. He wished to study civilization—which for him was essentially the history of human progress. But his study was not of the details of art and architecture, or the myriad of man's accomplishments in the ascent since the Fall. He was vitally concerned to understand the reasons for the emergence and submergence of human progress through time; to understand why history revealed periods when the creative energies of men seemed to slumber, and periods when they seemed to manifest themselves in unwonted energy. He strode colossus-like across details and posited climate, the quality of people, and culture as a triadic causation of human progress. He sought to reveal the environmental platform through space and time whereon man had been presented with his climatic circumstance, which in turn brought about migration, hastened the processes of selection, and facilitated or denied the advance of culture. He refused to countenance the march of civilization as chance. In a letter to historian Wallace Caldwell, Huntington later reflected,[31]

> it seems to me that there is no justification for talking about "progress" as the result of chance. What actually seems to happen is that for one or two billion years life on this earth has been trying experiments—unconsciously of course. Almost every conceivable method of life has been tried by some plant or animal. Man has tried all sorts of methods of getting a living, organizing society, and bringing up children. Most of these attempts are complete failures, or else lead to forms of life or of social organization which can progress to a certain point, but there reach a limit. The limits are set in the first place by the physical environment and its relation to food, movement, climate, and so forth. They are also set by the innate qualities of the organism. Thus the evolution of plants, animals, mankind, and society has been a process of trial and selection under the rigid control of physical environment and biological heredity at all times.

It was an epic undertaking, this juggling with a thesis of multiple causation, synthesizing it with the facts as revealed by archaeologists, paleontologists, geologists, anthropologists, historians, et al. That was why he wished to work with a team of specialists from a variety of disciplines. In fact, he accomplished that much by consulting specialists on the Yale faculty (especially Yale historians Michael I. Rostovtzeff, Raymond P. Dougherty, and Kenneth S. Latourette) and by corresponding with an international academic circle, spanning a variety of disciplines and encompassing a multiplicity of competences. Many of his correspondents became a part of that team without realizing it. Huntington exchanged several hundreds of letters with these men, who provided him with suggestions, information, references, and copies of their own works. Included among the historians with whom Huntington corresponded were: Henry Adams, Ernest Barker, George H. Blakeslee, James H. Breasted, James Bryce, Wallace Caldwell, Douglas Caruthers, Will Durant, Herbert A. Gibbons, James H. Robinson, Sir Mark Aurel Stein, Arnold J. Toynbee, Frederick J. Turner, and Lyon G. Tyler. Correspondents other than historians who also constituted part of his loosely knit team included: Henryk Arctowski, Oliver E. Baker, Harry E. Barnes, George G. Chisholm, William Morris Davis, Edward R. Dewey, S. Colum GilFillan, Frank H. Hankins, Roland M. Harper, J. Russell Smith, T. Griffith Taylor, Samuel Van Valkenburg, Stephen S. Visher, and Raymond H. Wheeler.

Huntington was very much aware of the intellectual distance which separated students of climatic influence, heredity, and cultural causation. He wished to create a synthesis of the three branches of study to reveal further the process and progress of civilization. His interest in the matter was not ephemeral; as early as 1907 he had concluded *The Pulse of Asia* with a chapter entitled "The Geographic Basis of History." When a work emerged concerning the sweep of civilization at least through recorded time, he was swift to seize upon it, to make notes to himself about it in his own cabalistic language, sometimes to correspond with the author, and perhaps to review the book where it might best be appreciated. He read Andrew R. Cowan's *Master Clues in World History* (1914) with interest, but was much more excited by the scope of Oswald Spengler's *The Decline of the West* (translations of 1926 and 1928 by Charles F. Atkinson). Huntington was a serious student of rhythms and cycles and was able to appreciate the Spenglerian arrangement of the historic process. Yet he was more prepared to concede the cause of oscillations to be biologic rather than Spenglerian.[32] In contributing a three thousand word review of H. G. Wells's *The*

Outline of History in *The Literary Review*,[33] Huntington opined that Wells should seek the aid of a group of specialists and should rewrite his book. Huntington was elaborating on a notion that was beginning to form in his own mind—that the mainsprings of civilization should stand revealed. His review won attention: editor of *The Literary Review*, Henry S. Canby wrote, "I don't know whether I have told you how many laudatory comments have come to me about your review of Wells' History. It seems to be considered the best review that has appeared on this side of the water."[34]

In 1926 Canby published a Huntington article on "The History of Human Progress,"[35] it being essentially a review of *The History of Civilization* edited by C. K. Ogden in eight volumes. Huntington there philosophized on the need for a history of human progress and suggested that such a volume might best be executed by a main author who, working very closely with a dozen or twenty collaborators and imbibing their various viewpoints, would then write a draft of the history to be submitted to each of his colleagues for his review. Only then should the main author write his final manuscript. This opinion on how such a history would best be written stemmed from the fact that Huntington had in mind just such a task. Several of Huntington's academic friends had urged him to write a book summarizing his thought. Huntington was concerned as to whether he should summarize his work with documentation, or whether he should reveal more proofs of his findings. Perhaps a letter from author Herbert A. Gibbons helped resolve his thought: "Your reputation is well enough established for you to abandon the fear of owing us your results without too much process."

Huntington wrote two books summarizing much of his previous work, dwelling on result and omitting process: *The Pulse of Progress* (1926) and *The Human Habitat* (1927). The first of these volumes, *The Pulse of Progress*, included much of what he had written previously, but a new five-chapter digression into a history of the Jews revealed him as a knowledgeable biblicist and as a geographer who could apply his principles well. His attempts to explain some of man's behavior on the land through history did not find an equal among his peers in the twenties. In the preface to that book he wrote that a history of human progress should be written which would take full account of recent advances in thought. He suggested that preparatory to this undertaking persons having original ideas along these lines

should set them forth in such a way that they could be subjected to criticism.[36] He had a remarkable capacity for the en-
joyment of legitimate criticism, which was invariably taken into
account when he revised a book, or wrote articles pertaining
to criticized matter. It was in the quest for such criticism that
Huntington had written *The Pulse of Progress*, summarizing his
work to that time. In "The Rhythm of Progress and Decay," the
first chapter of that book, he posited the remainder of his life's
work with the assertion that all history is a record of pulsations,
that no country, race, or type of civilization moves steadily forward, or steadily backward. He believed that one of the main
tasks of history is to explain why nations or smaller communities
constantly undergo such pulsations. Of the innumerable factors
involved he felt that all could be summed under "the three headings of physical environment, heredity, and social or cultural
environment."[37] *The Human Habitat* (1927) further recapitu-
lated his own work. But again, it revealed that the man seemingly had to break new ground whenever armed with a pen:
"The Terrestrial Canvas,"[38] "The Relation of the Soil to Aristocracy and Democracy,"[39] and "An Example of Transporta-
tion"[40] were additions to his previous work.

He began to plan his book on civilization. He wrote to the
Yale University Press, and inquired less formally of the houses
which had published other writings of his as to their interest in
such a venture. Editors placed plans before readers, committees,
and other evaluators, then became dilatory in reply until the
Depression intervened and interred further discussion. Yet Huntington was determined to execute his scheme. He realized the
time it would take, "in order to do it properly, I ought to spend
at least five years, possibly ten."[41] To release himself from the
bondage of earning a living he decided to write some textbooks.

CHAPTER XIII

Toward the Mainsprings of Civilization

The design for the study on "civilization" was already in his mind. He realized that the book would be large and complex in scope and, unlike some of his other books, would not be suitable for use as a classroom text. Yet it was the man's ambition to write such a volume. Eventually the first half of his manuscript on civilization was published in 1945 as *Mainsprings of Civilization*. The second half of the manuscript, tentatively entitled "The Pace of History" never was completed; the three chapters extant of this latter work were published posthumously.[1]

It was the financial insecurity of the civilization study that plagued him. Publishers would not commit themselves to a long-term plan, especially when it involved an advance against royalties. Even the Yale University Press shunned involvement in a scheme of such proportions. Consequently Huntington determined to write a book, or series of books, that would provide sufficient income during the thirties to make possible his study of civilization. Unfortunately, the combined royalties from all his writing aside from *Principles of Human Geography* had amounted to less than five hundred dollars a year during the latter twenties. Income from *Principles of Human Geography* might well have sponsored his intended undertaking, but owing to an ill-conceived arrangement with Sumner Cushing, the latter's widow received six-tenths of the royalties of that book; Huntington received four percent of three dollars for each copy sold.

When in 1928, A. W. Abrams was requested to revise the New York State curricula for the fourth and fifth grades, he wrote to Huntington proposing a joint authorship of an elementary geography series. The two men corresponded on the matter, secured an understanding, and proceeded to author some elementary geography. Abrams proposed and Huntington composed. The work had not long been commenced when Charles Seaver of the Macmillan Company proposed to Huntington that he join C. B. Benson and F. M. McMurry in preparing a series of elementary school geography books.[2] No expense was to be spared. Huntington dissolved his agreement with Abrams at the cost of $500, which Macmillan provided. Within one month of meeting Seaver, and agreeing to terms, Huntington was able to write to McMurry,[3] "I have finished a first draft of North America but it is much too long. . . ."

The three authors divided the work, agreed to frequent meetings and exchange of manuscripts, and planned travel. Huntington was to visit the southern part of the United States, South America, and Europe during the next thirty months. Benson was to travel to Japan, China, Indo-China, also to India and across the Indian Ocean, to the Cape, then to Cairo and on into Europe. McMurry confined himself to some travel in the United States. Huntington and Benson, accompanied by their wives, journeyed through the Appalachians to Georgia then to New Orleans and home via the Mississippi Valley. While in the valley Huntington studied the effects of the flood of 1927. By May 30, 1928, Huntington could write to McMurry,[4] "I enclose a tentative draft of a manuscript on part of the South. . . ." Meanwhile at Huntington's suggestion the company secured the services of cartographer Samuel Van Valkenburg, then with Clark University. Conference followed conference.

On September 29th, 1928, Huntington sailed from New York on board the S. S. *Calamares*. He then travelled through Cuba, Panama, Colombia, Ecuador, Peru, Bolivia, Chile, Argentina, Uruguay, Paraguay, Brazil, Trinidad, and Barbados, before returning to New Haven February 7, 1929. He had secured many photographs, taken many notes, and written more manuscript which he sent to Benson and McMurry. He had been especially pleased to meet Hoxmark and Mossman of the Argentine, with whose work in long-range weather forecasting he was quite familiar. Otherwise Huntington noted the progress shown in the cities, the fact that the Indians did not share in this progress, and evidences revealed by Inca terraces which he felt substantiated climatic change since their construction on the west slope of the Andes.[5]

Nine months later, Huntington, his wife, and three children journeyed to Europe, taking with them a seven-passenger Buick motor car. He drove over 17,000 miles and visited every country west of the Soviet Union and Jugoslavia with the exception of Portugal and Lithuania. He had wished to enter the Soviet Union but was refused permission to enter, probably owing to *"The Suicide of Russia,"* an article he had published in 1925.

The three children were placed at school in Nice, Geneva, and Constantinople—where Ellsworth's brother, George, was Vice-President of Robert College. The brothers and their wives travelled together much that summer. In December, 1929, the oldest boy, Charles, was allowed to accompany his parents to Cairo, thence up the River Nile to Assuan. Here the family parted company; Huntington continued equatorward while Mrs. Huntington and Charles returned to Constantinople. Huntington journeyed through the Sudan, Uganda, stayed some days on the margins of Lake Victoria, visited Ruwenzori and Nairobi before taking ship for Cairo from Mombassa. All the while Huntington was maintaining correspondence with co-workers Benson and McMurry. While Huntington was travelling in Europe and Africa, Benson was journeying westward from Japan, through southeast Asia, the Indian subcontinent and Africa. Benson, too, was composing manuscript as he travelled and parts of these manuscripts he sent to Huntington for criticism and revision; Huntington, in turn, sent them to McMurry in New York. Whether or not such extensive travel was necessary in the preparation of elementary texts for grades four to seven is a moot point. Certainly Huntington had been granted the opportunity to travel Europe, Africa, and South America in a manner not possible at any other time in his life.

The Macmillan Company published *Living Geography*, Book One; *How Countries Differ*; and *Living Geography*, Book Two: *Why Countries Differ*, in February, 1932. Notwithstanding the economic recession, the texts did sell and Huntington derived from them not less than one thousand dollars a year for the remainder of the decade. Occasionally his annual royalty approached two thousand dollars. However, with costs rising, his family growing up, and with little improvement in his Yale salary, he was still unable to free himself from all other obligations and concentrate upon his study of civilization. Even while writing manuscript for *Living Geography* he undertook a revision of his previously published *Business Geography*. The revision became so substantial that the new book, published in 1933 as *Economic and Social Geography*,[6] sold concurrently with *Business Geography*. Samuel Van Valkenburg helped substantially with the numerous maps.

Another manuscript enterprise developed as a result of his association with Van Valkenburg: in 1928 the latter had commenced the writing of a European geography text. After completing the manuscript he could not find a publisher. A large part of the problem resided in the fact that Van Valkenburg was not writing in his native language. When Van Valkenburg revealed his predicament to Huntington, the latter revised several chapters of a "Europe" manuscript which he had written during the twenties.[7] That manuscript too, had failed to meet with a publisher's favor. In fact when Visher asked Huntington in 1928 if he could quote parts of the manuscript for a text which he and Blanchard were preparing, Huntington sent him what was nearly a finished manuscript, and gave him permission to use as much of it as he wanted. *Economic Geography of Europe* by William O. Blanchard and S. S. Visher was published by McGraw Hill Book Co. in 1931, but not before Huntington had read, edited, and criticized the Visher part of the text. Visher had borrowed only a little from Huntington's manuscript. Consequently this previously written manuscript was available for the Van Valkenburg manuscript. Huntington selected certain of his chapters, added them to what Van Valkenburg had written, then vigorously edited the whole. The result was the 48-chapter, 651-page *Europe* by Van Valkenburg and Huntington published by John Wiley & Sons, 1935.

After his return from Europe in 1930 and during the following decade Huntington gave more of his time to community lecture engagements and addresses and to civic affairs. Professionally he gave more and more of his time during the 1930s to the American Eugenics Society. His decision as to whether or not he should agree to give or write an article was governed largely by the suggested payment accompanying the invitation. But if the invitation came from a church, local civic group, or school, inevitably he gave his services free of charge.

He retained a close relationship with the New Haven Church of the Redeemer. When the pastor announced his resignation in 1931, Huntington was elected to a small steering committee to choose another pastor. He visited several churches, some in Connecticut, some farther afield, and listened to Sunday morning sermons, in the hope that he would be able to suggest a new pastor. While he gave to that church, he and other members of his immediate family continued to send two hundred dollars annually to his father's church in Milton, and continued that contribution throughout the years of economic depression. He retained an interest in providing religious education in the schools of Connecticut, an interest which he had furthered in the twenties as President of the New Haven Council of Churches. He spoke before several church groups of his travels, addressed the New Haven Normal School, entertained, and was entertained by, Yale clubs including the Oriental Society, the Questioners, and the Inquirers. He lectured out of state to the National Council of Geography Teachers, to the University of Rochester, the American Society of Heating and Ventilating Engineers, the Fortnightly Club of Schenectady, the Eastern Sociological Conference, 'the Schoolmen's Week' in Philadelphia. Various of his lectures or publications were reported in the *New York Times* or the *Tribune*. He was asked to write to congressmen on behalf of numerous causes, was requested to be present at the launching of Sir Hubert Wilkins's *Nautilus*, and was selected by the Aristogenic Association as one of a group of Americans whose characteristics should be noted and filed away for a century for the benefit of future generations. The Buffalo Museum of Science requested from him an autographed photographic portrait, the British Economic Advisory Council requested him to review one of Uvarov's papers on climate and insects for the *Monthly Weather Review*, and Grenfell Price visited him in New Haven to discuss the possibilities and problems of white settlement in the tropics. O. J. Sieplein of the Department of Sun Ray Research of the Joseph H. Adams Foundation, and Arnett of Arnett Atheneum, Oklahoma, were two of many who journeyed to New Haven to talk with Huntington of their researches accomplished and intended.

There were so many demands upon Huntington's time that inevitably some work intended fell by the wayside; such was the case with a children's book of stories based upon his own Asiatic experiences which Huntington had commenced in the summer of 1928. The crowded schedule also meant that Huntington was not inclined to teach in a summer school, notwithstanding attractive invitations which came to him periodically. Thus his income dwindled in the years of depression: articles were not so easily sold to magazines, and royalties declined. Three publishing houses ceased paying Huntington royalties altogether. When his friend Wells retired from *Harper's Magazine*, and Huntington could no longer place his articles with that magazine, another of his main sources of income disappeared. Upon receiving an invitation from Harlan H. Barrows to teach two courses at the University of Chicago summer school, 1931, in the wake of the recently retired J. Paul Goode, he accepted. It was the first summer school he was to experience as a faculty member.

He offered two courses, "Climate and Man," and "Europe." He wrote to Barrows requesting that a stenographer be made available to make a record of his lectures. The "Climate and Man" lectures constituted essentially an intended fourth (but unpublished) edition of *Civilization and Climate*; the "Europe" lectures became an integral part of *Europe* by Van Valkenburg and Huntington. The summer school gave Huntington a chance to become better acquainted with Griffith Taylor and some of the other Chicago geography staff, including Harlan H. Barrows, Charles C. Colby and Robert S. Platt. The students too were enthusiastic in support of his classes: ". . . he was very much a stimulating scholar, mixing lecture with discussion and questions. He had the full attention of the class though he was less formal than most of the Chicago group."[8] Huntington taught the following summer at Clark University; returned to Chicago to teach in the autumn of 1937, replacing a sick Wellington Jones; and taught in the Harvard summer school of 1940. He found it necessary to decline invitations from the University of British Columbia for the summer of 1936 and from Syracuse University in 1941.

By teaching longer periods on some days of the 1931 Chicago summer school, Huntington was able to dash to Matamek factory on the estuary of the Matamek River, Saguenay County, Quebec, Canada in time to be present for the opening of one of the most intense conferences ever held concerning biological cycles. The conference had been called by Copley Amory of Boston and included thirty scientists and Canadian federal and provincial officials. Amory, for some years, had been interested in the fact that sometimes the fish, bird, and animal populations of that part of Canada were very abundant, and sometimes very scarce. At the conference, which lasted from July 23 to August 1, cycles of 30 months to 260 years or more were discussed with reference to fluctuations in trees, insects, fish of the sea, fish of the rivers, game birds, birds of prey, mice, rabbits, bacteria and parasites, reproduction, diseases, and deaths among human beings. Of twenty-five papers delivered before the conference Huntington contributed two: "The Ebb and Flow of Human Population" and "Climatic Cycles." Additionally he prepared a report of the conference which was published as "Matamek Conference on Biological Cycles."[9] Huntington also prepared a résumé of the conference for *Science*[10] and helped edit an abstract of papers and discussions.[11] A limited number of copies of the full proceedings of the conference was made available later in 1932, under the supervision of Copley Amory.[12]

Forerunners to the Matamek Conference had been two conferences sponsored by the Carnegie Institution of Washington, D.C. The first of these, called by President Merriam of the Carnegie Institution, was held December 8 and 9, 1922. Leading investigators had there delivered papers, engaged in discussion, and exchanged views on cyclic phenomena. Huntington had also offered two papers at that conference: "Cycles of Health" and "Causes of cycles."[13] A second conference on cycles, not attended by Huntington, had been sponsored by the Carnegie Institution in 1928. Both of these had attracted the attention of Amory. Following the Matamek Conference, Amory corresponded with and visited several of the participants of that meeting. He planned another conference of similar design later in the decade, but international tensions militated against such a meeting. Nevertheless, Amory's enthusiasm and continuing correspondence on the matter came to the attention of Edward R. Dewey. Amory, Dewey, and Huntington formed the nucleus of a committee in 1940, which conceived the design for what eventually became the Foundation for the Study of Cycles.[14] Huntington's advice at the founding was as invaluable as were Dewey's labors and Amory's connections and longstanding enthusiasm for the work. Some of Huntington's research on cycles was later published by the Foundation for the Study of Cycles. The decade of the thirties found Huntington studying more and more cycles, seeking their causation, and their applicability. It brought him into close contact with the persons and researches of Charles Elton, Harlow Shapley, Julian Huxley, Halbert Gillette, Henry L. Moore, Charles E. P. Brooks, and Henry H. Clayton. His research on cycles was detailed. Hundreds of letters and hundreds of pages of calculations attest his quest for the revelation of periodicities in phenomena. It was all an important part of the book which was forming in his mind—the book on civilization.

By the thirties Huntington's work was known and sought internationally. When he was invited by the organizers of the 1932 Rome Population Conference to present a paper, he sent them a rewritten version of "The Ebb and Flow of Human Population" which was published in the Congress Proceedings. Months later, when H. Arctowski invited him to contribute to a memorial volume of the Geographical Society of Lwow in honor of the seventieth birthday of the Polish geographer and founder of the Society, Eugeniusz Romer, Huntington provided "The Selective Action of Migration."[15] The following year he contributed an article to a memorial volume of *Geografiska Annaler* celebrating the seventieth birthday of the Swedish explorer, Sven Hedin. Huntington took the occasion to summarize his thought on climatic pulsations, and in so doing, committed to paper what he had recently spoken at the Franklin Institute in Philadelphia. Perhaps he would not have been tempted into a summation of the pulsatory climatic thesis, but the notion of historic variations of climate had been strongly criticized by A. Penck and J. W. Gregory on the occasion of the Centennial Celebration of the Royal Geographical Society (1930). In reply, Huntington wrote:[16]

> Many authorities, however, who have studied the problem on the spot and not merely from a distance, strongly oppose this tendency. Berkey and Morris for example, state that evidence collected by the expeditions of the American Museum of Natural History points unequivocally to historic pulsations of climate in Mongolia. Leakey in Central Africa, and Trinkler and de Terra in Central Asia arrive at a similar conclusion. Shortly before his sad death in an automobile accident Dr. Trinkler urged me to write an article pointing out the fallacies of Professors Penck and Gregory. The present article, therefore, not only pays homage to Dr. Hedin's marvellous half century of work in exploring Central Asia, but honors the memory of Dr. Emil Trinkler, whose explorations in that same region owed much to the inspiration of Dr. Hedin.

And while Huntington was rendering a summation of his pulsatory climatic hypothesis, the first three volumes of Arnold J. Toynbee's *A Study of History* appeared. Huntington was jubilant, for here was an historian making use of the geographer's offering. He wrote to Toynbee:[17]

> I have just gotten hold of your *Study of History*. . . . It seems to me that you have made one of the really great contributions to history. In the first place, your conception of civilization as a species gives to history as a whole a unity and a significance which, to me at least, it has never had before. In the second

place, you are the first to do what historians have long talked about—that is, to make a real synthesis of geography and history. From this point of view I am sure that your work is going to mark an epoch of methods of historical interpretation.

Then Huntington wrote to his friend Henry Canby, editor of *The Saturday Review of Literature*, requesting that he review the Toynbee volumes. Before Canby could reply, Huntington had read them and written the review.[18] He urged Canby to secure review copies of the volumes for he wanted them for his own shelves. He wrote to numerous of his friends about his discovery of Toynbee, typical of which was a brevity to Roland Harper,[19] "Toynbee is the first historian to really thoroughly accept the relationship of geography to history, and make it function." Huntington exchanged further correspondence with Toynbee in which he made suggestions concerning "geographical interpretation" and "The relative degree of challenge that constitutes the optimum." Civilization as a species treated by an historian, provided him with the historical plot into which he could weave his numerous theses. Toynbee wrote to Huntington,[20] "I am very deeply indebted to you. I have studied your work for years and it has worked its way right into my own thought." The two men exchanged correspondence over the next decade which did much to bring Huntington's viewpoint before the historians via further volumes of *A Study of History*. Marginalia adorn Huntington's private copy of *A Study of History*, which he read and reread while advancing his own work on civilization. And, too, correspondence and exchange of publications with Mark Aurel Stein was of benefit to Huntington's thought.

He decided to invite Yale historian Raymond P. Dougherty (Professor of Assyriology and Babylonian Literature) to study with him the inner border of the Fertile Crescent. Dougherty accepted and Huntington anticipated receipt of the professional historian's viewpoint. They expected to devote much of the academic year 1934–35 to a prolonged trip along the dry inner edge of the Crescent as far as Teima in the southwest and Koweit in the southeast. Huntington had hired an assistant who, for eighteen months, prepared a card catalogue of all ruins mentioned near or beyond the limits of present cultivation in the

Crescent of the thirties. He had discussed the matter seriously with Bertram Thomas and James Breasted and concluded that the journey should be made. But the unexpected death of Dougherty, coupled with a nonavailability of funds for such an undertaking, prevented him from travelling to that part of the world a second time (the first had been in 1909).

He remained instead in New Haven and sought relationships of names to accomplishment and crime, sought further evidence of climatic optima for plants and animals, and supervised Miss M. Howarth, who was writing a social geography of New Hampshire. When he received an invitation to present a paper at the International Geographical Congress to be held at Amsterdam in 1938, he readied for delivery "The Productivity of the Soil," but was obliged to have it read in his absence owing to financial circumstance.[21] Each of these contributions was in its own way a summary of some larger piece of research which he had undertaken and each of which constituted a part of his book on civilization.

Time and again Huntington recommenced his book, only to find himself turned aside by a matter which he felt should be made the subject of a little more research. But in 1935 it really did seem as though he were going to complete the task. He signed a contract with the Wiley Company, accepted an advanced royalty, then bantered with his live-wire friend, J. Russell Smith:[22]

> I am writing away as ever. The thing that I am trying to do now is to divest myself of the fact that I am a geographer or anything else and really look at the whole problem of civilization without bias; of course that is an impossibility, but at least it represents a good ideal.

Smith:[23]

> According to your letter of the twenty-fifth of February, your book on which you are now working might be entitled "Civilization Seen By a Disembodied Spirit," or "As The Man in The Moon Saw It."
>
> As you see it, how big is this book, and about what would its title be, and who is to publish it? and when. It sounds interesting.

Huntington:[24]

> Neither your "disembodied spirit" nor "the man in the moon"
> has the right perspective. The perspective that I want is that of
> the man from Mars. Such a man would see a book called Civili-
> zation, and at his distance it would need four or five hundred
> pages to give an outline of the subject. The final details would
> take a five-foot shelf. But I am not planning anything about
> them now. I am going to finish the book as soon as I can, but
> it may take a year.

Nevertheless two more areas of research were yet to be undertaken before "Civilization" was written. The first of these
concerned a study of the importance of the season in which
people are born. Huntington was writing on this theme in his
tentative manuscript on Civilization in 1936.[25]

> . . . that book (Civilization) is being postponed because, much
> to my surprise, I have been obliged to write another before get-
> ting out the main book. This other book is called "Season, Sex,
> and Genius." It is a study of the month of birth. I find that the
> month of birth, or rather, of conception, is a very important
> matter. Not only does the number of births vary systematically
> from season to season, but the proportion of the sexes varies
> similarly. So does the average length of life and the degree to
> which people display genius. It sounds simple to say these things
> but to really find out the facts has required a very complicated
> series of studies.

In an effort to measure the contribution of different types of
people to the progress of civilization he visited Washington,
D.C. and investigated the records of the F.B.I., Bureau of Patents, and Bureau of the Census. From the vast mass of statistics
which he and co-workers had gathered, Huntington sought to
infer other information concerning the quality of people. He
perceived a favorable season of birth for man and proceeded to
investigate the matter for a chapter of his long-delayed book on
civilization. He opined that man, like all other higher animals,
has a definite seasonal rhythm of reproduction and concluded
that babies born in later winter or early spring were endowed
with a superior inheritance. The work interested him so much

that he wrote "now I have spent a large part of my time on it for nearly a year."[26] He offered "Season, Sex and Genius" to Wiley who published it as *Season of Birth—Its Relation To Human Abilities*. Time and again, what started as an interesting set of paragraphs became a book.

Huntington regarded the book as perhaps his best from a scientific point of view, yet sales were disastrous, and the book remained little known. He addressed "The American Association on Mental Deficiency" (May, 1937) on "Physiological Relationships of Season of Birth,"[27] and *Science Digest* published an article excerpted from Chapter I of *Season of Birth*. Probably the most favorable of many reviews which were written of the book appeared in *The Journal of the American Medical Association* (1938).[28] Among the geographers R. B. Hall seemed most enthusiastic:[29] "I have read your book "Season of Birth," and enjoyed it tremendously. I think you have grasped one of the most vital problems in the whole geographical field. . . ."

Only one more extended stint of research separated him from a final assault on his book, "Civilization": his ozone hypothesis. Huntington examined the circulation dates of nonfiction books in forty-two libraries for a period of twenty years. Analysis of these data showed a maximum of intellectual activity in the early spring. That finding coincided with Huntington's earlier researches concerning students marks and the percentage of persons passing civil service examinations, and Joseph Rossman's discoveries concerning applications for patents or amendments to such applications. Huntington was perplexed by a spring maximum of mental activity when conditions of health are poor, coming only a little after the highest death rate of the year. And as physical well-being increased during the summer, improvement in mental activity failed to continue. "Altogether, it looks as if some unknown factor provided a mental stimulus which causes intellectual activity to increase during January and February while health is at its lowest, and to reach a maximum not far from March." He advanced the hypothesis that atmospheric ozone may provide the answer to the conundrum. Huntington had already written a manuscript on the rôle of ozone as an attempt further to reveal the relationships between weather, seasons, and mental activity. The manuscript, "Ozone, Health and Progress," had been completed in September, 1939, and was offered to the Wiley Company for publication as a book. In the preface to the manuscript Huntington wrote:[30]

This book is part of a prolonged attempt to analyze the physical factors which help or hinder the progress of civilization. The
attempt began with *The Pulse of Asia.* It reached full development in *Civilization and Climate,* and has been continued in
The Character of Races and several other books. The present
book, like its immediate predecessor, *Season of Birth,* was written almost unintentionally because a new phase of the broad
study of the effect of physical environment upon history demanded more intensive investigation. In each of these cases the
chance reading of an article suggested a new method by which
climate and weather may influence human welfare. Further inquiry disclosed an unexpected wealth of evidence which had
previously been overlooked. Thus the subject grew until a book
was written.

Huntington developed the value of the hypothesis by suggesting and demonstrating that ozone may have provided the psy-
chological stimulus which accounts for much of recorded history. Probably the ozone hypothesis reached a greater number
of people via the newspaper. In 1939 Louis Barail, a French-
speaking Swiss who had been a professor of biophysics at the
University of Geneva until he came to the United States in 1936,
organized an "International Congress of Biophysics, Biocosmics
and Biocracy." Huntington was made a member of the organizing committee of the Congress and president of the section of
biocosmics. In that capacity he gave a paper entitled "Climatic
Relationships of Ozone and Health," parts of which found their
way into many newspapers. Huntington prepared a paper for the
Association of American Geographers meeting in Chicago,
"Ozone, Health, and Progress," for a section on the "theory of
environmentalism" which Roderick Peattie was urging.
    Huntington undertook no further new researches before he
plunged into his book "Civilization." But the Wiley Company
insisted that he revise *Economic and Social Geography* and
Principles of Human Geography. That was accomplished in
1939 and both books appeared in 1940. *Principles of Economic
Geography* replaced the 1933 title, *Economic and Social Geography.* In the preface to the new edition, which was essentially
the fourth major revision of *Business Geography* (1922), Huntington wrote "most of the material is entirely new." Yet since he
borrowed material from previous editions, he acknowledged as
assistants F. E. Williams and S. Van Valkenburg. S. S. Visher

was also acknowledged for his painstaking criticism of the entire manuscript. Only weeks later the fifth edition of *Principles of Human Geography* appeared. Huntington also wrote in the preface to that book, of nearly 600 pages, "Approximately half of the material is new." The task of compiling revisions of both books simultaneously led him to thrust aside many matters demanding his attention. For weeks at a time he would banish all his incoming correspondence unopened to a desk drawer. Later Huntington would explain to his correspondent what had happened. Yet during the thirties and forties his vigorous activity in eugenics retained. Soon after the beginning of World War II he tried to help several European scientists escape Nazi-dominated Europe and find positions in the United States. He accommodated Mrs. Evelyn Phelps Brown—wife of Oxford University economist Henry Phelps Brown—and her two children in his home for several months as part of a scheme inspired by the British Eugenics Organization and supported by The American Eugenics Society. He had written separate letters to President and Mrs. Franklin D. Roosevelt urging that "red tape" be cut to save the depletion of the Oxonian eugenic treasury.

Time had hurried by and Huntington was already in his sixties, well aware that his book on civilization could wait no longer. He had signed a contract for the book with Wiley Company in 1935, and had received royalties in advance of publication. The president of Wiley Company in 1941 had begun to wonder where the manuscript was. The time-consuming task of earning money had slowed Huntington enormously. *Living Geography* had not provided the income he had anticipated. For three years Huntington edited and rewrote children's "geography drama" radio manuscripts for the Columbia Broadcasting Corporation; throughout the decade he reviewed a substantial number of books for pay, chiefly for *The Saturday Review of Literature*. He gave talks and addresses for pay; sold "interviews" and written pieces of work to newspapers whenever possible, and accepted an editorial post with an education film-making company.

Numbers of people who had read Huntington on eugenics wrote to him that he was against motherhood, religion, the South. Others wrote inquiring if he could determine the sex of children before conception. Astrologers wrote to him seeking his endorsement of their activities. Cranks wrote to him in droves, usually requesting money in order to fulfill a messianic vision.

Numbers of people wrote asking questions which arose from his books, others wrote on matters related to some of his books; in time he replied to all. On a more serious plane he exchanged correspondence with innumerable men working on problems similar to his own, men from a variety of disciplines. School teachers sought his advice on curricula, use of his own books, and bibliography for their school libraries. Frequently school children wrote to him requesting that he address their class, which he sometimes did if the school were close by, and on more than one occasion had a group of children travel from another state to visit him in his office on a Saturday or Sunday. In the early forties when Huntington had lent his name as sponsor to numerous political causes, he was assailed by champions of the people. He was harassed when his name was mentioned in a book on social nudism; and again was harassed because social scientist Harold Rugg—at the time held responsible in some quarters for subverting the mind of youth—also mentioned his work in footnotes. Many individuals devoted to causes wrote to Huntington for his endorsement, and invariably he lent his name if the reasons seemed admirable. Then there were the scholars who wrote to exchange news and views.

Beginning in 1940 he worked hard at the book on civilization. More and more discretionary duties devolved upon his secretary. He wrote to J. W. Goldthwait, his friend of graduate school days,[31] "My greatest fear now is that I shall grow too old to do good work before I can finish the things I have laid out." And to Rudolf Bertheau, Secretary of the American Eugenics Society, he wrote,[32] "The fact is that I am simply determined that I must get my book on Civilization written. You will remember that I have been trying to write this book ever since you've known me. Now I am trying to throw everything else overboard in order to get it done. Hence you and the Eugenics Society and lots of other things are not getting a fair deal."

But he did allow one more large interruption: in December, 1940 he read Raymond H. Wheeler's 1,000-page manuscript "History of Climate in Relation to the Rise and Fall of Governments." Huntington considered the work so valuable ("I believe you have hold of one of the great contributions of human knowledge.")[33] that he spent three weeks upon it, criticizing the whole in eighteen pages and writing an introduction to it. Following Huntington's suggestions, Wheeler divided the large manuscript into three volumes and composed a smaller one-volume summary of the whole. Continuing into 1943 Huntington assisted him with his work, deriving much of worth for his own work on civilization.

When Ralph H. Brown, Secretary of the Association of American Geographers wrote to Huntington in February, 1942, requesting a brief account of his past year's activity for inclusion in a newsletter, Huntington noted:[34]

> At last I am writing a book which I have planned for more than twenty years. The tentative title is "Civilization: A Study of Geography, History, Culture, and Heredity." The book has two purposes. The first is a preliminary attempt to strike a fair balance between geography, biological and cultural factors in the evolution of civilization and in history. This of course is an extremely hard thing to do. No one can expect to make more than a beginning in it.
>
> The second purpose is to bring together the various parts of my own theory of Civilization. These parts have been published in some twenty-five different books and many articles. They are nowhere gathered together, with the result that many people who think that some particular phase is over-emphasized, do not realize that this is more or less balanced by other phases elsewhere.

Robert M. Yerkes, Stephen S. Visher and Raymond H. Wheeler each read the manuscript and provided the criticism which Huntington sought; Edward R. Dewey read and criticized the section on cycles. The manuscript was finally completed in the spring of 1944.

The whole had been written with the storm clouds of war gathering in Europe. His three children, now grown, were all in service; one son was in the Pacific theatre, a second son was in France, and a daughter undertook service with the Red Cross in Europe (1945). Anxiety for the welfare of his children was constantly upon him. When he was informed that his younger son, George Herbert Huntington II, had been killed in action in France (1944), it was a desperately sad occasion for the man: "It is the hardest thing that has ever come into my life."

Mainsprings of Civilization appeared in May, 1945. Huntington purchased reviews of the book from clipping services by the pound weight. The book sold 10,000 copies in its first year. Even the Quartermaster Corps of the United States War Depart-

Toward the "Mainsprings"

ment, Jersey City, ordered a thousand copies. Letters requesting a lecture from Huntington or elucidation of a point in his book were frequent. Many magazine writers visited Huntington, then quoted and misquoted him in their columns. Huntington had been made quite tired by the innumerable tasks associated with his book, and upon publication took a one-month vacation in Maine. "The result was excellent. When I came home after being down in Maine I felt as young as ever and ready to tackle a volume which really is the concluding part of *Mainsprings of Civilization*."[35]

Huntington referred to a manuscript which he began to compose at once, tentatively entitled "The Pace of Culture," then re-entitled "The Pace of History." The work was in reality a part of *Mainsprings of Civilization*.[36]

> . . . reviews of *Mainsprings of Civilization* have made me realize more than ever that I ought to write what was originally intended as the fourth part of that book. That part was to be a study of the main elements of civilization and of its historical progress in the light of the ideas set forth in Parts One to Three, which have now been published as *Mainsprings of Civilization*. Inasmuch as I am now almost 69 years old it is quite clear that if I am to do a job of this kind I ought to get at it at once. . . .

The exclusion of this study from "Mainsprings" was dictated by the time he had already invested in that book and by the very considerable demands upon his time from other quarters. Besides, the publishers had already waited a decade for the manuscript. He embarked upon the study in September, 1945, and on October 16 Wiley Company sent Huntington a contract for what was to have been a sequel to "Mainsprings." Huntington had outlined some of his thoughts:

THE PACE OF HISTORY

Factors which may influence a change in mental attitude of peoples.

I. Biological Factors
    A. Hereditary (i.e. involving a change in actual and biological composition)
       1. Selective migration, either
         a. Inward
         b. Outward

c. Internal, e.g. country to city, province to province
2. Selective death rates, due to
    a. Disease, epidemics, plague, etc., new diseases
    b. War, including displacement and death of population as well as of fighters
    c. Famine, and other disasters, e.g. flood, earthquakes, etc.
3. Selective birthrates
    a. Rural vs. urban
    b. One racial group vs. another
    c. One social or economic class vs. another
    d. Religious vs. non-religious groups (celibacy)
4. Occurrence of Genius
    a. Extent to which genius is hereditary
    b. Extent to which genius or at least high achievement is due to vigor
    c. Extent to which genius or at least high achievement is due to opportunity
    d. Extent to which genius or at least high achievement is due to training
B. Physiological (i.e. involving increase or decrease in physical vigor, esp. reproduction vigor)
    1. Diet, influenced by
        a. Amount of food, depending on weather, methods of agriculture, density of pop., methods of taxation, land tenure, etc.
        b. Kind of food, e.g. nutritive quality, varying according to amount of meat, milk, etc.; quality of soil both originally and after being cultivated; density of population and consequent limitations as to amount of cereals vs. other types
    2. Disease
        a. Direct effect of diseases such as influenza, tuberculosis, syphilis, malaria, etc. upon general energy of people
        b. Indirect effect through creation of conditions of fear or hope, tendencies toward migration
        c. Variation due to changes in medical practice, introduction of new people, new ideas, etc.
    3. Weather
        a. Direct effect of pulsations on health, alertness, and reproduction, etc.

  b. Indirect effects through disease, crops, disasters, etc.
  c. Indirect effects through migration, political discontent, wars, etc.
  4. Mode of Life. Effect of changes in
      a. Percentage of rural, and urban, industrial, poor, rich, etc.
      b. Clothing and shelter, e.g. ease and cheapness of procuring warm clothes, time and energy available with poor heat and light vs. good heat and light
      c. Differences due to occupation. Degree to which one social and economic group compares with another in vigor because of different modes of life arising from occupational differences

II. Cultural Factors
  A. Material Culture
      1. Inventions or discoveries that
          a. Raise the standard of living
          b. Create a new balance in war
          c. Influence the amount and paths of trade
          d. Open up new avenues for further invention
          e. Change the mode of life
          f. Influence health, and alter the deathrate through diet, disease, protection from weather, etc.
          g. Alter the rates of marriage, birth, etc.
          h. Open new lands for occupation
          i. Open new resources for exploitation
          j. Induce migration
          k. Throw old resources, lands, methods, etc. out of use
  B. Immaterial Culture
      1. New ideas as to
          a. Art
          b. Literature
          c. Science and Engineering
          d. Philosophy
          e. Music
          f. Drama
          g. Politics
          h. Business
  C. Desire for Change
      How effective is this?
  D. Completion of Progress then possible along a given line, and hence turning to new lines

Securing copies of Lawrence B. Phillips's *The Dictionary of Biographical Reference* (1881), *Dictionary of American Biography* (1943), Herbert A. Giles's *A Chinese Biographical Dictionary* (1898), *The Dictionary of National Biography* (1882), *Larousse du XX Siècle* (1928–33), *Encyclopaedia Britannica* (14th edition, 1929), and *Nouvelle Biographie Génerale* (Paris, 1855), he proceeded to compile lists of many thousands of names of persons throughout space (the world) and time (approximately 800 B.C to the twentieth century). Individuals who had won eminence sufficient to warrant inclusion in these works were plotted in notebooks, arranged by decade, country (town or province), and occupation. Graphs were then to be made comparing the fluctuations in the number of famous men revealing oscillations between progress and stagnation. While this work was advancing with the aid of two assistants, Huntington proceeded to re-read Spengler, Wells, Toynbee, Caldwell, and Sorokin in order to make extensive notes concerning their work. By November of 1946 he could write:[37]

> . . . My chief news is that I am carrying on a rather large investigation of 100,000 persons who have distinguished themselves in history. My purpose is to classify and analyze these people in both space and time. I want to do something toward establishing the relation between geography and history on a much firmer statistical basis than has hitherto been attempted.

A heart attack in October, 1946, confined him to his room for several weeks, but by January of the following year he had returned to the work with energies unabated. In March (1947) he wrote to Henry and Evelyn Phelps-Brown:[38]

> . . . You may be interested to know that I am working away now quite steadily on a book which will complete "Mainsprings of Civilization." I am almost driven to despair, however, by the thought that I have to read so much. At a low reckoning there are a thousand books which I ought to read before trying to discuss the whole problem of civilization. At a high reckoning I shall not be able to read more than a score or two of them. If I try to read more I shall never finish my own book. It is a terrible thing to think how ignorant one is after seventy years of trying to learn something.

When death interrupted the study in October, 1947, only chapters one, three, and four were in typed form. Chapter two was in outline form, and several notebooks, clippings and note-cards had been amassed. Alas, the study had to die with the man. It robbed him of a sense of fulfillment, for he had wished to provide a full résumé of his life's thought in readily accessible form. It was the volume dealing with culture that Huntington especially wished to see published.

Perhaps this program of writing might have been completed had Huntington supported fewer causes, and undertaken less writing for fellow workers and publishers. For the Office of War Information Huntington wrote "German v. Nazis" (1945), and "One Thousand Years of Eugenics in Iceland" (1943); he allowed himself to be appointed an advisor to the Climatic Section in the Quartermaster Corps of the Army (1943–45); was President of the Connecticut Branch of the League of Nations Association (1941–45), and for a lesser time President of the Connecticut Branch of the United Nations Association; in 1942 accepted an advisory position within the National Association of Manufacturers, from which vantage point he could urge a spirit of international cooperation and a flight from isolationism at the conclusion of the war. For this group he wrote numerous confidential tracts which were discussed in committee, and from which emerged policy statements made known to the government. Of his work with this association he wrote to Professor A. Missenard of France:[39]

> The plan for a Trusteeship Council, which was finally adopted at San Francisco, was based primarily upon a memorandum which I prepared for the National Association of Manufacturers. This memorandum was adopted also by the United States Chamber of Commerce and by our two great labor organizations, the A.F.L. and the C.I.O. Thus it was presented at San Francisco, and with some modifications was adopted. Therefore, I feel that I had a real part in framing the present organization of the United Nations. I also helped in preparing the main memoranda upon which the statements of the Charter as to the Economic and Social Council were based.

In 1944, although himself a Republican, Huntington campaigned vigorously for the Democratic Party since they advocated a policy of internationalism. When the United Nations headquarters was to be established in the United States, the latter's State Department requested Huntington to submit a memorandum concerning the seat of that institution. Huntington actively opposed manifestations of hysteria. He opposed the work of the Dies Committee (1943), wrote to President Roosevelt of his outrage concerning the Earl Browder case (1944), was a relentless opponent of the Un-American Activities Committee (1946), and actively opposed the establishment of a postwar peace-time military conscription.

When Huntington invested his concern in a political cause he invariably wrote to not less than a dozen members of the Senate and the House of Representatives—to the same people who had requested advice, suggestions, pamphlets and manuscripts from him. Invariably his letters to the politicians were listened to, and on occasion read in whole or part before the Congress. Such a letter read *in toto* was his protestation against the Un-American Activities Committee. Huntington accepted invitations from Governor Baldwin of the State of Connecticut to serve on state-wide committees relating to United War and Community Funds and celebrations attending the 32nd Birthday of the Republic of China. He lectured frequently on the need for postwar international cooperation, to clubs and groups throughout New England. And additionally during the course of writing "Mainsprings" and its sequel "The Pace of History," Huntington wrote several articles, authored "The Quality of People," the first chapter in *America at War, A Geographical Analysis*,[40] prepared "The Influence of Geography and Climate Upon History" for inclusion in *Compass of the World*,[41] revised his chapter in *Our National Resources and Their Conservation*,[42] accepted a commission to write a "Dictionary of Economic Geography,"[43] and agreed to join with Van Valkenburg and Pauline Schwartz in writing "Geography in Human Affairs."[44] By August, 1946, 45 chapters and over 500 pages of manuscript had been written. It never was published.

When Griffith Taylor requested Huntington to write the introductory chapter to *Geography in the Twentieth Century* (1951), Huntington agreed to write on the philosophy of his geography. Realizing the size of his writing program, Huntington wrote to Secretary Noel Sargent of the National Association of Manufacturers on September 18, 1947,

I have come to the conclusion that I had better resign as a member of the Advisory Group. . . . My reason for resigning is not health, for I am now well enough to come, but the fact is that I have laid out plans for at least three books which I want to write before I die. . . .

Huntington died on October 17, 1947. Posthumously Mrs. Huntington offered Taylor the last piece her husband had written, "Geography and Aviation,"[45] which Taylor accepted in lieu of his friend's intended essay concerning his geographical philosophy.

CHAPTER XIV

The Geography of Ellsworth Huntington: Some Thoughts and Reflections

When Huntington arrived in Cambridge, September, 1901, he met William Morris Davis, then fifty-one years of age, at the height of his creativity, offering his variety of physiography to students who frequented the Harvard Yard. Part of that offering was an insistence that ontography was to supplement physiography in the erection of a total schema, which would constitute the discipline. Huntington's first page of notes taken as a student of Davis in Geology 6 (February 9, 1903) stated that much. Lake Goljeuk, the canyons of the Euphrates, the plains, the mountains, the physiographic drama of Asiatic Turkey, had excited Huntington's curiosity and had led him to Harvard, there to investigate the complexities of the physical environment. At Harvard he learned much of scientific method, witnessed scholarly procedures, and felt the intense excitement of scholarship about him. With Davis he attended scientific meetings, and with Davis ventured into the field. With Davis, Huntington travelled as assistant on the Pumpelly expedition in 1903, and while on that expedition gathered evidences which enabled him to advance the thesis of a uniform postglacial trend toward desiccation.[1] And it was Davis who made possible Huntington's 1905–1906 expedition to Asia with R. L. Barrett, resultant to which Huntington wrote *The Pulse of Asia* while resident in Cambridge, and while in frequent consultation with Davis. In 1905 Huntington felt that change had been uniform and in the direction of desiccation: in 1907 he enunciated the idea of climatic pulsations of varying magnitude within historic time, and concluded his book with a chapter analyzing the impact of climatic pulsations upon human affairs.[2] In dedicating his book to Davis "first of modern geographers," he was acknowledging his debt for help of an immediate type, and for the receipt of a professional point of view. He had become familiar with Davis's life history, and was especially impressed with the man's accomplishment in transforming " a mere mass of undigested facts into a well-developed science . . . the systematizing of the science of physiography." He recognized Davis's belief that younger men should systematize what was then regarded as the other half of the field—ontography, and wrote of these matters in "William Morris Davis, Geographer."[3] Frequently throughout his life Huntington stated that Davis had been the greatest scientist he had ever known; frequently he acknowledged that his work derived from his mentor's inspiration and viewpoint.

Clearly revealed in Huntington's earlier writings was the posture of an environmentalist; that is, he continually sought the effect of the environment upon the individual and human society. His assertions that the environment in particular instances led to individual action later won for him the appellation "environmental determinist," and all that such implied. Yet at the time such "determinism" was slowly winning its way with perfect respectability as reviews of *The Pulse of Asia*, and "The Roorbach Questionnaire" reveal. His quest for a definitive revelation of climatic pulsations took him through Asia, Europe, the United States, Central and South America, and Africa. *Palestine and Its Transformation* (1911), *The Climatic Factor as Illustrated in Arid America* (1914), followed *The Pulse of Asia* to form a triumvirate of books then without peer on the subject of postglacial climatic change. With "The Solar Hypothesis of Climatic Changes," and the companion volumes *Climatic Changes* and *Earth and Sun* Huntington fundamentally rested the case for climatic pulsation within historic time. He revisited the theme frequently, assumed it in much of what he wrote, and made formal summary of the matter in 1935 on the occasion of Hedin's seventieth birthday in "Climatic Pulsations." Meanwhile his bold scheme, imaginatively wrought, involving tree rings, lake levels, valley terraces, dunes, disappearing rivers, wilderness ruins and the whole apparatus of indices for climatic change, was applied to history; revealed was an ever-changing climatic milieu explaining nomadic migrations, the fortunes of kings, the downfall of empires, outbursts of intellectual advance, amidst a congeries of lesser matters concerning rhythms and the grape harvest in Sweden, chestnuts in Scotland, the olive at Paris, the design of the Roman toga, the freezing of the Rhine *et al.*

When Huntington wrote *The Pulse of Asia*, singularly few of his contemporaries subscribed to the thesis of climatic pulsations in historic time. When, in 1916, he sent a questionnaire on this matter to the members of the Association of American Geogra-

phers, to a list of geologists selected by Joseph Barrell, to the
Climatic Committee of the Ecological Society of America, and
to some meteorologists, the response was overwhelmingly in support of the pulsatory hypothesis.[4] The intellectual spectacle was
lauded, fêted, denied, damned, but it was not ignored.

Commencing in 1915 Huntington's published thought began
to assume a new direction; he began to study and attempt measurements of the effect of climatic conditions upon human efficiency. Measurement of the performance of thousands of factory
workers and students suggested to Huntington temperature
optima for the human; approximately 60–65°F outdoor temperature for physical efficiency and 40°F for mental activity.
Later, these figures were revised.[5] Huntington presented the
spectre that a very hot or a very cold or a monotonous climate
might impair release of the highest energies of the human race.
The thesis had serious import for all peoples living beyond the
confines of certain sectors of the humid middle latitudes. Law-
yers, businessmen, mayors, ambassadors, and countless others—
many from "the South"—derided; others dismissed the charge
as that of climatic determinism returning in a new guise. It
should be noted, however, that Huntington did not think climate all-determining. He conceded the vital rôle of culture and
heredity in the development and maintenance of civilization. Yet
he felt that the rôle of climate had not been rendered explicit
and was not properly understood. In view of his own special capacity for revealing the mechanics of the celestial apparatus it
is not surprising that he dwelt so considerably on climate as a
force in human affairs. In the preface to *Civilization and Climate* Huntington wrote, "When the volume was first planned, I
contemplated a discussion of all the factors and an attempt to
assign to each its proper weight." Yet he decided to analyze the
rôle of climate and its relationship to civilization, leaving the
discussion of the rôles of heredity and culture for later volumes.
Even so he did not omit the rôles of heredity and culture. Chapter two was devoted to an analysis of "Race or Place," and elsewhere one finds:[6]

> Even if our climatic ideas are correct, it will still be true that the
> ordinary events of the historical record are due to the differing
> traits of races, the force of economic pressure, the ambition of
> kings, the intrigues of statesmen, the zeal of religion, the jeal-

ousy of races, the rise of men of genius, the evolution of new political or social institutions, and other similar circumstances.

In any event Huntington only claimed that where civilization had risen to a high level, the climate appeared to have possessed the qualities which he had found to be most stimulating for human activity. He did not insist that the climate had caused the civilization. "This philosophy has been worked out with much richness of detail in . . . *Climate and Civilization* [*sic*], with which no student of Geography should remain unacquainted," wrote J. Russell Smith.[7] And of the same work economist Simon N. Patten wrote "I can frankly say that no book in a decade, and few new books in my whole career have at first reading influenced me so profoundly as this one."[8]

Analysis of nine million deaths in the United States, France, and Italy and their relation to temperature and humidity, and attention to a further fifty million deaths led Huntington to offer and define more precisely the ideal climate for the human race. His studies of the environmental circumstances surrounding death led him to lecture before plumbers and steamfitters, doctors and hospital groups, workingmen's groups and health leagues. His studies relating to climatic health were frequently published in plumbers' magazines and medical journals. He is probably the only American geographer to have been awarded a prize for published research by the National Anesthesia Research Society (1920). He was quite convinced that "the climate that the world most needs is one where the summer average is about 64°, and the winter average about 40°, and where a constant succession of storms brings frequent alternations of cold and heat, moisture and dryness, cloud and sun." The whole was summed up in *World-Power and Evolution*. Climate, health, business, and the erection and maintenance of civilization were closely examined horizontally through land surface and vertically through time. "Every important aspect of human knowledge must be considered in its relation to both space and time" he wrote in the preface to *World-Power and Evolution*, which again revealed his intellectual concern to provide an environmental basis for the historic record. Although he had written several articles on eugenics, that was his first book which stressed the importance of the matter. "We must give ten-fold or a hundred-fold greater weight to the great problem of eugenics." Of "training, heredity, and physical environment" he remarked "it is idle . . . to say that one is any more important than the others." And he stated bluntly of man,[9]

> He preserves the sick and weakly instead of letting them die; he permits an economic and social system which causes the people with greatest mental power to have the fewest children, while the stupid breed like rabbits. . . .

The book had been written during the years of World War I and the preface authored while Huntington was with the Military Intelligence Division in Washington, D.C. His faith in human nature, and in the inevitability of human progress, had been jarred. The enlightenment which he could offer mankind by providing analysis of the influence which the physical environment exerts and has exerted upon the human organism seemed remote. He began to think that a change in the composition of mankind was necessary if mankind were to avoid future war. He joined eugenic societies and held office in them, wrote what he frankly termed "propaganda tracts," studied U.S. immigration laws and gave advice to Congress on the matter, talked and lectured on the subject formally and informally. He studied the results of consanguineous marriage among the ancient Jews and Egyptians; the results of immigration and natural selection; the stimulating effect of atmospheric ozone; the optimal season of birth for people who later attained much; and he calculated that people with blond hair and blue eyes attained greater longevity than others under similar circumstances. He was especially concerned that the percentage of people from better families in the United States was decreasing, and that consequently the percentage of the poorer type of person (he often called them "stupid") was increasing. *The Character of Races* (1924), *The Builders of America* (1927), *Tomorrow's Children: The Goal of Eugenics* (1935), *After Three Centuries* (1935), and perhaps *Season of Birth* (1938) were Huntington's larger contributions to a field which, on the intellectual plane, he studied to wrestle with civilization's history, and which, on the contemporary plane, he studied because of his fear that the human stock of his own country was showing signs of degeneracy. This was the second great phase of his life inquiry.

Meanwhile, he was conscious of the need to study the rôle of culture in determining the route of civilization through time. Environment, heredity, and culture proved a difficult triumvirate with which to juggle, and while he turned his hand to the study of cultural manifestations repeatedly and with obvious interest, he never laid siege to the concept in quite the same way as he had his studies of environment and heredity. After completing *Mainsprings of Civilization* (1945) he gave himself unremittingly to the study of culture and its rôle in the cause of civilization, but death interrupted the labor.[10]

Huntington did contribute substantially to the geographer's apparatus. He was one of the first geographers in the United States to insist upon the worth of the isopleth, to investigate cycles effectively, to insist upon mathematical measurement rather than inaccurate generalization, and to use the correlation coefficient extensively. He authored the first substantial textbook concerning the principles of human geography in the United States; he provided four textbooks enabling the field of economic geography to take hold; and authored several other books dealing with the general principles of geography, the effects of climate, and the nature and causes of climatic change. His writing and his maps were extensively reproduced by fellow geographers. His books were used throughout the United States educational system, in high school, college, university, and graduate school, in departments of geography, sociology, economics, and anthropology. When Clark University initiated a one-year floating university which journeyed around the world, two of Huntington's books were used as texts (*Business Geography* and *Principles of Human Geography*). Several of his books were listed as distinguished by the American Library Association, the League of Nations Non-Partisan Association, and the Business Administration and Economics Group of the American Textbook Services. Superintendents, principals, and presidents requested and accepted his advice on the matter of textbook selection.

He was a founding member of the Association of American Geographers, had helped organize the New Haven meeting of 1912, had been elected its First Vice President for 1913, and President for 1923, and Councillor for 1924. He also served as reader of papers for the *Annals*. He delivered a total of eighteen papers before the group in the years 1904 to 1941, and in the first fifty years of Association history followed Mark S. W. Jefferson, S. S. Visher, Ray H. Whitbeck, Derwent S. Whittlesey, and Wallace W. Atwood in number of papers delivered at the annual meetings. He was one of the youngest men ever elected to the Presidency of the Association. During his Presidential year he made several efforts to improve the quality of the Association's *Annals*: he proposed payment for articles, annual prizes for the best articles submitted, grouping articles by subject matter into a separate number of the *Annals* and enlargement of the periodical. He urged a permanent secretary for the Association. He was adamant that the best men for it should be secured and retained. To that end he worked hard to have Richard E. Dodge retain office in the Association. Also during that Presidential year he selected the five-man "Committee on Geographic Provinces." He contributed more articles to *The Geographical Review* in the years 1902–1922 than did any other geographer, and remains second only to Mark Jefferson in the total number of papers published in that periodical.[11] He served for a time as an associate editor of the *Bulletin of the American Geographical Society* and *The Geographical Review* and wrote many reviews which were published in that periodical. He was a founding member of the advisory council of *Economic Geography*. He lectured to audiences of the American Geographical Society, the Geographical Society of Philadelphia, the Chicago Geographical Society, and the Harvard Travellers Club. His services were constantly requested by colleges and clubs. It is probable that he gave over seven hundred public addresses during his career. Aside from forty years' service to Yale he taught in summer schools at Chicago (1931), Clark (1932), Harvard (1940), and for the autumn semester at Chicago (1937). He advised many students concerning their careers and helped many graduate students with their dissertations.

Huntington remains the most prolific geographer in United States history as well as the most widely reviewed, and also the most widely read (by laymen, as well as by students). In the first two decades of the century, in the wake of Davis's statement, "the essential in geography is a relation between the elements of terrestrial environment and the items of organic response," Huntington's work was not attacked because he sought, or found, 'response.' He was charged with being too speculative, hurried, unscientific, and popular, but he could not be attacked for positing environmental determinism, when variants of that theme fairly dominated the mainstream of geography in the country.

During the 1920s, however, a noticeable shift in the nature of geography in the United States began to take place. Second-

and third-generation geographers descended from W. M. Davis began to emerge with their own point of view. Physiography was taught by separate departments of geology, or routinely offered when demanded by geography students. Microstudies in geography began to emerge in substantial numbers, and this at a time when Huntington was entering upon his prolonged study of heredity. Huntington was studying heredity as part of his scheme for analyzing the growth, rise, and decline of civilization: geographers assumed that Huntington was making of heredity another branch of the geographic inquiry. That geographers should study matters other than geography for extended periods of time had not occurred to the new generation. As the size of areas studied diminished, and as the studies became more detailed, so the prevailing point of view grew more distant from Huntington's viewpoint. During the thirties, what was probably the mainstream of geography in the United States slid past Huntington. Lucien Febvre's *A Geographical Introduction to History* (1925) and Carl Sauer's "The Morphology of Landscape," were only two of several publications to question the validity of geographical determinism. Almon E. Parkins's "The Geography of American Geographers," summarizing some thirty definitions of the field sent to him by leading geographers in 1930, '31, and '32, further cast doubt on the posture of determinism. Bowman's *Geography in Relation to the Social Sciences* (1932) largely ignored determinism and determinists, and Hartshorne's *The Nature of Geography* (1939) considered environmental determinism as an historic piece rather than as a stance with which living geographers had endowed themselves. The thirties had been a sober decade in United States geography, at the end of which the discipline had been given a direction and a locus. American geographers seemed to know what was acceptable and what was not, and geography departments and their seminars began to function with that knowledge. Probably the American university seminar system did more to remove "determinism" from the locus of professional respectability than the published works on that subject. What the seminars did not investigate so carefully were the writings of geographers themselves. The sweeping generalization had fallen from favor, though Taylor, Peattie, and Visher openly accepted the validity of, and even encouraged, inquiries of this scope. A reaction against all forms of determinism had set in and all forms of environmentalist thought were considered with suspicion. Doubtless this was in part due to the refinement through which the discipline was passing.

Huntington had not concerned himself with these niceties. A one-man department, already approximately sixty years of age, with a prearranged plan to span his life's allotment, he was not about to change radically his professional intellectual style. Besides, he did not have a particularly good opinion of most American geographers; he regarded them as rather mediocre and productive of little original thought.[12]

> . . . I may be too hard on my fellow geographers, but I feel that you can almost count on your fingers the ones who do any appreciable amount of really original thinking. They write good descriptions, but they are not using the kind of mentality which is evident in the discussion of principles by physicists, for example.

Since Huntington's opinion of his contemporaries was such, it was only with a practiced patience that he could silently endure detractors who opined that he had constructed a deterministic scheme in which climate was nearly all-determining. In his published work and in his correspondence Huntington insisted that civilization was the product of three forces: environment, heredity, and culture. He expressed this point of view in 1915 in the preface to *Civilization and Climate*. Nine years later, in *The Character of Races*, he wrote further of the need to study climate, heredity and culture in order to reveal the historic process. He stated that *The Character of Races*[13]

> is the logical companion of *Civilization and Climate*. Each illustrates a great principle which had generally been overlooked in the study of history. Neither pretends to be complete, for where a new subject is first presented the mere limitations of space, as well as the dictates of psychology, make it necessary to concentrate upon a single theme. For a complete, well-rounded view of history one must combine these two books with many others which discuss such matters as geographic location and natural resources; human inventions, discoveries, and ideas; the influence of men of genius; the economic forces that bind mankind so closely; the growth and pressure of population; and the interplays of war, religion, intrigue, and human ambition. Some day the progress of science will give us a scientific history in which all these factors, as well as the factors of climate and natural selection, are co-ordinated and given due weight.

In the preface to *The Human Habitat* (1927) Huntington wrote,[14] "Physical environment never compels man to do anything; the compulsion lies in his own nature. But the environment does say that some courses of conduct are permissible and others impossible." And in reviewing Ernest Barker's *National Character and the Factors in its Formation*, (1927) Huntington again revealed his sympathy with the 'possibilist' point of view:[15]

> In discussing physical environment Dr. Barker's main thesis is one which geographers are at last coming to recognize. The environment does not say to man you must do this or that. It merely says "here are the possibilities. Choose which you will. Or choose one now and another later." He might perhaps do well to go somewhat farther in pointing out that the environment limits the possibilities—only a few may prove profitable at a given stage of human progress. . . . Again and again he harks back to the idea that "man's choice determines his environment more than the environment determines his choice."

Six years later in *Economic and Social Geography* (1933) he reminded his readers that[16] "geographic environment merely offers opportunities to man. Man's own will determines which of the various opportunities he will accept, and how far he will go in using them."

Huntington thought that he had made his position clear from his writings, yet he had written so very much that his audience did not comprehend his scheme. He enjoyed legitimate criticism of his work; in fact he frequently sought a partner with whom he could exchange manuscript in the quest for criticism. He was delighted when someone offered him a new idea or improved one extant. And he was pleased to receive many hundreds of letters from readers of his books and articles, making suggestions for an improved revision. This type of criticism Huntington valued, but criticism based on an inaccurate reading of his work annoyed him, though it was an annoyance to which he became accustomed over the decades. Especially was he annoyed with the type of extended and careless criticism amounting to dismissal which Sorokin offered in *Contemporary Sociological Theories*. He was annoyed by inaccurate reporting of his addresses or publications in newspapers or magazines—an annoyance which he invariably suffered in silence. But if a review appeared in one of the professional periodicals misrepresenting his position, Huntington was very apt to make reply to both editor and author. Of one part of a review-essay by J.O.M. Broek concerning Huntington's *Principles of Economic Geography*, published in *The Geographical Review*, Huntington wrote:[17]

> . . . You conscientiously and in general correctly attempt to analyze my position, but you fail to find out what that position is. That is not surprising, for you cannot be expected to read everything I have written, nor can I be expected to put everything into every book, regardless of the subject. Nevertheless, it is unfortunate. Again and again I have reiterated the idea that the relation of the geographical environment to man changes as culture advances. I have applied this idea specifically to the Mediterranean problem in a paragraph on page 430 of *Principles of Economic Geography*, in several pages (507ff) of *Principles of Human Geography*, in a whole chapter of Europe, and in various other books. . . .

He levied the same criticism at E.G.R. Taylor following publication of her article, "Whither Geography? A Review of Recent Geographical Texts."[18]

> . . . Perhaps my worst sin is that I have published my theories in so many and such diverse books that very few people really understand my full theory of civilization. According to that theory, climate is only part of one of three great determiners of civilization. It is indeed the most important phase of geographical environment, but it is far from the only phase. And in addition to physical environment we have two other equally important fields to consider. One is biological inheritance as to which our knowledge is sadly deficient and the other is cultural inheritance . . .

He was immeasurably delighted when a reviewer recognized that he appreciated the rôle of heredity and culture in addition to that of environment. When Lester Klimm reviewed *The Geographic Factor* by Whitbeck and Thomas in the *Bulletin of the Geographical Society of Philadelphia*, he wrote:[19]

> . . . a complete reading of Huntington's works would leave a critical reader with a much truer picture of that author's breadth of outlook and realization of the total situation. Huntington can

hardly be accused of ascribing everything to climate when at least half of his work has dealt with the influence of selective migration which he saw, very early, strongly modified the climatic influence.

Huntington wrote to Klimm at once[20]

> . . . It is a great pleasure to find somebody who freely recognizes the fact that I devote as much time to other things as to climate. I have indeed been criticized by some people as ascribing everything to race and inheritance but they were persons who knew little or nothing about geography. My constant attempt is to strike an even balance between environment and heredity. Moreover, I repeatedly emphasize the fact that social and physical environment are coordinating factors whose effects are entirely mixed. Nevertheless, to my despair, I find any number of people quoting me as if I thought climate were the only factor in determining human progress.

Huntington had written and thought a great deal about the process of natural selection exerted by selective migrations throughout history. He published much on the theme, and in correspondence revealed that he considered the major weakness both of Frederick J. Turner and Halford J. Mackinder to be their failure to take into account this form of selection.[21] He was not a Lamarckian: "I certainly feel no assurance whatever that environment produces changes. It may select certain types for preservation, but that is quite a different matter. . . ."[22] He had grown up in an age which derived much from the concept of the unity of nature and Darwinian evolution; "he reasoned Darwinly."[23]

Huntington believed that an environment, not a locality, exerted influence upon man. In *The Pulse of Asia* and other of his earlier works Huntington reveals the thoroughgoing determinism of the day, based on little more than intelligent observation obtained from much travel, a determinism derived from impressions. In "The Geographer and History" Huntington criticized such sweeping generalization (including two quotations from his own writing in *The Pulse of Asia*):[24]

> In the first place they are too sweeping and parts of them are couched in the form of positive statements of facts, whereas they

are really theories to which many able scholars take exception.
In the second place, even if they are fundamentally true, they
give the impression that geographical influences are more direct
than is actually the case.

His Asiatic researches reveal that it was the psychic and subjective source of his being that perceived an environmental influence upon mankind. Huntington, too, was aware of this. Commencing with the measurement of factory performance, student
marks, and the like, Huntington objectively sought to measure
the influence of environment on human physiology. His studies
thenceforth were largely contributions to the emerging field of
physiological climatology, which is in itself an admission to a
form of determinism, but one based on careful measurement.
Huntington conceded that heredity and the cultural milieu
shared with climate a responsibility for movement in civilization.
Yet that part of his research dealing with climate seemed to attract most attention and was what first typed him. Huntington
had carefully considered the matter of the degree of influence
exerted by climate on human life and in so doing helped establish "physiological climatology" as a respected area of study. His
understanding of the man-milieu relationship went beyond the
summary language he used to describe that understanding. In
1932 he wrote to George Hubbard:[25]

> . . . I used to use the words "control" and "determine." Now
> my tendency is very strongly to say "permit" and "favor." I feel
> that what the environment does is mainly first to offer a choice
> of different conditions which man may utilize and then favor
> one type of activity rather than another. I think we need to ex-
> ercise a great deal of care in our statements and I realize that I
> have not been careful enough thus far.

He wrote to Van Valkenburg in 1934 distinguishing[26]

> between geographic responses and geographic determinism. No
> sane geographer can fail to believe in responses. When one gets
> out of breath in going up a hill, that is a geographic response,
> and so is the location of London. Miss Semple and Ratzel went
> to the extreme of making it appear that if a certain type of geo-
> graphic environment prevailed man was forced to live in a cer-
> tain way. American geographers, with their tendency to be

stampeded, have become afraid of the idea of determinism and some . . . fail to appreciate the difference between absolute determinism and what may be called voluntary responses.

Huntington did ponder some of the philosophical implications of his intellectual stance. In particular he queried the matter of process versus content in his published work, and again he pondered the matter of that final unfettered leap of the mind which leads intuition to assertion. These matters are revealed in correspondence with people sympathetic to his endeavor. In such a letter to Walter Pitkin—who had shown friendship to some at least of Huntington's thought in his *A Short Introduction to the History of Human Stupidity*—Huntington wrote,[27] "I often wonder about the relative value of stimulating by unproved ideas as compared with genuine discoveries which may not be sensational, but which are of permanent value. . . ." Huntington enjoyed his thought, and trod boldly where the less sure of the species may well have hesitated. He was not afraid to venture an hypothesis. It was his way of receiving criticism, and testing the worthiness of an idea. If the idea were wrong, criticism set him right quickly.

He was only incidentally interested in the business of defining geography. He was forever impatient to get on with doing it.[28] Yet he did have a fundamental idea as to what he believed was properly the core of the geographic inquiry. He expressed himself informally on the subject in a letter to C. R. Dryer in 1921:[29] "I still hold out pretty strongly that geography is the study of distribution, and that when we study a region the main thing is to know why a certain group of conditions are located in a certain region. The map is the thing." He never wavered from his belief that this was essentially at the heart of the geographical investigation. More formal renditions of his concept of the nature of geography may be found in "The Science of Geography,"[30] 1912, and in responses to the Parkins statement "The Nature of Geography,"[31] and the Report of the Committee on Research in the Earth Sciences dated April 1, 1939.[32] On numerous other occasions he penned parts of his belief as to what geography was for him, and in 1931 wrote "The Content of Modern Geography." The article was rejected by the editors of *The Geographical Review* and the *Annals of the Association of American Geographers*. It was never published. Gladys Wrigley felt that the matter needed more discussion prior to publi-

cation, and Derwent Whittlesey's advisors felt that the *Annals*
should publish the results of original field investigations. Huntington wrote:[33]

> . . . it seems to me that . . . geography is primarily the science
> which deals with the distribution of all sorts of phenomena upon
> the earth's surface, and with the reasons for this distribution. It
> answers the following questions concerning any of these phe-
> nomena: Where is it? What other phenomena accompany it?
> Why is it there? The geographer may be called upon to discuss
> anything from rocks and plants to machines and poetry. He does
> not explain how these things come into existence, nor how they
> behave. He merely finds out how the geographic surroundings
> —earth, air, water, plants, animals, and man's own activities—
> cause them to be more abundant and better developed in some
> regions than in others.

He essentially remained unpublished on this matured conception of the nature of geography, notwithstanding invitations
from the editor of *The Encyclopaedia Brittanica,* and *Survey
Volumes of the Social Sciences* to provide them with surveys of
recent developments in the field. Huntington refused them. He
much preferred investigating for himself, to writing of the work
of previous investigators. Frequently he would address an educational assemblage and talk for a while of his conception of
geography, but very often such talks became a forum for the
propagation of those branches of the field which he thought
needed further investigation. In correspondence with his contemporaries his appreciation of what was geographic occasionally emerged.

He had conceived the idea of writing a volume or volumes
on civilization during the early twenties—perhaps earlier—but
paused only long enough to scribe *The Pulse of Progress* which
summarized some of his more important thought to that time,
then lunged on until eventually *Mainsprings of Civilization* was
published in 1945. His dream of a team of collaborators formally at work on the project never did materialize. But by way
of correspondence he harnessed such a team to his cause, though
the various members of that team were unaware of the larger
context.

When Huntington wrote "Geography and History," a review-
article of T. Griffith Taylor's *Environment and Nation,* he again

insisted that "a rational understanding of history requires a good knowledge of the changing physical background upon which the historical events occur."[34] It prompted Preston E. James to urge Huntington to deliver a paper on the subject at the next meeting of the Association of American Geographers.[35] Huntington obliged with "Geography and History,"[36] presented before the Association in December, 1938, at Cambridge, Massachusetts, and subtly rearranged in *Mainsprings of Civilization*. Perhaps, in sum, the largest of his undertakings was the attempted provision of an environmental platform since postglacial time upon which man had acted out the drama of history. His efforts attracted the attention of historians in the United States; notable among those utilizing something of Huntington's work and viewpoint were Michael Rostovtzeff, Will Durant, James H. Breasted, James H. Robinson, and Harry E. Barnes.

Huntington roamed the earth in the wake of that early inspiration, enduring extremes of heat and cold, crossing plains, mountains, and rivers, and basins, travelling on camel, donkey, horse, pullman, auto, or ship. He was one of a very few American geographers of his time to have travelled North, Central and South America, Europe, Asia, Africa, and Australia. The experience was invaluable. Few indeed were the authors who could repudiate editorial invective in quite the same way.[37] "I can scarcely take seriously the remarks of a man . . . who says a camel cannot stand the cold although I myself have used camels where the thermometer fell to 17° below zero."

Authors wished to quote him, copy his maps, borrow his photographs; authors of books teaching English composition quoted his prose as a model of its kind.[38] Publishing houses urged him to give them an opportunity to publish his manuscripts, and would sign a contract merely on the basis of a letter from Huntington stating that he was going to write a book on such and such a subject. Editors consulted him concerning the validity of work which had been placed before them. He investigated vigorously and wrote amply, in the spirit of his time, at least until the mid 1920s. If favor from authority in American geography came to be less evident after 1930, that was because a new point of view and perhaps a new social structure had made itself apparent. Huntington continued his work in the manner of his grand design, continued through the Great Depression and the Second World War—imbued with the inevitability of human progress, inspired by the inner forces of religion, remem-

bering an earlier life of letter writing and fine conversation which
he continued into his later years in another age. He tired a little
of those people who put their head on one side, looked wise,
criticized loudly, and wrote little themselves. But he suffered
them quietly.

Many were the particular criticisms levelled against Huntington. He stood accused of attempting to consolidate some rather
weak positions by taking much for granted, adopting a position
of doubtful scientific validity, and rallying from it with a prose
style that invited comparison. That one may be taken in by guile
is not the fault of Huntington; the reader is at liberty to create
his own distance. But the audience which read much of Huntington's published work frequently did not have the intellectual
apparatus to discount what was doubtful, spun as it was in a web
of gossamered prose and scientific assumption. There were out-
right errors in his work on occasion, and in rather indiscrimi-
nately adopting secondary sources as authoritative, the history
which Huntington attempted to synthesize with his geography
was hardly adequate. When he sought to measure, he may have
quantified with an insufficient apparatus. In his dismissal of error
noted publicly, Huntington may have seemed cavalier. In *Climatic Changes* he had written, "Alpha Centauri was nearest the
sun at the climax of the last glacial epoch."[39] In fact the sentence should have read, "Alpha Centauri will be nearest the sun
some 28,000 years hence." Although Huntington had taken his
data from a misprinted Bulletin of the Lick Observatory, and
although he demonstrated that the error did not detract from the
results of his study, the matter was not readily forgotten.

In his earlier years he frequently sent an article to the editor
of a publication, then followed it with an unannounced revision
some weeks later. And sometimes he made drastic revision on
proof sheets. These habits must have been disconcerting to editors, and they reveal a certain impatience on his part to complete
a piece of work and begin another. And, too, there were those
occasions when he wrote something to please an editor because
at one time or another he had committed himself. Late in November, 1911, he wrote:[40]

> Wednesday I had no classes. Accordingly I cleared the decks for
> an article on the Arabian Desert and Human Character. I had
> half promised it for the Journal of Geography. . . . They wanted
> it on hand by December 1 at the latest. So I got to work and

hustled. I had had no time to touch it, or even think about it till Japan was off my hands. I had not time to think out any new thoughts; so I cribbed selections from Palestine, strung them together, and wrote around them. The article went into the mail that night smoking hot. I never wrote anything half so fast before, and I shall be curious to see whether it is good for anything when it gets cold.

He did go fact-gathering in support of his scheme, and frequently advanced only by making the most daring and speculative conjecture—the mind flinging itself beyond the facts, intuitively—*voilà*, solar system, space, time, stars, electronic discharge, sunspots, variability, pulsations, glaciation, and mutation.[41] Some accepted Huntington's premise that a notion no matter how established should be allowed life until proved false; others instantly derided. That, in some measure, was what made Huntington a colorful figure. One was for or against his procedure.

Yet one should constantly bear in mind that out of economic necessity Huntington wrote for two audiences. As research associate in geography at Yale he made his scientific contribution; as head of a household he wrote in popular vein for magazines and textbooks—with wide distribution. It is ironic to think that his remuneration for "The New Astrology," which straddled nine pages in *The New Century*, and which took him one morning to write, was in excess of that for the book *Earth and Sun* which—in some 300 pages—treated of the same matter in a much more thorough and scientific manner. He was obliged to make his living with his pen after 1915. His research associate post with professorial rank never provided more than a meagre percentage of the salary attaching to a Yale professorship. Continuously he was obliged to write what he called "pot-boilers" and endure what he termed "scullery work" (probably relating to correction of radio scripts) to meet the expenses of family life. That he succeeded in devoting such a large amount of his time to the higher undertaking is a tribute to the man as scientist.

There were some curious dualisms in Huntington's work which others noticed and perhaps noted as contradictions. Huntington's insistence on a hierarchy of innate competence, and consistent inquiry into the eugenic cause in the 1930s, was perhaps unfortunate. When he proposed on the eve of World War II that Caucasians with blond hair and blue eyes were possessed

of greater longevity than others, his utterance seemed peculiarly
non sequitur. When a colleague reviewed *Mainsprings of Civilization* six years after Huntington's death he wrote:[42]

> An overvaluation of certain alleged findings in this field could
> lead directly to Buchenwald and Dachau. Huntington clearly
> disassociated himself from such diabolical argument, but the un-
> aware reader may not be as discerning, and an initial warning
> sign is necessary.

His perpetual spoken and written concern that the poorer
families were multiplying at a faster rate than the superior families was a curious spectacle in a society insisting upon a political
equality, from which variety of equality all other equalities
seemed inferable. He analyzed the superiority of Puritan families, then wrote the history of the Huntington family, revealing
that the family was Puritan in its New World origin, had a constitution, an association, a hymn, and a prayer. Yet he supported
a local cooperative movement, was a long-time member of a local
teachers union, and on numerous occasions asserted that the economic system of the United States was "barbarous." When he
proclaimed that Newport, Rhode Island, offered a climatic environment which most nearly approximated the ideal in the
United States, skeptics felt that Huntington's ethnocentrism was
revealing itself.

Much indeed has been spoken and written of Huntington's
work. Commentary has been both laudatory and damning. In
fact, it is probably not too much to say that Huntington was the
most controversial figure in United States geography in the first
half of the twentieth century. Posthumously criticism of him has
mounted almost in proportion to the distance from the age
which the critics are criticizing, all of which well illustrates John
K. Wright's "Law of the disparagement of the past."[43] When the
Russian Y. G. Saushkin wrote of, ". . . . the late Ellsworth Huntington, whose work is not even taken seriously by the young
geographers," it was in the wake of a visit to the United States.[44]
When Thomas W. Freeman wrote *The Geographer's Craft*, he
selected Huntington as representative of geographic craftsman-
ship in North America;[45] in reviewing that book in *Economic
Geography* Andrew H. Clarke wrote:[46]

> . . . Indeed, in a gloomily humorous vein, an American reviewer
> is led to wonder if some, perhaps unconscious, anti-American

bias had not motivated the writer to choose the figure whom most contemporary American geographers might most avidly choose to forget rather than, say, William Morris Davis, Mark Jefferson, Ellen Churchill Semple, or Isaiah Bowman. . . .

Since, to the later twentieth century, Ellsworth Huntington has become an image of unscientific "scientism" and unscholarly historical generalization, the widespread circulation of whose writings may have delayed the progress of American geography for a generation, perhaps the most charitable thing to do is to try to ignore the fact that Freeman included him as "of interest for his attempt to study the totality of the influence of climate on man."

Huntington's critics have suggested that he ventured into fields other than his own, whereas development of a critical faculty with regard to his work might have been more productive. And, of course, his latter-day critics insisted that he was an environmental determinist, and that at a time when environmental determinism had fallen into disrepute owing in part to the blandishments of geography authors of high school texts. If he was a fellow traveller of the determinists, he was continually weighing, assaying, and reshaping his postulates—perhaps assessing too many value judgments, very likely producing too much too soon—yet nonetheless emerging with a new form of determinism, more moderate, supple, subtle, and versatile than anything which had come before—one might well add "or since." It never did receive a name.

Less well known are the feelings of scholars from different fields who were encouraged or inspired by the man and his works, only some of whose feelings are excerpted. In the year of his death (1943) Aurel Stein wrote to Huntington, "My combined archaeological and geographical interests make me realise fully the important service your investigations have rendered both to historical and geographical research."[47] Carl Sauer later wrote, "Perhaps I would have become interested in the larger reaches of human time anyway but I must acknowledge that Huntington gave me a push at the right time."[48] Sir Archibald Grenfell Price opined that Huntington "deeply influenced my professional life and work, and at the same time, showed me how much a really great and really humble scientist could effect."[49] Stephen B. Jones, one-time colleague of Huntington at Yale, reflects, "If I had to pick the 'most unforgettable character' from among my acquaintances, past and present, my choice might very well be Ellsworth Huntington. He was certainly the scholar and gentleman, and was both dynamic and patient."[50] Nathaniel Weyl reckons Huntington to be "one of the most neglected innovating minds in the American social sciences."[51]

Sympathetic though critical evaluation of some of Huntington's work is available in, "A Critique of the Climatic Hypothesis of Ellsworth Huntington," (1931), by Stanley Stevens;[52] "Huntington and Bowman: A Comparative Study of Their Geographic Concepts," (1952) by James M. Smythe;[53] "An Evaluation of Some Geographical Concepts of Ellsworth Huntington," (1963) by Clark A. Akatiff;[54] and especially in "Huntington and His Critics: the Influence of Climate on Civilization," (1968) by John E. Chappell, Jr.[55] Subsequently Chappell has written other pieces in an attempt to encourage a serious reconsideration of Huntington's thought.[56] And O.H.K. Spate appreciatively perceived Huntington's endeavour in "Toynbee and Huntington: A Study in Determinism."[57]

Numerous authors have written books that have acknowledged the worth of at least some of Huntington's work. These include in particular *The Environmental Basis of Society* (1925) by Franklin Thomas; *Fresh Air and Ventilation* (1925) by C-E.A. Winslow; *Climate Through the Ages* (1926) by C.E.P. Brooks; *Geography of American Notables* (1928) and *Scientists Starred, 1903–1943 in American Men of Science* (1947) by Stephen S. Visher; *Climate Makes the Man* (1942) and *World Power and Shifting Climates* (1963) by Clarence A. Mills; *Climate and the Energy of Nations* (1942) by Sydney Markham; and *Temperature and Human Life* (1949) by C-E.A. Winslow and Lovic P. Herrington.

Reviews of his books were published in many countries. Many an eminent affixed his name to a critically appreciative review of a Huntington-authored book. Such reviews by Carl L. Becker, George G. Chisholm, Douglas W. Johnson, Hugh Robert Mill, Simon N. Patten, Sir Napier Shaw, and Ray H. Whitbeck are worthy of study as a subject in themselves. They offered no sustained conceptual opposition to Huntington's work, only a congeries of suggestions for improvement. It was not until after Huntington's death that abrupt dismissal of the man's thought became vogue.

Huntington enjoyed his geography. He knew what he wanted to do and had a very well-defined sense of problem. He rallied evidence to his point of view and built only with that evidence.

Rarely did he produce evidence which ran contrary to the point for which he strove. Huntington adopted the method of the adversary principle. In his published work he did not weigh the pro and con, but took the pro and left the con to his critics, inviting them to build large principles which might then be opposed. It was an important part of Huntington's method. And he refused to be intimidated by those who inquired, "Is this geography?" If he seemed to some rather subjective, to be writing with an air of certainty about matters hardly provable, that was because he was a pioneer. His own form of art in perception he mixed with scientific prosecution, to become a veritable pied piper; and a very large audience paid to revel with him through his pages. He was an invaluable irritant to many geographers. To others he gave a helpful stimulus. The spectacle was far too large to be ignored—an isolated geographer at the full pitch of his bent, subject to ever increasing criticism, building a scheme revealing the place of man twixt the cosmos and microcosmos. The performance was little short of drama, and there were those in the audience who applauded and demanded curtain calls. In fact the legacy of the man is so pervasive that one has to allow that in his lifetime he became part of that moving force which is the culture of a nation. Probably no twentieth-century American geographer stood forward so prominently as the representative of the aggregate knowledge of his age.

His work flowered into a systematic expression which warrants pursuit with as much perspicuity as is available to the task. His was an innate active scholarship, which responded with growth to every new experience which came to him. Inevitably this meant changes of emphasis in his thought, and in the resultant pattern which he committed to paper. One can concede that these changes in his thought were all a part of growth in his quest; or one can regard them as contradictions. To a degree one derives from Huntington in proportion to the sympathy one extends to his undertaking. If he was outside the mainstream of American geography for his last twenty years, he compelled at least one generation of geographers to search their hearts lest the truth be not in them. Whether a mainstream existed or not, or whether most American geographers were working toward disparate ends matters little. In the one case he was a dissenter, and in the other, a minority opinion. That he continued to function as of old, and consummate the work of an earlier period with a monumental overview of civilization is performance indeed.

NOTES

Notes to Chapter I

1. *See* The Huntington Genealogical Memoir 1633–1915.
2. *See* "My Brother Ellsworth," an essay written by Henry Strong Huntington, Jr., Spring, 1967.
3. *See* "My Brother Ellsworth," an essay written by Ruth H. Fletcher, Spring, 1967.
4. A. K. Teele to Richard Cobb, March 15, 1900.
5. Reprinted in *The Beloit Daily Free Press*, Vol. XV, No. 298, p. 1.
6. From Beloit College Report Cards sent to Ellsworth Huntington.
7. Father to Ellsworth Huntington, October 17, 1893.
8. Father to Ellsworth Huntington, October 17, 1893.
9. Father to Ellsworth Huntington, December 24, 1894.
10. Mother to Ellsworth Huntington, April 4, 1897.
11. Mother to Ellsworth Huntington, April 24, 1897.
12. Mother to Ellsworth Huntington, December 8, 1895.
13. Ellsworth Huntington to Father, February 19, 1917.
14. Father to Ellsworth Huntington, March 26, 1895.
15. Professor G. L. Collie to Richard Cobb, April 16, 1900.
16. G. F. Hanson (State Geologist and Director) to G. J. Martin, June 3, 1966.
17. *Transactions of the Wisconsin Academy of Sciences*, Vol. 11, pp. 249–254, 1897.
18. Ellsworth Huntington to Father, February 11, 1897.
19. Father to Ellsworth Huntington, February 17, 1897.
20. Professor G. L. Collie to Richard Cobb, April 16, 1900.
21. *The Congregationalist*, October 14, 1897, p. 528.
22. *See* Diary I, of Ellsworth Huntington, September 16, 1897–December 28, 1897.

Notes to Chapter II

1. Harpoot has been variously spelled, e.g., Harput, Charpoot, Kharput. *See* *Appendix C . . . A note on the spelling of some place names.*
2. Notebook A. (September 16, 1897–December 28, 1897), pp. 31, 32. For the account of Huntington's journey to Harpoot see Notebook A, pp. 1–120.
3. *The Round Table*, Vol. XLIV, (February 18, 1898, No. 19, pp. 184–186. Vol. XLIV, February 25, 1898, No. 20, pp. 193–196.)
4. *The Missionary Herald*, Vol. XCIX, January, 1903, No. 1, "The Growth, Influence and Needs of Euphrates College," by M. A. Melcon, pp. 13–15.
5. Notebook C, (March 18, 1898–October 29, 1899) pp. 68–69.
6. Notebook D, pp. 10–15.
7. Notebook E, p. 11.
8. Notebook D, "The Geology of the Harpoot Group of Mountains in Asiatic Turkey," p. 12.
9. Notebook D, "The Geology of the Harpoot Group of Mountains in Asiatic Turkey," pp. 11–12.

10. Notebook C, inserted page, numbered 6.

11. Notebook C, p. 8.

12. Notebook C, inserted page, numbered 8.

13. Notebook C, inserted page, numbered 4.

14. Notebook C, p. 36.

15. Notebook C, p. 192.

16. "Electric Phenomena in the Euphrates Valley," *Monthly Weather Review*, Vol. 28, No. 7, p. 286 and 290, July 1900.

17. "The Climate of Harput Turkey," *Monthly Weather Review*, Vol. 29, No. 6, pp. 250–253, June, 1901.

18. Notebook E, p. 13.

19. C. F. Lehmann to Richard Cobb, Corresponding Secretary of Harvard University, March 25, 1900.

20. Ellsworth Huntington to G. C. Collie, October 24, 1899, (copy of the letter; Notebook C, pp. 175–200, see p. 177).

21. Ellsworth Huntington to G. C. Collie, October 24, 1899, (copy of the letter; Notebook C, pp. 175–200, see pp. 178–179).

22. "Through the Grand Canyon of the Euphrates on a Raft," p. 2, unpublished essay by Ellsworth Huntington.

23. Notebook, (February 12, 1900–August 13, 1901) p. 116.

24. Ellsworth Huntington to Henry S. Huntington, April 18, 1900.

25. T. H. Norton to F. W. Putnam, February 1, 1901.

26. Ellsworth Huntington to Theresa Gaytes, June 19, 1901.

27. Notebook, (August 18, 1901–August 29, 1902) p. 50.

28. Notebook, (August 18, 1901–August 29, 1902) p. 50.

29. *Verhandlungen der Berliner Anthropologischen Gesellschaft*, February 17, 1900, pp. 140–152; November 17, 1900, pp. 572–575; November 16, 1901, pp. 173–209.

30. Notebook (August 18, 1901–August 29, 1902), p. 75.

Notes to Chapter III

1. Graduate School, Record of Ellsworth Huntington, Office of the Registrar, Harvard University.

2. Ellsworth Huntington to Mother, December 8, 1901.

3. Notebook submitted to J. B. Woodworth, Geology 8, May 12, 1902, "A Sketch of the physiography and geology of Asia Minor as a whole and of the Harpoot Mountains," pp. 1–52; "Asia Minor—bibliography and analysis of," pp. 53–82.

4. Unpublished 8,000-word essay.

5. *The Geographical Journal*, Vol. XX, No. 2, August 1902, pp. 175–200.

6. *Bulletin of the American Geographical Society*, Vol. 34, October and December 1902, pp. 301–310, 384–393.

7. Ellsworth Huntington to Mother, December 8, 1901.

8. F. B. Wright to Ellsworth Huntington, January 11, 1902.

9. *Records of the Past*, Vol. I, Part VI, June 1902, pp. 163–171.

10. *Records of the Past*, Vol. II, Part V, May, 1903, pp. 131–140.

11. *Proceedings of the American Association for the Advancement of Science,* pp. 422–423, 1902.

12. "Far from the Track in Utah," unpublished article, 10,000 words.

13. *Journal of Geology,* Vol. XI, 1903, pp. 46–63.

14. *Bulletin of the Museum of Comparative Zoology at Harvard College,* Vol. XLII; Geological Series, Vol. VI, No. 5, February 1904, pp. 199–259.

15. W. M. Davis to Ellsworth Huntington, February 17, 1904.

16. A Mormon Summer, an unpublished article, p. 2.

17. *Explorations in Turkestan with an account of the Basin of Eastern Persia and Sistan.* Carnegie Institution of Washington Publication, No. 26, April, 1905, p. 3.

18. *My Reminiscences,* Raphael Pumpelly, Vol. II, Henry Holt and Company, 1918, pp. 698–700.

19. James Barton to Richard Cobb, Corresponding Secretary, Harvard University, March 1, 1900.

20. Thomas Norton to Ellsworth Huntington, September 30, 1902.

21. Diary 1903B, (April 18, 1903–June 22, 1903), pp. 46–47.

22. Diary 1903B, pp. 57–58.

23. Diary 1903B, p. 68.

24. Diary 1903B, p. 62.

25. Diary 1903B, p. 73.

26. Diary 1903B, p. 77.

27. Diary 1903B, pp. 111–115.

28. Diary 1903B, p. 116.

29. Diary 1903C, (June 1903–August 19, 1903) p. 40.

30. "With a Minbashi in Turkestan," *Appalachia,* Vol. XI, No. 1, 1905, pp. 17–27.

31. Diary 1903C, pp. 101–102.

32. Diary 1903C, p. 111.

33. Diary 1903C, p. 145.

34. Diary 1903F, (August 19, 1903–September 26, 1903) pp. 9–10.

35. Diary 1903F, p. 51.

36. *Petermanns Mitteilungen aus Justus Perthes Geographischer Anstalt* 1900, Nr. 131, XXXVIII, pp. 1–378.

37. Diary 1903F, p. 85.

38. Diary 1903F, p. 79.

39. *Principles of Human Geography,* 5th edition, 1940 (John Wiley and Sons), Chapter 2, "An Example of Human Geography," pp. 16–26.

40. Diary 1903F, pp. 77–78.

41. *Explorations in Turkestan with an account of the Basin of Eastern Persia and Sistan,* Carnegie Institution, 1905, 324 pages.

42. *Bulletin of the American Geographical Society,* Vol. 36, 1904, pp. 217–220.

43. W. M. Davis to Ellsworth Huntington, March 10, 1904.

44. Unpublished article.

45. Diary 1903H (November 23, 1903–January 7, 1904), p. 74–75.

46. W. M. Davis to Ellsworth Huntington, February 17, 1904.

47. Diary 1903H, pp. 113–114.

48. *Asia: A Geography Reader*, 1912, Rand McNally Company, Chapter X, "The Waterless Land of Persia," pp. 97–111.

49. *Bulletin of the American Geographical Society*, Vol. 37, No. 5, 1905, pp. 271–281.

50. *Explorations in Turkestan*, Carnegie Institution, 1905, p. 315.

51. Notes by Ellsworth Huntington, Yale University archives.

52. *Explorations in Turkestan . . . Expedition of 1904*, edited by Raphael Pumpelly, Vol. 1, pp. 217–232.

Notes to Chapter IV

1. Robert LeMoyne Barrett, *Harvard College Class of 1898 Quindecennial Report*, June, 1913, p. 21. See also: "Robert LeMoyne Barrett, 1871–1969; Last of the Founding Members of the Association of American Geographers" by G. J. Martin. *The Professional Geographer*, February 1972, Vol. XXIV, No. 1, pp. 29–31.

2. *Bulletin of the American Geographical Society*, January 1905, Vol. 37, No. 1, p. 49. For a similar statement of purpose see: *The Geographical Journal*, March 1905, Vol. XXV, No. 3, p. 327.

3. Journal, 1905, pp. 4–5, personal papers of Ellsworth Huntington.

4. The book is inscribed: "December 31, 1904 With the best wishes for a successful journey and a safe return. Charles R. Lanman"

5. Journal, 1905, p. 36, personal papers of Ellsworth Huntington.

6. "The Value of Kashmir," *Bulletin of the American Geographical Society*, 1906, Vol. 38, No. 11, pp. 657–682.

7. *Journal of Geology*, 1906, Vol. 14, No. 7, pp. 599–617.

8. *The Geographical Journal*, April, 1907, Vol. XXIX, No. 4, pp. 456–457.

9. Journal, 1905, pp. 158–159, personal papers of Ellsworth Huntington.

10. Journal, 1905, p. 163, personal papers of Ellsworth Huntington.

11. Journal, 1905, p. 274, personal papers of Ellsworth Huntington.

12. "Mr. Barrett and Mr. Ellsworth Huntington in Central Asia," *The Geographical Journal*, February 1906, Vol. XXVII, No. 2, pp. 177–179.

13. *Servant of Sahibs*, by Ghulam Rassul Galwan, W. Heffer & Sons Ltd., Cambridge, England, 1923 (reprinted 1924), 282 pages.

14. "Changes of Climate and History." Unpublished paper delivered before the Association of American Geographers, 1906.

15. *The Geographical Journal*, October 1906, Vol. XXVIII, No. 4, pp. 352–367.

16. *Bulletin of the American Geographical Society*, 1906, Vol. 38, No. 12, pp. 764–765.

17. The paper was not listed in the *Annals of the Association of American Geographers*. See abstracts of program, 1906.

18. "The Border Belts of the Tarim Basin," *Bulletin of the American Geographical Society*, 1906, Vol. 38, No. 2, pp. 91–96.

19. Journal, 1906, p. 404, personal papers of Ellsworth Huntington.

20. *Bulletin of the American Geographical Society*, 1907, Vol. 39, No. 2, pp. 65–77.

21. *Bulletin of the American Geographical Society*, 1907, Vol. 39, No. 3, pp. 137–146.

22. *The Geographical Journal*, June 1907, Vol. XXIX, No. 6, p. 674.

23. Journal, 1906, p. 461, personal papers of Ellsworth Huntington.

24. See also: *Bulletin of the American Geographical Society*, 1906, Vol. 38, No. 4, p. 236.

25. J. S. Keltie to Ellsworth Huntington, January 4, 1906. "It is quite evident that your researches will be a very valuable addition to the general work of Sven Hedin. Hedin has, no doubt, done excellent work in clearing the way for more detailed investigation, and your observations on what you call physiography, and what I call Physical Geography of the great Plateau are most suggestive."

26. *The Times*, January 6, 1906, p. 8.

27. *The Geographical Journal*, June, 1906, Vol. XXVII, No. 6, pp. 627–628.

28. Address to the Royal Geographical Society, 1906. *The Geographical Journal*, July 1906, Vol. XXVIII, No. 1, pp. 1–7.

29. W. M. Davis to Ellsworth Huntington, April 4, 1906.

30. W. M. Davis to Ellsworth Huntington, April 14, 1906.

31. *Bulletin of the American Geographical Society*, 1907, Vol. 39, No. 5, pp. 268–272.

32. Ellsworth Huntington to J. E. Wolff, May 21, 1906, Harvard University Archives.

33. *The Pulse of Asia*, Houghton Mifflin Company, Boston, November, 1907, p. 415.

34. W. M. Davis to Ellsworth Huntington, December 23, 1906.

35. Change of Climate and History (editorial correspondence), *The Christian Work and Evangelist*, January 12, 1907, Vol. 82, p. 45.

36. H. E. Gregory to W. M. Davis, January 23, 1907.

37. W. M. Davis to Ellsworth Huntington, January 25, 1907.

38. No record of the thesis exists in the Harvard University Archives.

39. *Bulletin of the Geological Society of America*, October, 1907, Vol. 18, pp. 351–388.

40. Minutes—the Division of Geology, Harvard University, Dec. 21, 1903–Dec. 7, 1916, pp. 119, 124 and 125.

41. Robert DeC. Ward to Ellsworth Huntington, March 18, 1908.

42. The contract was established April, 1907.

43. W. M. Davis to Ellsworth Huntington, May 26, 1907.

44. H. E. Gregory to Ellsworth Huntington, June 3, 1907.

45. November, 1907.

46. *The Pulse of Asia*, p. 359.

47. W. M. Davis, to Ellsworth Huntington, November 14, 1907.

48. D. W. Johnson to Ellsworth Huntington, January 11, 1908.

49. *Bulletin of the American Geographical Society*, 1908, Vol. 40, No. 4, pp. 252–254.

50. *The Pulse of Asia*, Houghton Mifflin Company, 1919.

Notes to Chapter V

1. "Yale University, Department of Geology, History of Department, 1802–1915," compiled by H. E. Gregory, p. 164–165.

2. "Yale University, Department of Geology, History of Department, 1802–1915," compiled by H. E. Gregory, p. 167.

3. Schuchert, C., "Joseph Barrell, 1869–1919," *National Academy of Sciences, Biographical Memoirs*, 12:9, 1929.

Members of the Geology Department, Yale University, 1907: Barrell, Bowman, Dana, Eaton, Ford, Gregory, Huntington, Irving, Lull, Matthewson, Pirsson, Robinson, Schuchert, Ward. (Hiram Bingham was added to the faculty in December, 1907.)

4. H. E. Gregory, A. G. Keller and A. L. Bishop: *Physical and Commercial Geography*, Ginn and Co., 1910.

5. A. G. Keller and A. L. Bishop: *Commercial and Industrial Geography*, Ginn and Co., 1912.

6. A. Heilprin, 1907: Mark Jefferson, 1916: H. E. Gregory, 1920: E. Huntington, 1923: M. Campbell, 1927: I. Bowman, 1931.

7. Letter, E. Huntington—John Phelan, March 8, 1926.

8. Letter, I. Bowman—M. Jefferson (undated. Written on train en route to Chicago, almost certainly 1908.)

9. "Professor Penck's Lectures," *Bulletin of the American Geographical Society*, Vol. 50, No. 11, 1908, p. 687. Professor Penck of the University of Berlin began his course of lectures in the Peabody Museum of Natural History, Yale University on October 13. The subject of the ten lectures was Problems of Glacial Geology: 1. Glaciers and Climate   2. Glaciers and Water   3. Glaciers and Moraines   4. Older Moraines and Glaciers of the Great Ice Age   5. Climate of the Ice Age   6. Different Glacial Systems   7. Interglacial Times   8. Chronology of The Great Ice Age   9. Antiquity of Man   10. Glacial Earth Sculpture. "The Under Side of Faculty Life," *Yale News*, Vol. XXXII, No. 36, Tuesday, November 3, 1908, p. 1.

10. *Bulletin of Yale University*, Second Series, No. 7, June, 1906, President's Report, p. 75.

11. Yale University Catalogue 1907–1908, pp. 176–178.

    A1. *Physical and Commercial Geography* (This is also the A course in Anthropology.)

        Professor Gregory, Dr. Bishop, Mr. Bowman, Mr. Huntington, Mr. Boggs, Mr. Beck, and Mr. H. P. Fairchild.

    The physical features of the land; ocean; climate; the natural distributions of flora, fauna, minerals, etc.; the conditions of human life as affected by natural environment.

    B7. *Geography of Asia* Mr. Huntington

    The regional geography of the Nearer East, India, and Central Asia; types of physical environment in relation to types of human activity; the life relationships of the physiography of Asia. Lectures, maps, and library work.

    C7. *Geographic Controls in History* Mr. Bowman and Mr. Huntington
The geographic elements of man's environment as a factor in history, individual study of the geographic conditions affecting the history of a limited region in America or in Asia.

Huntington also participated in "Selected Studies in Language, Literature, History and the Natural and Social Sciences."

12. *Yale University Catalogue*, 1907–1908, p. 246.

13. "The Present Trend of Geography in the United States," R. H. Whitbeck, *The Geographical Journal*, Vol. XXXV, No. 4, April, 1910, pp. 419–425.

14. E. J. Dimock—G. J. Martin, March 12, 1969.

15. Henry W. Hobson—G. J. Martin, February 6, 1969.

16. Alexander W. Harbison—G. J. Martin, February 18, 1969.

17. *See* Appendix D.

18. W. M. Davis—E. Huntington, November 5, 1908.

19. E. Huntington—application for Ph.D. degree. Yale Archives (Graduate School, undated.)

20. E. Huntington papers deposited in the Sterling Library, Yale University.

21. J. Barrell, Administrative Committee, Yale Graduate School, May 28, 1909.

22. C. Schuchert to A. W. Philips, Dean, Graduate School, Yale University, May 18, 1909.

23. *See* the Hadley and Angel correspondence files, Yale University Archives.

24. H. E. Gregory, *The '96 Half-way Book*, by Clarence Day, Jr., Class Secretary, Yale College, New Haven, 1915, p. 153.

25. H. S. Canby, *Alma Mater: The Gothic Age of The American College*, 1936, G. W. Pierson, Volume One of *Yale: College and University 1871–1937*, 1952.

26. E. Huntington to George Huntington, October 27, 1907.

27. E. Huntington to W. M. Davis, October 28, 1907.

28. W. M. Davis to E. Huntington, November 2, 1907.

29. George W. Pierson, Vol. I, *Yale: College and University 1871–1937*, p. 295.

30. L. Bacon, *Semi-Centennial: Some of the Life and Part of the Opinions of Leonard Bacon*, 1939, pp. 32–33.

31. I. Bowman, *The Journal of Geography*, Vol. VII, No. 3, November, 1908, pp. 59–61.

32. H. S. Canby, *Alma Mater: The Gothic Age of the American College*, p. 161.

33. His first major address by invitation while a faculty member at Yale was before the American Geographical Society November 26, 1907. Huntington addressed the Society on "A Journey Across the Himalaya Mountains in the Unexplored Salt Desert of Lop." *Bulletin of the American Geographical Society*, Vol. XXXIX, No. 9, 1907, pp. 751–752: He addressed the National Geographic Society January 17, 1908; "Medieval Tales of the Lop Basin in Central Asia:" and he addressed the Philadelphia Geographical Society February 3, 1909; "A Raft Trip Down the Euphrates River."

34. R. S. Woodward to E. S. Dana, November 16, 1912.

35. E. Brückner to E. S. Dana, November 26, 1912.

36. A. Penck to E. S. Dana, November 26, 1912.

37. E. S. Dana to Hanns Oertel, December 30, 1912.

38. E. Huntington to President A. T. Hadley, October 22, 1914.

Notes to Chapter VI

1. *Monthly Weather Review*, Vol. 36, Part I, November, 1908, pp. 359–364; Part II, Summary 1908, pp. 446–450.

2. Isaiah Bowman, "Geographic Relations in Chile and Bolivia," *Annals of the Association of American Geographers*, Vol. 1, 1911, p. 105.

3. *The Geographical Journal*, Vol. XXXIII, No. 3, March, 1909, pp. 267–278.

4. *Annals of the Association of American Geographers*, Vol. 1, 1911, p. 113.

5. W. M. Davis to E. Huntington, April 24, 1908.

6. *Bulletin of the American Geographical Society*, Vol. 40, No. 9, 1908, pp. 513–522.

7. *History of the Class of 1909*, Yale College, edited by Harold P. Stokes, Vol. 1, Yale University, 1909, p. 162.

8. E. Huntington to T. Wells, November 21, 1908. T. Wells to E. Huntington, November 28, 1908.

9. "Dr. Ellsworth Huntington Returns to Asia," *Bulletin of the American Geographical Society*, Vol. 41, No. 2, 1909, p. 102.

10. *National Geographic Magazine*, Vol. 21, September, 1910, pp. 761–775.

11. E. Huntington to J. S. Keltie, March 8, 1910.

12. E. Huntington to Ruth Huntington, January 3, 1908.

13. *Who's Who in America*, Vol. VII, 1912–1913, p. 2336.

14. R. S. Woodward to E. Huntington, April 16, 1908.

15. R. S. Woodward to E. Huntington, January 5, 1910.

16. "The First Dendrochronologist," Robert F. Heizer, *American Antiquity*, XXII, 2, 1956, pp. 186–188.

17. *Carnegie Institution of Washington, Yearbook* No. 9, 1910, pp. 57–58.

18. *Bulletin of the American Geographical Society*, Vol. 42, September, 1910, pp. 641–661.

19. *The Geographical Journal*, Vol. XXXVI, No. 6, December, 1910, p. 732.

20. R. S. Woodward to E. Huntington, October 8, 1910.

21. D. T. Macdougal to E. Huntington, September 3, 1910.

22. E. Huntington to R. S. Woodward, February 21, 1911.

23. "The Secret of the Big Trees," by Ellsworth Huntington, 1913, p. 10.

24. *Monthly Weather Review*, Vol. 37, No. 6, June, 1909, pp. 225–237.

25. "The Secret of the Big Trees," by Ellsworth Huntington, Department of Interior Publication, 1913, p. 14.

26. *The Geographical Journal*, Vol. XL, No. 3, September, 1912, pp. 264–280 and pp. 392–411.

27. *Annual Report Smithsonian Institution*, 1912, pp. 383–412.

28. E. Huntington to W. M. Davis, May 8, 1912.

29. E. Huntington to W. M. Davis, November 14, 1911.

30. C. J. Kullmer to E. Huntington, September 28, 1910.

31. C. J. Kullmer to E. Huntington, January 30, 1911.

32. C. J. Kullmer to E. Huntington, February 6, 1911.

33. E. Huntington to C. J. Kullmer, October 24, 1911.

34. E. Huntington to C. J. Kullmer, September 29, 1911.

35. E. Huntington to C. J. Kullmer, October 24, 1911.

36. *Annals of the Association of American Geographers*, Vol. 2, 1912, p. 115.

37. *Annals of the Association of American Geographers*, Vol. 2, 1912, p. 116.

38. *Annals of the Association of American Geographers*, Vol. 2, 1912, p. 115.

39. E. Huntington to R. S. Woodward, April 23, 1912.

40. E. Huntington to C. J. Kullmer, April 26, 1912.

41. E. Huntington to W. H. Hobbs, April 23, 1912.

42. *Bulletin of the American Geographical Society*, November, 1912, Vol. 44, No. 11, pp. 801–822.

43. *Annals of the Association of American Geographers*, Vol. 3, 1913, pp. 115–116.

44. *Bulletin of the American Geographical Society*, January, 1913, Part 1, Vol. 45, 1913, No. 1, pp. 1–12; Part II, Vol. 45, 1913, No. 2, pp. 107–116.

45. *The Geographical Journal*, Vol. XLI, No. 6, June, 1913, pp. 588–589.

46. *Bulletin of the American Geographical Society*, Vol. 43, No. 9, 1911, pp. 641–659.

47. *Characteristics of Existing Glaciers*, The Macmillan Company, New York, 1911, 301 pages.

48. *Bulletin of the Geological Society of America*, Vol. 24, December 26, 1913, p. 687.

49. E. Huntington to Colonel H. D. Borup, October 11, 1912. The Crocker Land Expedition was postponed in the summer of 1913 when the 27-year-old son of Col. Borup drowned while canoeing in Connecticut only weeks prior to the date of departure. Despite a later Crocker Land Expedition, Huntington's suggestions were not carried out in the detail he proposed. Hobbs reveals the history of his glacial theory in his autobiography. (*The Autobiography of William Herbert Hobbs*, J. W. Edwards, 1952, pp. 222).

50. E. Huntington to J. C. Toumey, July 12, 1912. E. Huntington to A. W. Evans, July 12, 1912.

51. *The Climatic Factor as Illustrated in Arid America*, 1914 by Ellsworth Huntington.

52. *See* "Tree Growth and Climatic Interpretations," *Quaternary Climates*, Publication No. 352, Carnegie Institution of Washington, 1925, pp. 155–204.

53. For a contemporary elaboration and criticism of Huntington's work in dendrochronology see "Dendrochronological evidence of climatic pulsation in Huntington's work" by Clark A. Akatiff; chapter IV of "An Evaluation of Some Geographical Concepts of Ellsworth Huntington," (M.A. thesis, University of California, Los Angeles, 1963).

54. *Carnegie Institution of Washington, Yearbook, No. 11*, 1912, p. 74.

55. *Carnegie Institution of Washington, Yearbook, No. 11*, 1912, p. 74.

56. *The Climatic Factor as Illustrated in Arid America*, p. 211.

57. E. Huntington to Charles Schuchert, September 4, 1912.

58. E. Huntington to C. S. Alden, April 29, 1912.

59. E. Huntington to W. B. Lombard, December 5, 1911.

60. E. Huntington to Dr. Rose, December 5, 1911.

61. E. Huntington to E. J. Swift, December 5, 1911.

62. E. Huntington to C. Stuart, December 5, 1911.

63. J. McKeen Cattell to E. Huntington, November 11, 1911.

64. E. Huntington to W. M. Davis, November 21, 1911.

65. "Clark University's Work in Geography," *Bulletin of the American Geographical Society*, Vol. 44, No. 1, 1912, pp. 47–48.

66. *The Journal of Race Development*, January, 1912, Vol. 2, pp. 256–281.

67. *Japan and Japanese-American Relations*, edited by G. H. Blakeslee and G. E. Stechert, 1912, pp. 42–67.

68. E. Huntington to T. B. Wells, December 6, 1913.

69. T. B. Wells to E. Huntington, December 18, 1913.

70. *Civilization and Climate*, 1915, p. 8.

71. *Bulletin of the American Geographical Society*, Vol. 43, No. 4, April, 1911, pp. 241–265.

72. *Civilization and Climate*, 1915, Appendices A and B, pp. 297–313.

73. E. Huntington to T. B. Wells, May 18, 1914.

74. T. B. Wells to E. Huntington, July 28, 1914.

75. *Harper's Magazine*, January, 1915, Vol. CXXX, No. DCCLXXVI, pp. 234–244.

76. *Harper's Magazine*, February, 1915, Vol. CXXX, No. DCCLXXVII, pp. 367–373.

77. *Harper's Magazine*, May, 1915, Vol. CXX, No. DCCLXXX, pp. 943–951.

78. *The Literary Digest*, May 22, 1915, Vol. L, No. 21, p. 1210.

79. A. Phelps Stokes to E. Huntington, May 7, 1915.

80. *The Geographical Journal*, "A Measure of Civilization," Vol. 47, No. 1, 1916, pp. 51–54.

81. J. G. Bartholomew to E. Huntington, February 2, 1916.

82. *The Geographical Journal*, April, 1910, pp. 395–419, Vol. 33.

83. *Bulletin of the American Geographical Society*, Vol. 47, No. 3, March, 1915, pp. 184–189.

84. Henry Strong Huntington undertook this manuscript following his retirement as minister of the Congregational Church, Milton, Massachusetts in 1907. The manuscript consisting of 25 chapters and 212 pages was completed in 1914; it never was published.

85. *Yale Review* III, 1913, pp. 507–519.

86. *The Journal of Race Development*, Vol. 5, No. 2, October, 1914, pp. 185–211.

Notes to Chapter VII

1. Henry Adams to E. Huntington 11 Jan. 1910.

2. Madison Grant to E. Huntington April 10, 1912.

3. "The Desiccation of Eur-Asia," *The Geographical Journal*, Vol. 23, June 1904, No. 6, pp. 722–734.

4. "L. S. Berg," by J. A. Morrison, *The Geographical Review*, October, 1951, No. 4, Vol. XLI, pp. 673–675.

5. Lev S. Berg, "Vopros ob Izmenenii Klimata v Istoricheskuiu Epokhu." *Zemlevedenie*, 1911, No. 3.

6. W. L. G. Joerg to E. Huntington, March 16, 1914.

7. "Das Problem der Klimaänderung in geschichtlicher Zeit" (*Geographische Abhandlungen* hrsg. v. A. Penck, Bd. X, Heft 2.) Leipzig, B. G. Teubner, 1914. In—8, 70 p. 3M. 60.

8. *Le Turkestan Russe*, A. Woeikof. Libraire Armand Colin, Paris 1914, p. 360.

9. *Civilization & Climate*, 2nd edition with a new introduction 1922.

10. *Bulletin of the American Geographical Society*, Vol. 47, 1915, No. 9, p. 708.

11. *Annales de Géographie*, Jan. 15, 1914, Vol. 23, No. 127, pp. 1–30.

12. E. Huntington to Francois Herbette, Feb. 12, 1914.

13. *Overland to India*, by Sven Hedin, 2 vol., Macmillan & Co., 1910.

14. *Overland to India*, Vol. 2, pp. 188–189.

15. *Overland to India*, Vol. 2, p. 189.

16. *Overland to India*, Vol. 2, pp. 224–225.

17. *Overland to India*, Vol. 2, p. 225.

18. Berlin; Weidmann 1910 (132 pages) pp. 16–30.

19. *The Geographical Journal*, Feb. 1914, No. 2, Vol. XLIII, pp. 148–172: also March 1914, No. 3, Vol. XLIII, pp. 293–313.

20. "Is the Earth Drying Up?", *The Geographical Journal*, March 1914, No. 3, Vol. XLIII, p. 307.

21. "Climatic Changes," *The Geographical Journal* No. 2, Vol. XLIV, Aug. 1914, pp. 203–210.

22. *The Geographical Journal*, No. 4, Oct. 1915, Vol. XLVI.

23. *Journal of Geography*, Jan. 1912, pp. 163–168.

24. *Bulletin of the American Geographical Society*, Vol. 44, 1912, No. 6, pp. 432–440.

25. *Bulletin of the American Geographical Society*, Vol. 44, 1912, No. 6, pp. 440–447.

26. *Bulletin of the American Geographical Society*, Vol. 44, 1912, No. 6, p. 441.

27. *The American Historical Review*, Jan. 1913, Vol. XVIII, No. 2, pp. 213–232.

28. E. Huntington to J. S. Keltie, July 11, 1913.

29. J. S. Keltie to H. G. Lyons, 26 Sept. 1913.

30. J. S. Keltie to E. Huntington, 1 Oct. 1913.

31. E. Huntington to J. S. Keltie, Oct. 18, 1913.

32. H. J. Mackinder to J. S. Keltie, 23 Oct. 1913.

33. *The Geographical Journal*, No. 1, Jan. 1914, Vol. XLIII, pp. 19–32.

34. Mark Jefferson to Ellsworth Huntington, Dec. 26, 1912.

35. *Bulletin of the American Geographical Society*, 1915, Vol. 47, No. 9, p. 708.

36. E. Huntington to W. L. G. Joerg, March 19, 1914.

37. E. Huntington to R. E. Dodge, April 23, 1914.

38. R. E. Dodge to E. Huntington, August 18, 1914. The 44-page article is with the Huntingtonia, Yale.

39. *Bulletin of the Geological Society of America*, Vol. 25, November 2, 1914, pp. 477–590.

40. Abstract, "Solar Hypothesis of Climatic Changes," *Bulletin of the Geological Society of America*, Vol. 25, March 30, 1914, pp. 82–83.

Notes to Chapter VIII

1. Teachers' Manual of Geography for Grades VII and VIII (for use in either elementary schools or junior high schools), The Commonwealth of Massachusetts Bulletin of the Board of Education, 1918, Number 6 (Elementary Education Service, State House, Boston, Massachusetts), 54 pages.

2. *Journal of Geography*, Vol. XV, November, 1916, pp. 87–91.

3. J. Byers to E. Huntington, September 6, 1916.

4. E. Huntington to G. W. Benton, December 20, 1916.

5. W. W. Livengood to E. Huntington, December 23, 1916.

6. Huntington and Cushing entered into an arrangement whereby Cushing should received a 6% royalty and Huntington a 4% royalty on the 'human geography'; royalty rates were to be reversed on "Commercial and Industrial Geography."

7. E. Huntington to G. W. Benton, August 17, 1917.

8. W. W. Livengood to E. Huntington, September 6, 1917.

9. E. Huntington to W. W. Livengood, August 30, 1917.

10. E. Huntington to Mark Jefferson, March 9, 1920.

11. *Bulletin of the Geographical Society of Philadelphia*, Vol. XVIII, No. 3, July, 1919, pp. 341–352.

12. *Journal of Geography*, Vol. XIX, No. 7, October, 1920, pp. 1–5, and 255–259.

13. Charles B. Stoll, Vice President, Textbook Division, Wiley Company to G. J. Martin, January 26, 1967.

14. E. P. Hamilton, Secretary, John Wiley and Sons, to E. Huntington, June 27, 1921.

15. *Jimbun chirigaku gairon*. Translated by Fushimi Yoshio, edited by Ishibashi Goro, Tokyo, Sekizensha (1927).

16. Quoted . . . Wiley advertisement for fifth revised edition of *Principles of Human Geography*, October, 1940.

17. *Scottish Geographical Magazine*, Vol. XXXVII, No. 4, October, 1921, 286–287.

18. *The Geographical Journal*, Vol. LXVIII, No. 2, August, 1921, pp. 143–144.

19. *La Géographie*, XXXVII, No. 3, March, 1922, p. 295.

20. *Nature*, Vol. 107, No. 2703, August 18, 1921, pp. 774–775.

21. Isaiah Bowman to Harlan H. Barrows, March 3, March 11, and June 13, 1921.

22. *The Geographical Review*, Vol. 12, No. 1, January, 1922, pp. 157–160.

23. Harlan H. Barrows to Isaiah Bowman, June 15, 1921.

24. W. M. Davis to E. Huntington, July 9, 1921.

25. E. Huntington to W. M. Davis, August 2, 1921.

26. W. M. Davis to E. Huntington, August 22, 1921.

27. W. M. Davis to E. Huntington, September 11, 1921.

28. E. Huntington to J. Willitz, June 15, 1921.

29. *The Geographical Review*, Vol. 15, No. 2, April, 1925, pp. 285–294.

30. W. W. Atwood to E. Huntington, March 15, 1924.

31. E. Huntington to W. W. Atwood, March 17, 1924.

32. *Economic Geography*, Vol. 1, No. 2, July, 1925, pp. 143–172.

33. *The Geographical Review*, Vol. 15, No. 3, July, 1925, pp. 499–500.

34. *The Bulletin of the Geographical Society of Philadelphia*, Vol. XIV, No. 1, January, 1916, p. 34. "Award of the Kane Medal to Dr. Ellsworth Huntington."

35. G. B. Roorbach to E. Huntington, October 29, 1915.

36. *The Bulletin of the Geographical Society of Philadelphia*, Vol. XIV, No. 1, January, 1916, pp. 1–21.

37. *The Bulletin of the Geographical Society of Philadelphia*, Vol. XIV, No. 1, January, 1916, pp. 21–24.

38. J. Russell Smith to E. Huntington, November 1, 1915.

39. *Proceedings of the Nineteenth International Congress of Americanists*, 1915, pp. 150–164.

40. Abstract published in *Annals of the Association of American Geographers*, Vol. VI, 1916, p. 127. See also *The Geographical Review*, February, 1916, Vol. I, No. 2, pp. 132–133.

41. Carl P. Birkinbine, "Variations in precipitation as affecting water works engineering." *Journal of the American Waterworks Association*, Vol. 3, 1916, No. 1, pp. 1–62. *The Bulletin of The Geographical Society of Philadelphia*, Vol. XIV, No. 3, July, 1916, pp. 37–38, "Climatic Variations and Water Works Engineering" by Ellsworth Huntington.

42. *Proceedings of the Second Pan-American Scientific Congress*, Vol. 11, Government Printing Office, Washington, 1917, pp. 411–431.

43. *The Quarterly Journal of Economics*, Vol. XXXI, February, 1917, pp. 173–208. Noted in *The Geographical Review*, Vol. III, No. 5, May 1917, pp. 401–402.

44. *The Quarterly Journal of Economics,* Vol. XXXI, February, 1917, p. 185.

45. C. R. Dryer to E. Huntington, October 28, 1917.

46. J. P. Goode to E. Huntington, December 5, 1916.

47. O. E. Baker to E. Huntington, June 18, 1917.

48. E. Huntington to H. E. Bourne, November 7, 1916.

49. *The Geographical Review*, Vol. I, No. 3, March, 1916, pp. 192–202.

50. *The Geographical Review*, Vol. 2, No. 3, September, 1916, pp. 169–183.

51. *The Geographical Review*, Vol. 3, No. 3, March, 1917, pp. 188–211; Vol. 3, No. 4, April, 1917, pp. 303–316.

52. I. Bowman to E. Huntington, January 21, 1916.

53. I. Bowman to E. Huntington, May 15, 1916.

54. I. Bowman to E. Huntington, June 6, 1916.

55. Published as "Climate and the Evolution of Civilization" in *The Evolution of the Earth and Its Inhabitants*, edited by R. S. Lull, pp. 147–193, 1918.

56. *The Boston Evening Transcript*, December 20, 1915.

57. "The Pilgrim Memorial Institution," unpublished article by E. Huntington; also, *The Boston Evening Transcript*, June 28, 1916.

Notes to Chapter IX

1. "War Services of Members of The Association of American Geographers," *Annals of The Association of American Geographers*, Vol. IX, 1919, pp. 53–70.

2. E. Huntington to I. Bowman, April 7, 1917.

3. *The Geographical Review*, Vol. 7, No. 1, January, 1919, pp. 24–35.

4. E. Huntington to W. M. Davis, April 4, 1917.

5. Unpublished article, "Proposal for the Application of a New Scientific Method to a Phase of Military Training."

6. E. Huntington to G. E. Hale, April 4, 1917.

7. V. C. Vaughan to E. Huntington, April 21, 1917.

8. V. C. Vaughan to E. Huntington, July 28, 1917.

9. The visit was made on October 30, 1917.

10. E. Huntington to I. Bowman, January 23, 1918.

11. Ellsworth Huntington to Cornelia Huntington, January 7, 1919.

12. "A Statement of Geographical War Work in Great Britain," unpublished 6-page report to the Division of Geology and Geography of the National Research Council, June, 1918.

13. Memorandum. E. Huntington to General Churchill, May 26, 1919.

14. August 15, 1918. (Military Monograph Sub-section of M.I.2) 3 pages.

15. *The Geography of Europe*, 1918, Foreword, p. 8.

16. J. R. Smith to E. Huntington, October 31, 1918. The other men who provided manuscript for the book included Herbert Bassett, N. A. Bengtson, C. E. Bonnett, A. P. Brigham, C. C. Colby, S. W. Cushing, Leon Dominian, V. C. Finch, W. H. Haas, G. R. Mansfield, E. B. Mathews, C. J. Posey, A. L. Pugh, J. R. Rich, G. B. Roorbach, J. Russell Smith, R. H. Whitbeck, and F. E. Williams.

17. Memorandum. E. Huntington to General Churchill, May 26, 1919.

18. Memorandum. E. Huntington to General Churchill, May 26, 1919.

19. *The Geographical Review*, Vol. 11, April, 1921, pp. 212–216.

20. *The Geographical Review*, Vol. 11, April, 1921, pp. 227–242.

21. *The Geographical Review*, Vol. 11, April, 1921, pp. 243–264.

22. *Mexico and The Caribbean*, edited by G. H. Blakeslee, pp. 44–53.

23. *The Journal of International Relations*, Vol. 11, No. 2, October, 1920, pp. 224–233.

24. General Churchill to E. Huntington, July 18, 1919.

25. Charles Walcott to E. Huntington, April 28, 1919.

26. Unpublished article, 5 pages.

27. Yale University Press, 1919, 287 pages.

28. Memorandum. Colonel John M. Dunn to E. Huntington, December 23, 1918.

29. Memorandum, Colonel John M. Dunn to E. Huntington, December 26, 1918.

30. *Asia*, Vol. XVIII, No. 6, June, 1918, pp. 480–489.

31. F. T. Allan—E. Huntington, March 26, 1919.

32. "Introduction to New Edition," vii-xxi, *The Pulse of Asia*, 1919.

33. *Scribner's Magazine*, Vol. 77, February, 1925, No. 2, pp. 155–160.

34. Anson Phelps Stokes to E. Huntington, July 11, 1918.

35. *The American Review of Reviews*, Vol. LVIII, No. 3, September, 1918, pp. 287–291.

36. Bjorn Helland-Hansen and Fridtjof Nansen: Temperaturschwankungen des Nordatlantischen Ozeans und in der Atmosphare: Einleitende Studien uber die Ursachen der klimatologischen Schwankungen. *Kristiania Videnskapsselskapets Skrifter: Mat. -Naturv. Klasse*, 1916, Art. 9 (pp. 1–341). Christiania, 1917.

37. E. Huntington, "Coincident Activities of the Earth and the Sun," *The Popular Science Monthly*, Vol. LXXII, June, 1908, pp. 492–502.

38. E. Huntington, "Solar Disturbances and Terrestrial Weather," *Monthly Weather Review*, Vol. 46: pp. 123–41, 168–77, 269–77, March, April, June, 1918.

39. *The Geographical Review*, Vol. 5, No. 6, June, 1918, pp. 483–491.

40. Yale University Press, 1922, xiii, 329 pages.

41. *Earth and Sun*, Yale University Press, xxv, 296 pages.

42. *Modern Medicine*, Vol. 1, No. 1, May, 1919, pp. 13–22. Reprinted as "Interpretation of Death Rate by Climographs" in *Metal Worker, Plumber, and Steam Fitter*, Part 1, Vol. 92, No. 7, August 15, 1919, pp. 193–195. Part 2, Vol. 92, No. 9, August 29, 1919, pp. 251–253 and p. 274. Part 3, Vol. 92, No. 11, September 12, 1919, pp. 306–308 and p. 311.

43. *Ecology*, Vol. 1, No. 1, January, 1920, pp. 6–23. Reprinted in *Monthly Weather Review*, Vol. 48, September, 1920, pp. 501–505, Review and Discussion by J. B. Kincer, Meteorologist, U.S. Weather Bureau, pp. 505–507, "Discussion by Author" (Ellsworth Huntington).

44. *Modern Medicine*, October, 1919, Vol. 1, No. 6, Part 1, Humidity, pp. 463–468. Vol. 1, No. 7, Part 2, Variability, pp. 555–558.

45. *The Modern Hospital*, April, 1920, Vol. XIV, No. 4, Part 1, The Ideal Conditions of the Air, pp. 271–275.

46. *The Modern Hospital*, April, 1920, Vol. XIV, No. 5, Part 2, Methods of Air Control and Their Results, pp. 348–353.

47. *School*, Vol. XXXII, No. 16, December 16, 1920, p. 271.

48. I. Bowman to E. Huntington, August 9, 1919.

49. Huntington was awarded one of the second prizes by the National Anesthesia Research Society for meritorious research, October, 1920.

50. E. Huntington to G. G. Wyant, May 10, 1919.

Notes to Chapter X

1. A. P. Stokes to E. Huntington, December 5, 1916.

2. E. Huntington to A. P. Stokes, December 11, 1916.

3. E. Huntington to J. Barrell, March 12, 1917.

4. Minutes of the Geological Faculty of Yale, 1919–1932, W. E. Ford, Secretary.

5. Minutes of the Geological Faculty of Yale, 1919–1932, W. E. Ford, Secretary.

6. E. Huntington to J. R. Angell, October 31, 1921.

7. E. Huntington to J. R. Angell, November 11, 1921.

8. E. Huntington to J. R. Angell, November 16, 1921.

9. J. R. Angell to R. D Salisbury, November 23, 1921.

10. R. D Salisbury to J. R. Angell, November 25, 1921.

11. J. R. Angell to John C. Merriam, December 28, 1921.

12. E. Huntington to J. R. Angell, May 31, 1922.

13. J. R. Angell to J. C. Merriam, November 20, 1922.

14. H. S. Graves to J. R. Angell, March 31, 1925.

15. E. Huntington to A. M. Huntington, July 10, 1925.

16. T. W. Farnham to E. Huntington, July 13, 1925.

17. E. Huntington to W. L. Cross, May 25, 1926

18. E. Huntington to J. R. Angell, February 18, 1929.

19. J. R. Angell to E. Huntington, December 17, 1926.

20. E. Huntington to J. R. Angell, October 24, 1927.

21. J. R. Angell to E. Huntington, October 29, 1927.

22. J. R. Angell to E. Huntington, November 9, 1927.

23. C. H. Warren to J. R. Angell, November 14, 1927.

24. W. L. Cross to J. R. Angell, November 8, 1927.

25. E. Huntington to J. R. Angell, March 12, 1928.

26. J. R. Angell to E. Huntington, March 17, 1928.

27. Records of the Yale Corporation's Prudential Committee, April 13, 1929.

28. J. R. Angell to W. L. Cross, March 23, 1929.

29. C. H. Warren to E. Huntington, April 15, 1927.

30. C. H. Warren to E. Huntington, April 15, 1927.

31. E. Huntington to J. R. Angell, March 21, 1928.

32. E. Huntington to J. R. Angell (copy to Deans), September 17, 1928.

33. E. Huntington to J. R. Angell, February 18, 1929.

34. Charles Seymour to E. Huntington, February 19, 1929.

35. *The Geographical Review*, Vol. 12, No. 1, January, 1922, pp. 100–115.

36. *The Geographical Journal*, Vol. LX, No. 6, December, 1922, pp. 445–446.

37. C. H. Crickmay to G. J. Martin, January 2, 1970.

38. Geoffrey W. Crickmay to G. J. Martin, July 23, 1967.

39. C. A. Connaughton to G. J. Martin, April 28, 1970.

40. E. S. Deevey, Jr., to J. Chappell, November 25, 1969.

41. J. Doris Dart to G. J. Martin, October 2, 1969.

42. W. C. Smith to G. J. Martin, December 12, 1969.

43. E. M. Weyer to G. J. Martin, May 14, 1970.

44. E. Huntington to R. V. Coleman, March 23, 1926.

45. A. G. Price to G. J. Martin, August 25, 1970.

46. E. Antevs to G. J. Martin, July 20, 1970.

Notes to Chapter XI

1. "Geographical Environment and Japanese Character," *The Journal of Race Development*, Vol. 11, No. 3, Jan. 1912, pp. 256–281.
See also: "The Adaptability of the White Man to Tropical America," *The Journal of Race Development*, Vol. 5, No. 2, Oct. 1914, pp. 185–211 and "A Neglected Factor in Race Development," *The Journal of Race Development*, Vol. 6, No. 2, Oct. 1915, pp. 167–184.

2. *The Geographical Review*, Vol. 2, No. 6, December, 1916, pp. 458–463.

3. E. Huntington to R. L. Davis, September 10, 1936.

4. E. Huntington to Madison Grant, August 27, 1925.

5. *The Yale Review*, Vol. VI, No. 3, April, 1917, p. 670.

6. *The Yale Review*, Vol. VII, No. 2, January, 1918, pp. 337–348.

7. E. Huntington to J. H. Breasted, April 7, 1921.

8. E. Huntington to Carl C. Brigham, January 16, 1923.

9. E. Huntington to Stella Piari, May 3, 1924.

10. E. Huntington to H. F. Perkins, June 17, 1933.

11. Albert Johnson to Leon F. Whitney, March 4, 1926. (Reproduced in Report of The President of The American Eugenics Society, Inc., June 1926, pp. 6–7.)

12. E. Huntington to Charles Scribners Co., June 20, 1921.

13. *Temples and Towers: A survey of the World's Moral Outlook*, compiled by George Vaughan, 1941, pp. 139–140.

14. E. Huntington to Rosina Hahn, June 26, 1925.

15. T. G. Taylor to E. Huntington, December 19, 1924.

16. G. G. Chisholm to E. Huntington, March 24, 1925.

17. E. Huntington to P. H. Belknap, May 11, 1926.

18. Preface viii–ix, *West of The Pacific*, 1925.

19. *See especially*, Chapter 17 "Aboriginal America and Modern Australia."

20. *White Settlers in the Tropics*, A. Grenfell Price, 1939, American Geographical Society, Special Publication, No. 23.

21. "The Vitality of White Races in Low Latitudes," *The Economic Record*, May, 1927.

22. "The White Settlement of Tropical Australia," Chapter IX, *The Peopling of Australia*, pp. 222–245, edited by P. D. Phillips and G. L. Wood, 1928.

23. *The Economic Record*, November, 1929, p. 185–201.

24. E. Huntington to George W. Pierson, November 17, 1941.

25. E. Huntington to T. J. Sullivan, February 16, 1943.

26. *The Builders of America*, E. Huntington and Leon Whitney, 1927, Preface V, Review was published, *New York Times*, September 29, 2. 6. 1927; Huntington's letter to the editor was published, *New York Times*, October 23, III, 5:7, 1927.

27. *New York Times*, September 29, 2.6., 1927; *New York Times*, October 23. III, 5:7, 1927.

28. E. Huntington to Frank Gordon, March 9, 1931.

29. *The Nation*, Vol. 125, No. 3239, August 3, 1927, pp. 105–107.

30. *The American Mercury*, Vol. XI, No. 44, August, 1927, pp. 438–443.

31. *The Outlook*, Vol. 146, No. 17, August 24, 1927, pp. 538–540.

32. *The Outlook*, Vol. 147, No. 1, September 7, 1927, pp. 21–23.

33. *The Yale Review*, Vol. XVII, No. 1, October, 1927, pp. 136–152.

34. *Eugenics*, Vol. 1, No. 1, October, 1928, pp. 6–14.

35. *The American Mercury*, Vol. XV, No. 57, September, 1928, pp. 13–19.

36. E. Huntington to Margaret Sanger, March 6, 1925.

37. The stenographic record (and Huntington's corrections) is with the Ellsworth Huntington papers at Yale University.

38. *The Yale Review*, Vol. XVII, No. 1, October, 1927, p. 151.

39. E. Huntington to G. K. Shull, February 12, 1929.

40. George Eastman and John Rockefeller virtually financed the Society until Eastman's death in 1932.

41. A considerable amount of Huntington's research on this subject remains unpublished.

42. A pamphlet published by the Society.

43. John Wiley and Sons, 1935, 139 pages.

44. "A Eugenics Program for the United States," 17 pages, published by the American Eugenics Society.

45. E. Huntington to George Christ, May 22, 1935.

46. American Eugenics Society, *Annual Report of the President*, 1937–38.

47. Copy with the 'Huntingtonia,' Yale archive and manuscript library.

48. The Committee included: Vernon Kellogg, Chairman; Ellsworth Huntington; Harry H. Laughlin; Raymond Pearl, Edward H. Thorndike; Clark Wissler.

49. *After Three Centuries:* A Typical New England Family, by Ellsworth Huntington and Martha Ragsdale. The Williams and Wilkins Company, Baltimore, Maryland, 1935, vi and 274 pages.

50. Sixth Reunion Huntington Family, 1938 (Geo. H. Ellis Co., 1938, 92 pages), pp. 24–41.

51. "Once More: What's In a Name?" p. 39.

52. *The Huntington Family Memoir.* Being a Continuous History of the Known Descendants of Simon Huntington (who left England for America in 1633) to 1915 (1205 pages).

53. "Once More: What's In a Name?" pp. 40–41.

54. E. Huntington to William G. Mather, October 21, 1940.

55. *Mainsprings of Civilization* (1945), p. 102

Notes to Chapter XII

1. *Political Science Quarterly,* Vol. XXXV, No. 3, September, 1920, pp. 393–410. He now spells his name S. Colum Gilfillan.

2. S. C. GilFillan to E. Huntington, November 19, 1924.

3. *Political Science Quarterly,* XXXIX, No. 3, September, 1924, pp. 458–484.

4. "Climate and History, as Recorded by the Big Trees." Article embodying labels for exhibit in the American Museum of Natural History . . . contained in "The Big Tree and Its Story," by George H. Sherwood, Guide Leaflet No. 42 of the American Museum of Natural History, 1924.

5. E. Huntington to Bruce Barton, November 12, 1925.

6. S. S. Visher to E. Huntington, January 25, 1920.

7. S. S. Visher to Dean Wilbur Cross, April 10, 1920.

8. E. Huntington to J. R. Smith, February 24, 1921.

9. *Science,* Vol. LVII, No. 1474, March 30, 1923, pp. 386–391.

10. W. J. Humphreys to National Book Buyers Service, February 5, 1923.

11. *The Geographical Review,* Vol. 15, No. 2, April, 1925, p. 257.

12. E. Huntington to S. S. Visher, February 2, 1920.

13. Australian National Research Council—E. Huntington, December 28, 1922. 1922.

14. E. Huntington to T. Griffith Taylor, June 27, 1921.

15. T. Griffith Taylor to E. Huntington, May 27, 1925.

16. E. Huntington to T. Griffith Taylor, February 23, 1925.

17. T. Griffith Taylor to E. Huntington, December 19, 1924.

18. T. Griffith Taylor to S. S. Visher, November 8, 1947.

19. *The Geographical Review,* Vol. 15, No. 4, 1925, pp. 563–583.

20. *Kokumin Toyo chiri to Kuhon*—Tokyo, Fuzambo, 1927, Tr. by A. Tsuyusaki.

21. *Kiko to bummei.* Tr. by Masato Masaki, 1938.

22. Written by E. Huntington, January 4, 1922.

23. E. Huntington to Lawrence Martin, November 28, 1924.

24. Lawrence Martin to E. Huntington, December 8, 1924.

25. *Annals of the Association of American Geographers*, Vol. XIV, No. 1, March, 1924, pp. 1–16

26. *New York Times*, February 10, 1924, Section 7, p. 14, cols. 1 and 2.

27. E. Huntington to Rosina Hahn, June 26, 1925.

28. R. N. Rudmose Brown to E. Huntington, February 15, 1924.

29. E. Huntington to S. C. GilFillan, July 7, 1924.

30. "Weather and Health, A Study of Daily Mortality in New York City," *Bulletin of the National Research Council*, No. 75, April, 1930, 161 pages.

31. E. Huntington to Wallace Caldwell, August 8, 1946.

32. *Journal of the National Institute of Social Sciences*, Vol. XII, November 1, 1927; p. 117.

33. *The Literary Review*, December 11, 1920, p. 4.

34. Henry S. Canby to Ellsworth Huntington, January 22, 1921.

35. *The Saturday Review of Literature*, July 24, 1926, Vol. 11, No. 52.

36. *The Pulse of Progress*, Preface v, 1926.

37. *The Pulse of Progress*, page 1.

38. *The Human Habitat*, Chapter 1, pp. 1–18.

39. *The Human Habitat*, Chapter 16, pp. 244–262.

40. *The Human Habitat*, Chapter 17, pp. 263–280.

41. E. Huntington to S. C. Gilfillan, January 28, 1928.

Notes to Chapter XIII

1. "Ellsworth Huntington and 'The Pace of History'," by Geoffrey J. Martin, *Connecticut Review*, pp. 83–123, October 1971, Vol. 5, No. 1.

2. Charles H. Seaver to E. Huntington, January 23, 1928.

3. E. Huntington to F. M. McMurry, February 27, 1928.

4. E. Huntington to F. M. McMurry, May 30, 1928.

5. E. Huntington to E. H. Carrier, March 8, 1929.

6. *Economic and Social Geography*, John Wiley and Sons, 1933, 630 pages.

7. S. C. Gilfillan and S. S. Visher had provided Huntington with three chapters for which Huntington had paid them.

8. John K. Rose to G. J. Martin, May 4, 1970.

9. Printed by Matamek Factory, Canadian Labrador, 1932, 32 pages.

10. "The Matamek Conference on Biological Cycles," *Science*, Vol. 74, September 4, 1931, pp. 229–235.

11. "Matamek Conference on Biological Cycles, Abstracts of papers and discussions," by Charles Elton, Matamek Factory, Canadian Labrador, 1933, 50 pp.

12. *Matamek Conference on Biological Cycles, Proceedings, 1932*, 315 pp.

13. See "Report of a Conference on Cycles," pp. 657–676, *The Geographical Review*, Vol. 13, No. 4. Special Supplement, October, 1923.

14. "Cycles, Rhythms and Periodicities," Foundation for the Study of Cycles, Foundation Reprint, No. 14: "Two Intriguing Cycles," Foundation for the Study of Cycles, Foundation Reprint, No. 15: "Broader Aspects of Environmental Cycles," Foundation for the Study of Cycles, Foundation Reprint, No. 16.

15. Memorial Volume of the Geographical Society of Lwow in honor of Eugeniusz Romer, edited by H. Arctowski, Lwow, 1934, pp. 495–517.

16. "Climatic Pulsations," *Geografiska Annaler*, 1935, p. 571.

17. Ellsworth Huntington to Arnold J. Toynbee, November 6, 1934.

18. *The Saturday Review of Literature*, Vol. XI, No. 22, December 15, 1934, p. 365 and 376.

19. Ellsworth Huntington to Roland M. Harper, November 13, 1934.

20. A. J. Toynbee to Ellsworth Huntington, November 21, 1934.

21. *Comptes Rendus du Congrès International de Géographie, Amsterdam, 1938*. Tome Deuxième, Travaux de la section IIIb, Geographique Economique, pp. 200–210.

22. E. Huntington to J. Russell Smith, February 25, 1935.

23. J. Russell Smith to E. Huntington, March 8, 1935.

24. E. Huntington to J. Russell Smith, March 14, 1925.

25. E. Huntington to S. C. Gilfillan, September 14, 1936.

26. E. Huntington to E. P. Hamilton, September 14, 1936.

27. Published as "Season of Birth and Mental Stability," *American Association on Mental Deficiency . . . Proceedings*, Vol. XLII, No. 2, 1937, pp. 116–124.

28. *The Journal of the American Medical Association*, Vol. III, No. 3, July 16, 1938, p. 347.

29. R. B. Hall to E. Huntington, May 20, 1938.

30. Unpublished manuscript, Yale University Archives.

31. E. Huntington to J. W. Goldthwait, May 21, 1940.

32. E. Huntington to Rudolf Bertheau, November 27, 1941.

33. E. Huntington to Raymond H. Wheeler, January 13, 1941.

34. E. Huntington to Ralph H. Brown, February 27, 1942.

35. E. Huntington to O. E. Geppert, November 23, 1945.

36. E. Huntington to S. S. Visher, August 31, 1945.

37. E. Huntington to Albert S. Carlson, November 26, 1946.

38. E. Huntington to Henry and Evelyn Phelps-Brown, March 29, 1947.

39. E. Huntington to A. Missenard, August 31, 1945.

40. "The Quality of People," In *America at War, A Geographical Analysis*, edited by Samuel Van Valkenburg, pp. 1–37, 1942.

41. *Compass of the World*, edited by Hans W. Weigert and V. Stefansson, pp. 174–189, 1943.

42. Chapter 21, "The Conservation of Man," pp. 466–484, *Conservation of Natural Resources*, edited by Guy-Harold Smith, 1950.

43. Unfinished at the time of his death.

44. Typed manuscript available in the Yale University archive library.

45. Chapter 22, "Geography and Aviation," pp. 528–542, *Geography in the Twentieth Century*, edited by T. Griffith Taylor, 1951.

Notes to Chapter XIV

1. "The Basin of Eastern Persia and Sistan," by Ellsworth Huntington, pp. 219–315. *Explorations in Turkestan with an account of The Basin of Eastern Persia and Sistan*, 1905.

2. *The Pulse of Asia*, 1907, Chapter 18, "The Geographic Basis of History," pp. 359–385.

3. "William Morris Davis, Geographer," pp. 32–33, *The Bulletin of the Geographical Society of Philadelphia*, Vol. X, No. 4, October, 1912.

4. Footnote 1, p. 185, "Climatic Change and Agricultural Exhaustion as Elements in the Fall of Rome," *The Quarterly Journal of Economics*, Vol. XXXI, February, 1917. Only five of these letters are with the Ellsworth Huntington papers at Yale.

5. . . . "mankind as a whole appears to work best when the mid-day temperature (not the average for the whole day) is about 63° to 70°, and feels most comfortable when at rest if the corresponding temperature is about 70° to 77°." *Mainsprings of Civilization*, 1945, p. 267.

6. *Civilization and Climate*, 1915, pp. 278–279.

7. *Industrial and Commercial Geography* by J. Russell Smith, 1925, p. 10.

8. *The Survey*, Vol. XXXV, No. 2, Feb. 12, 1916, p. 589.

9. *World-Power and Evolution*, 1919, p. 18.

10. An unfinished manuscript (The Pace of History) and hundreds of pages of notes reveal the dimensions of this interest.

11. *Geography in the Making* by J. K. Wright, 1952, p. 294.

12. E. Huntington to R. B. Wynn, February 16, 1945.

13. *The Character of Races*, 1924, Preface ix.

14. *The Human Habitat*, 1927, Preface vi.

15. *The Saturday Review of Literature*, March 24, 1928, Vol. IV, No. 35, pp 697–702.

16. *Economic and Social Geography*, 1933, page 16.

17. E. Huntington to J.O.M. Broek, November 17, 1941.

18. E. Huntington to E.G.R. Taylor, January 20, 1937.

19. *The Bulletin of the Geographical Society of Philadelphia*, Vol. XXXI, No. 4, October, 1933.

20. E. Huntington to L. E. Klimm, November 20, 1933.

21. E. Huntington to G. W. Pierson, November 17, 1941.

22. E. Huntington to J. B. Griffing, February 12, 1929.

23. S. C. Gilfillan to G. J. Martin, June 5, 1970.

24. "The Geographer and History," *The Geographical Journal*, January, 1914, pp. 19–32.

25. E. Huntington to George Hubbard, June 2, 1932.

26. E. Huntington to S. Van Valkenburg, November 30, 1934.

27. E. Huntington to W. B. Pitkin, June 21, 1941.

28. E. Huntington to R. H. Brown, April 30, 1925.

29. E. Huntington to C. R. Dryer, October 5, 1921.

30. *The Yale Review*, Vol. 2, No. 1, October, 1912, pp. 82–96.

31. E. Huntington to A. E. Parkins, November 24, 1931.

32. E. Huntington to P. E. James; *also see* E. Huntington and R. Hartshorne correspondence, October, 1939 (Yale University archives).

33. Unpublished manuscript, folder 533, "Huntingtonia" (Yale University archives).

34. *The Canadian Journal of Economics and Political Science*, Vol. III, No. 4, November, 1937, pp. 565–572.

35. P. E. James to E. Huntington, January 20, 1938.

36. "Geography and History," An Abstract, *Annals of the Association of American Geographers*, Vol. 29, No. 1, March, 1939, p. 78.

37. E. Huntington to W. W. Livengood, November 7, 1917.

38. Dana O. Jensen to E. Huntington, November 13, 1940. J. H. Coleman to E. Huntington, May 1, 1939.

39. *Earth and Sun*, 1923, Preface, xv.

40. E. Huntington to Henry S. Huntington, Jr., November 30, 1911.

41. "The New Astrology," *The Century Magazine*, Vol. 110, No. 1, May, 1925, pp. 106–114.

42. *The Itinerant Ivory Tower*, G. E. Hutchinson, 1953, pp. 78–79.

43. "On Medievalism and Watersheds in the History of American Geography," Chapter 10, pp. 154–167, *Human Nature in Geography*, 1966, by J. K. Wright.

44. *Soviet Geography: Review and Translation*, Vol. III, No. 3, March, 1962, p. 79.

45. *The Geographer's Craft*, Chapter 5, pp. 101–123, 1967.

46. "What Geographers Did: A Review," by Andrew H. Clark, *Economic Geography*, Vol. 44, No. 1, January 1968, pp. 83–86.

47. Aurel Stein to Ellsworth Huntington, April 22, 1943.

48. Carl O. Sauer to G. J. Martin, June 23, 1970.

49. A. Grenfell Price to G. J. Martin, August 25, 1970.

50. Stephen B. Jones to G. J. Martin, May 20, 1971.

51. Nathaniel Weyl to G. J. Martin, March 5, 1971.

52. An M.A. thesis completed at the University of North Carolina, 1931.

53. An M.A. thesis completed at the University of Toronto, 1952.

54. An M.A. thesis completed at the University of California, Los Angeles, 1963.

55. A Ph.D. dissertation, The University of Kansas, 1968.

56. "Climatic Change Reconsidered: Another look at 'The Pulse of Asia,'" *The Geographical Review*, Vol. 60, No. 3, July, 1970, pp. 347–373; "Climatic Pulsations in Inner Asia and Correlations between Sunspots and Weather," *Palaeogeography, Paleoclimatology, Palaeoecology*, Vol. 10, No. 2–3, fall, 1971, pp. 12–14; "Atmospheric Influences on Man: Quantitative Confirmation," *International Geography*, Vol. I, 1972, pp. 135–137.

57. *The Geographical Journal*, Vol. CXVIII, Part 4, December, 1952, pp. 406–424.

The Published Works of Ellsworth Huntington

"Experiments with Available Road-making Materials of Southern Wisconsin," *Transactions of the Wisconsin Academy of Sciences, Arts and Letters*, Vol. XI, September, 1897, pp. 245–249.

"On the road" in Turkey, *"The Round Table*, Vol. XLIV, No. 19, February 18, 1898, pp. 184–186 and 193–196.

"Electric Phenomena in the Euphrates Valley," *Monthly Weather Review*, Vol. 28, No. 7, July, 1900, pp. 286–287.

"The Climate of Harpoot, Turkey in Asia," *Monthly Weather Review*, Vol. 29, No. 6, June, 1901, pp. 250–253.

"Weitere Berichte uber Forschungen in Armenien und Commagene," *Sitzung der Berliner Anthropologischen Gesellschaft*, Vom. 16, November, 1901, pp. 173–209.

"The Prehistoric Mounds of Eastern Turkey," *Records of the Past*, Vol. I, Part VI, June, 1902, pp. 163–171.

"Through the Great Cañon of the Euphrates River," *The Geographical Journal*, Vol. XX, No. 2, August, 1902, pp. 175–200.

"The Valley of the Upper Euphrates River and Its People," *Bulletin of the American Geographical Society*, Vol. 34, No. 4, 1902, pp. 301–310; and Vol. 34, No. 5, pp. 384–393.

"The Hittite Ruins of Hîlar, Asia Minor," *Records of the Past*, Vol. II, Part V, May, 1903, pp. 131–140.

"The Hurricane Fault in the Toquerville District, Utah," with James Walter Goldthwait, *The Journal of Geology*, Vol. XI, No. 1, January-February, 1903, pp. 46–63; and *Bulletin of the Museum of Comparative Zoology*, Harvard, Vol. XLVII, February, 1904, pp. 199–259.

"With a Minbashi in Turkestan," *Appalachia*, Vol. XI, No. 1, 1905, pp. 17–27.

"The Mountains of Turkestan," *The Geographical Journal*, Vol. XXV, January-February, 1905, pp. 22–40, 139.

"The Mountains and Kibitkas of Tian Shan, *Bulletin of the American Geographical Society*, Vol. 37, No. 9, 1905, pp. 513–530.

"The Depression of Sistan in Eastern Persia," *Bulletin of the American Geographical Society*, Vol. 37, No. 5, 1905, pp. 271–281.

"A Geologic and Physiographic Reconnaissance in Central Turkestan," *Explorations in Turkestan, Expedition of 1903*, Raphael Pumpelly, Ed., Carnegie Institution of Washington, 1905, pp. 159–216.

"The Basin of Eastern Persia and Sistan," *Explorations in Turkestan, Expedition of 1903*, Raphael Pumpelly, Ed., Carnegie Institution of Washington, 1905, pp. 219–315.

"The Rivers of Chinese Turkestan and the Desiccation of Asia," *The Geographical Journal*, Vol. 28, No. 4, October 1906, pp. 352–367.

"Pangong: A Glacial Lake in the Tibetan Plateau," *The Journal of Geology*, October-November, 1906, pp. 599–617.

"The Vale of Kashmir," *Bulletin of the American Geographical Society*, Vol. 38, No. 11, 1906, pp. 657–682.

"The Border Belts of the Tarim Basin, *Bulletin of the American Geographical Society*, Vol. 38, No. 2, 1906, pp. 91–96.

"Some Characteristics of the Glacial Period in Non-Glaciated Regions, *Bulletin of the Geological Society of America*, Vol. 18, October, 1907, pp. 351–388.

The Pulse of Asia, Houghton Mifflin & Co., Boston, 1907, xxix and 415 pp. (Slightly revised editions appeared in 1919 and 1930.)

"The Depression of Turfan, in Central Asia," *The Geographical Journal*, Vol. 30, No. 3, September, 1907, pp. 254–273.

"Lop-Nor—A Chinese Lake." Part 1—"The Unexplored Salt Desert of Lop," *Bulletin of the American Geographical Society*, Vol. 39, No. 2, 1907, pp. 65–77. Part 2—"The Historic Lake (Lop-Nor)," Vol. 39, No. 3, 1907, pp. 137–146.

"Archaeological Discoveries in Chinese Turkestan," *Bulletin of the American Geographical Society*, Vol. 39, No. 5, 1907, pp. 268–272.

"The Historic Fluctuations of the Caspian Sea," *Bulletin of the American Geographical Society*, Vol. 39, No. 10, 1907, pp. 577–596.

"The Anglo-Russian Agreement as to Tibet, Afghanistan, and Persia," *Bulletin of the American Geographical Society*, Vol. 39, No. 11, 1907, pp. 653–658.

"An Archipelago of Sand Dunes in a Lake of Central Asia," Map, *Bulletin of the American Geographical Society*, Vol. 40, No. 1, 1908, pp. 1–6.

"Archaeology in the Center of Asia," *Records of the Past*, Vol. VII, Part II, March-April, 1908, pp. 96–107.

"The Climate of Ancient Palestine," *Bulletin of the American Geographical Society*, Vol. 40, Part 1, No. 9, pp. 513–522; Part 2,

No. 10, pp. 577–586; Part 3, No. 11, pp. 641–652.

"The Climate of the Historic Past," *Monthly Weather Review*, Part 1, "The Old World," Vol. 36, No. 11, 1908, pp. 359–364. Part 2, "The New World," Vol. 36, No. 13, 1908, pp. 446–450.

"Coincident Activities of the Earth and the Sun," *The Popular Science Monthly*, Vol. LXXII, June, 1908, pp. 492–502.

"Description of the Kurgans of the Merv Oasis," extracted from Publication No. 73 of the Carnegie Institution of Washington, *Explorations in Turkestan, Expedition of 1904*, Vol. I, Chapter XII, Part III, 1908, pp. 217–232.

"Kirghiz Nomads and Influence of High Plateaus, *The Journal of Geography*, Vol. 6, 1908, pp. 313–328.

"Medieval Tales of the Lop Basin in Central Asia," *National Geographic Magazine*, Vol. 19, No. 4, April, 1908, pp. 289–295.

"The New Province Two Thousand Years Old," *Harper's Magazine*, Vol. CXVIII, No. 793, December, 1908, pp. 19–29.

"A Raid on Kafir Kala," *The Round Table*, Beloit College, January 31, 1908, pp. 174–176.

"The Relation of Afghanistan to Its Neighbors," *Bulletin of the Geographical Society of Philadelphia*, Vol. VI, No. 4, 1908, pp. 111–119.

"The Afghan Borderland," *National Geographic Magazine*, Part 1, "The Russian Frontier," Vol. XX, No. 9, September, 1909, pp. 788–799; Part 2, "The Persian Frontier," Vol XX, No. 10, October, 1909, pp. 866–876.

"Life in the Great Desert of Central Asia," *National Geographic Magazine*, Vol. XX, No. 8, August 1909, pp. 749–760.

"The Mountaineers of the Euphrates," *National Geographic Magazine*, Vol. XX, No. 2, February, 1909, pp. 142–156.

"Railroads in Asia Minor," *Bulletin of the American Geographical Society*, Vol. 41, No. 11, 1909, pp. 691–696.

"Beyond the Dead Sea," *Harper's Magazine*, February, 1910, Vol. CXX, No. 717, pp. 419–430.

"The Burial of Olympia; A Study in Climate and History," *The Geographical Journal*, December, 1910, pp. 657–675, remarks on pp. 685–686.

"Across the Ghor to the Land of Og," *Harper's Magazine,* Vol. CXX, No. 719, April, 1910, pp. 667–678.

"A Canvas Boat on the Dead Sea," *Harper's Magazine*, Vol. CXX, No. 716, January, 1910, pp. 186–196.

"The Fallen Queen of the Desert," *Harper's Magazine*, Vol. CXX, No. 718, March, 1910, pp. 552–563.

"The Fringe of Verdure Around Asia Minor," *National Geographic Magazine*, Vol. XXI, No. 9, September, 1910, pp. 761–775.

"The Libyan Oasis of Kharga," *Bulletin of the American Geographical Society*, Vol. 42, No. 9, 1910, pp. 641–661.

"The Lost Wealth of the Kings of Midas," *National Geographic Magazine*, Vol. XXI, No. 10, October, 1910, pp. 831–846.

"Problems in Exploration: Central Asia," *The Geographical Journal*, Vol. 35, No. 4, 1910, pp. 395–419.

"The First Americans," *Harper's Magazine*, Vol. CXXII, No. 729, February, 1911, pp. 451–462.

"The Greenest of Deserts," *Harper's Magazine*, Vol. CXXIII, No. 733, June, 1911, pp. 50–58.

"The Karst Country of Southern Asia Minor, *Bulletin of the American Geographical Society*, Vol. 43, No. 2, 1911, pp. 91–106.

Palestine and Its Transformation, Houghton, Mifflin & Co., 1911, xvii and 443 pp.

"Physical Environment as a Factor in the Present Condition of Turkey," *The Journal of Race Development*, Vol. 1, No. 4, April, 1911, pp. 460–481.

"American Archaeology," *Harper's Magazine*, Vol. CXXIV, No. 740, January, 1912, pp. 291–301.

"The Arabian Desert and Human Character," *The Journal of Geography*, Vol. X, No. 3, January, 1912, pp. 169–175.

Asia, A Geography Reader, Rand McNally & Co., (Introduction by R. E. Dodge, 1912. (Slightly revised edition—1923.)

"Climatic Changes in the Nearer East: A Reply," *Bulletin of the American Geographical Society*, Vol. 44, No. 6, 1912, pp. 440–447.

"The Fluctuating Climate of North America," Part I—"The Ruins of the Hohokam," *The Geographical Journal*, Vol. XL, No. 3, September, 1912, pp. 264–280; Part II—"The Succession of Civilization," Vol. XL, No. 4, September, 1912, pp. 392–411. Reprinted in *Annual Report of the Smithsonian Institution, 1912*, Washington, 1913, Publication 2206, pp. 383–412.

"Geographical Environment and Japanese Character," *The Journal of Race Development*, Vol. 2, No. 3, January, 1912, pp. 256–281. Reprinted in *Japan and Japanese American Relations* (Clark University Addresses), edited by G. H. Blakeslee and G. E. Stechert & Co., 1912.

"The New Science of Geography," *Yale Review*, Vol. II, No. 1, October, 1912, pp. 82–96.

"The Peninsula of Yucatan," *Bulletin of the American Geographical Society*, Vol. 44, No. 11, 1912, pp. 801–822.

"The Physical Environment of the Southwest in pre-Columbian Days," *Records of the Past*, Vol. XI, Part III, May-June, 1912, pp. 128–141.

"The Secret of the Big Trees," *Harper's Magazine*, Vol. CXXV, No. 746, July, 1912, pp. 292–302.
Translation reprinted, "El Secreto del arbol gigantesio," *Bulletin of the Pan American Union*, 1912. Reprinted 1913, Department of the Interior, Washington, Government Printing Office.

"Changes of Climate and History," *American Historical Review*, Vol. 18, No. 2, January, 1913, pp. 213–232.

"Guatemala and the Highest Native American Civilization, *Proceedings of the American Philosophical Society*, Vol. LII, No. 211, September-October, 1913, pp. 467–487.

"The Shifting of Climatic Zones as Illustrated in Mexico, *Bulletin of the American Geographical Society*, Vol. 45, No. 1, 1913, p. 1–12 and Vol. 45, No. 2, pp. 107–116.

"The Adaptability of the White Man to Tropical America," edited by G. H. Blakeslee, *Clark University Addresses*, G. E. Stechert & Co., 1914, pp. 360–386.
The Journal of Race Development, Vol. 5, No. 2, October, 1914, pp. 185–211.

The Climatic Factor as Illustrated in Arid America, Publication No. 192, Carnegie Institution of Washington, 1914.

"The Geographer and History," *The Geographical Journal*, Vol. XLIII, No. 1, January, 1914, pp. 19–32.

"The Handicap of the Tropics," *Yale Review*, Vol. III, No. 3, April, 1914, pp. 507–519.

"The Mystery of the Yucatan Ruins," *Harper's Magazine*, Vol. CXXVIII, No. 747, April, 1914, pp. 757–766.

"The Solar Hypothesis of Climatic Changes," *Bulletin of the Geological Society of America*, Vol. 25, No. 2, 1914, pp. 477–590.

"Climatic Changes," pp. 93–94, "The Effect of Climate Versus Earth Movements, p. 94, "The Stages of Development of Playas," pp. 95–96, "The Curtailment of Rivers by Desiccation," p. 96, "The Agreement of Botanical, Chemical, and Physiographic Evidences of Climatic Pulsations," pp. 96–97, "The Death Valley Series," p. 97, *Carnegie Institution of Washington, Year Book No. 14*, 1915.

Civilization and Climate, viii and 333 pp., Yale University Press, 1915. (Second edition, 1922; and a much revised third edition, 1924, reprinted 1973, Archon Books, Hamden, Ct.)

"A Neglected Factor in Race Development," *Journal of Race Development*, Vol. 6, No. 2, October, 1915, pp. 167–184.

"Solar Activity, Cyclonic Storms, and Climatic Changes," *Monthly Weather Review*, Vol. 43, No. 12, December, 1915, p. 609.

"Terrestrial Temperature and Solar Changes," *Bulletin of the American Geographical Society*, Vol. 47, No. 3, 1915, pp. 184–189.

"Work and Weather," *Harper's Magazine*, Vol. CXXX, No. 776, January, 1915, pp. 233–244.

"Climate as a Factor in Colonial Administration," *Report of the Thirty-Fourth Annual Lake Mohonk Conference on the Indian and Other Dependent Peoples*, October, 1916, pp. 122–129.

"Climatic Investigations," *Carnegie Institution of Washington, Year Book No. 15*, 1916, pp. 88–90.

"Climatic Variations and Economic Cycles," *The Geographical Review*, Vol. 1, No. 3, March, 1916, pp. 192–202.

"Death Valley and Our Future Climate," *Harper's Magazine,*, Vol. CXXXII, No. DCCXCII, May, 1916, pp. 919–928.

Discussion of "Variations in Precipitation as Affecting Water Works Engineering," by Carl P. Birkinbine, *Journal of the American Water Work Association*, Vol. 3, No. 1, March, 1916, pp. 94–101.

"Our Immigrant Problem: A Discussion and Review," *The Geographical Review*, Vol. 2, No. 6, December, 1916, pp. 458–463.

"Prediction of Climatic Variations," *The American Museum Journal*, Vol. XVI, February, 1916, No. 2, pp. 96–103.

"The Water Barriers of New York City," *The Geographical Review*, Vol. 2, No. 3, September, 1916, pp. 169–183.

"Weather and Civilizations," *Bulletin of the Geographical Society of Philadelphia*," Vol. XIV, No. 1, January, 1916, pp. 1–21.

"Climatic Change and Agricultural Exhaustion as Elements in the Fall of Rome," *The Quarterly Journal of Economics*, Vol. XXXI, No. 2, February, 1917, pp. 173–208.

"The Geographical Work of Dr. M. A. Veeder," *The Geographical Review*, Vol. 3, No. 3, March, 1917, pp. 188–211; Vol. 3, No. 4, April, 1917, pp. 303–316.

"Maya Civilization and Climatic Changes," *Proceedings of the Nineteenth International Congress of Americanists*, Washington, December, 1915, Washington, 1917, pp. 150–164.

"Solar Activity, Cyclonic Storms and Climatic Changes," *Proceedings of the Second Pan-American Scientific Congress*, Vol. II, Government Printing Office, Washington, 1917, pp. 411–431.

"Temperature Optima for Human Energy," *Proceedings of the National Academy of Sciences*, Vol. 3, No. 2, February 15, 1917, pp. 127–133.

"Climate and the Evolution of Civilization," *The Evolution of the*

Earth and Its Inhabitants, edited by R. S. Lull, Yale University Press, pp. 147–193, 1918. (Revised for *The Evolution of Earth and Man*, edited by G. A. Baitsell, Yale University Press, 1929, pp. 330–383.)

The Geography of Europe; a presentation of some aspects of European geography for the use of members of the Students' Army Training Corps, edited by E. Huntington and H. E. Gregory, Yale University Press, 1918, 95 pp.

"Germany's Prospective Loot in Asia," *Asia*, Vol. XVIII, No. 6, June, 1918, pp. 480–489.

"Save Coal and Save Health, *The American Review of Reviews*, Vol. LVIII, No. 3, 1918, September, pp. 287–291.

Siberia and Eastern Russia, Military Handbook, 4 volumes, Washington Government Printing Office, 1918. ("Classified" and therefore not available.)

"Solar Disturbances and Terrestrial Weather," *Monthly Weather Review*, Vol. 46, No. 3, pp. 123–141; Vol. 46, No. 4, pp. 168–177; Vol. 46, No. 6, pp. 269–277, 1918.

"The Sun and The Weather: New Light on Their Relation," *The Geographical Review*, Vol. 5, No. 6, June, 1918, pp. 483–491.

Teachers' Manual of Geography for Grades 7 and 8, Elementary Education Service, State House, Boston, 1918.

"Air Control and the Reduction of the Death Rate After Operations," *Modern Medicine*, Vol. 1, No. 6, October, 1919, Part 1, Humidity, pp. 463–468; Part 2, Variability, No. 7, pp. 555–558.

"The Future of Palestine," *The Geographical Review*, Vol. 7, No. 1, January, 1919, pp. 24–35.

"The Interpretation of the Death Rate by Climographs," *Modern Medicine*, Vol. 1, No. 1, May, 1919, pp. 13–22.

"The Nature and Possibilities of Tropical Agriculture (with Sumner W. Cushing) *Bulletin of the Geographical Society of Philadelphia*, Vol. XVII, No. 3, July, 1919, pp. 83–97.

The Red Man's Continent, Yale University Press, 1919, ix, 183 pp.

"The Sun's Atmosphere: A Review of Bigelow's Work on the Sun," *The Geographical Review*, Vol. 8, No. 6, December 1919, pp. 350–354.

"The Adaptability of the White Man to the Tropics in Australia," *The Geographical Review*, Vol. 10, No. 2, August, 1920, pp. 110–111.

"Air Control and the Reduction of the Death Rate after Operations," *The Modern Hospital*, Vol. XIV, No. 1, January, 1920, pp. 10–15; Vol. XIV, No. 2, February, 1920, pp. 111–114.

"Climate and Human Efficiency in Korea, *The Geographical Review*, Vol. 10, No. 1, July, 1920, pp. 45–46.

"The Control of Pneumonia and Influenza by the Weather," *Ecology*, Vol. 1, No. 1, January, 1920, pp. 6–23.

"The Control of Pneumonia and Influenza by the Weather (a summary)," *Monthly Weather Review*, pp. 501–502, "Discussion by Author," pp. 505–507, Vol. 48, No. 9, September, 1920.

"The Factor of Health in Mexican Character," *Mexico and The Caribbean*, edited by G. H. Blakeslee, G. E. Stechert and Co., 1920, pp. 44–53.

"Have You Made Up Your Mind?," Campaign Literature, Published by Pro-League Independents, 67 Milk Street, Boston, October, 1920.

Principles of Human Geography, (with Sumner W. Cushing), John Wiley & Sons, Inc., xiv and 430 pp., 1920.

"The Purpose and Methods of Air Control in Hospitals," Part 1, The Ideal Conditions of the Air, *The Modern Hospital*, Vol. XIV, No. 4, April, 1920, pp. 271–275.

"The Purpose and Methods of Air Control in Hospitals," Part 2, Methods of Air Control and Their Results, *The Modern Hospital*, Vol. XIV, No. 5, May, 1920, pp. 348–353.

"Quantitative Mapping by Natural Regions, *The Geographical Review*, Vol. 10, No. 1, July, 1920, p. 47.

"The Rivalry Between Sugar Beets and Sugar Cane," (with Sumner W. Cushing), *Journal of Geography*, Vol. XIX, No. 7, October, 1920, pp. 255–259.

Letter to the editor of *The Geographical Review* (re "The Adaptability of the White Man to the Tropics in Australia"), Vol. XI, No. 3, July, 1921, pp. 475–476.

"Air Control as a Means of Reducing the Postoperative Death Rate," *American Journal of Surgery*, Anesthesia Supplement, Parts 1 & 2, Vol. XXXV, No. 7, July, 1921, pp. 82–90; No. 2, October, pp. 93–100.

"Atmospheric Moisture: Its Significance and Terminology," *The Geographical Review*, Vol. XI, No. 2, April, 1921, pp. 304–305.

"Dr. Leonard Hill on Ventilation, the Kata thermometer and Humidity, *"The Geographical Review*, Vol. XI, No. 2, April 1921, pp. 305–306.

"Memoir of Sumner Webster Cushing," *Annals of the Association of American Geographers*, Vol. 11, June, 1921, pp. 109–111.

"The Relation of Health to Racial Capacity: The Example of Mexico," *The Geographical Review*, Vol. XI, No. 2, April, 1921, pp. 243–264.

"What the Air Does to Us," *The Nation's Health*, Vol. III, No. 5, May, 1921, pp. 265–266.

Business Geography (with Frank E. Williams), John Wiley & Sons, x, 482 pp., 1922.

Climatic Changes: Their Nature and Causes (with S. S. Visher), xiii, 329 pp., Yale University Press, 1922.

"The Evolution of Climate in Northwestern Europe: A Review," *The Geographical Review*, Vol. 12, No. 1, January, 1922, pp. 126–130.

"Peat Deposits as Evidence of Climatic Change, *The Geographical Review*, Vol. 12, No. 1, January, 1922, pp. 142–143.

"Causes of Geographical Variations in the Influenza Epidemic of 1918 in the Cities of the United States," *Bulletin of the National Research Council*, Vol. 6, Part 3, No. 34, July, 1923, pp. 1–36.

"Cycles of Health," Report of a Conference on Cycles, Special Supplement to *The Geographical Review*, Vol. XIII, No. 4, October, 1923, pp. 662–664. "Causes of Cycles," pp. 667–669.

Earth and Sun; an hypothesis of weather and sunspots, Yale University Press, xxv, 296 pp., 1923.

"Influenza and the Weather in the United States in 1918," *The Scientific Monthly*, Vol. XVII, No. 5, November, 1923, pp. 462–471.

"The Lordly Sun, *Harper's Magazine*, Vol. CXLVI, No. DCCCLXXIV, March, 1923, pp. 440–448.

"Solar Cyclonic Explanation of Glaciation (with S. S. Visher), *The Pan-American Geologist*, Vol. 39, February, 1923, pp. 25–42.

"Temperature and Mortality in New York City," A Preliminary Report from the Committee on the Atmosphere and Man, *Statistical Bulletin of the Metropolitan Life Insurance Company*, Vol. IV, No. 2, February, 1923.

The Character of Races, as influenced by physical environment, natural selection and historical development, Charles Scribner's Sons, xvi, 393 pp., 1924.

"The Children of Ministers," *The Christian Work*, Vol. 117, No. 19, November 8, 1924, pp. 530–532.

"Climate and History, as Recorded by the Big Trees," *The Big Tree And Its Story*, by George H. Sherwood, guide leaflet No. 42 of the American Museum of Natural History, 1924.

"Environment and Racial Character," Chapter 8, *Organic Adaptation to Environment*, edited by Malcolm R. Thorpe, Yale University Press, 1924, pp. 281–299.

"Geography and Natural Selection. A Preliminary Study of the Origin and Development of Racial Character," *Annals of the Association of American Geographers*, Vol. XIV, No. 1, March, 1924, pp. 1–16.

Modern Business Geography, with Sumner Cushing, World Book Co., Yonkers, New York, viii and 352 pp., 1924.

"The Chinese Renaissance," *Scribner's Magazine*, Vol. 78, No. 3, September, 1925, pp. 253–260.

"Climatic Cycles and the Number of Animals," *The Geographical Review*, Vol. 15, No. 2, April, 1925, pp. 313–316.

"The Distribution of Domestic Animals," *Economic Geography*, Vol. 1, No. 2, July, 1925, pp. 143–172.

"The Minimum Standards of Australia," *Scribner's Magazine*, Vol. 78, No. 4, October, 1925, pp. 412–421.

"The New Astrology, *The Century Magazine*, Vol. 110, No. 1, May, 1925, pp. 106–114.

"The Suicide of Russia," *Scribner's Magazine*, Vol. 77, No. 2, February, 1925, pp. 156–160.

"Tree Growth and Climatic Interpretations," *Quaternary Climates* Publication No. 352, Carnegie Institution of Washington, 1925, pp. 155–204.

West of the Pacific, Charles Scribner's Sons, New York, 1925, xv, 453 pp.

"The Biological Antecedents of Jesus, *Scribner's Magazine*, Vol. 80, No. 1, July, 1926, pp. 53–59.

"The Effect of Overpopulation on Chinese Character," *Birth Control Review*, Vol. X, No. 7, July, 1926, pp. 221–222, 234. A similar piece in *Problems of Overpopulation*, Sixth International Birth Control Conference, edited by Margaret Sanger, Vol. II, pp. 43–65.

"The Handicap of Poor Land," *Economic Geography*, Vol. II, No. 3, July, 1926, pp. 335–357.

"History of Human Progress," *The Saturday Review of Literature*, Vol. II, No. 52, July 24, 1926, pp. 945–947.

The Pulse of Progress, Charles Scribner's Sons, vi, 341 pp., 1926.

"The Sifting Power of Cities," *Scribner's Magazine*, Vol. 80, No. 3, September, 1926, pp. 316–324.

"What the Weather Does to Us," *Scribner's Magazine*, Vol. 79, No. 6, June, 1926, pp. 571–577.

"Where Can Man Best Live?" *The Forum*, Vol. LXXV, No. 5, May, 1926, pp. 708–717.

The Builders of America (with Leon F. Whitney), William Morrow & Co., 1927, xiv, 368 pp.

"Business Cycles and the Weather," *The Philadelphia Purchaser*, March, 1927, pp. 9–15.

"The Descendants of Who's Who. What do They Tell of the Future of the Race?," *The Outlook*, Vol. 146, No. 17, August 24, 1927, pp. 538–540 (with Leon F. Whitney).

Readings in Sociology, edited by Jerome Davis and Harry E. Barnes, D.C. Heath and Co., 1927.

    "Gold, Distance, and Climate as Social Influences in California," pp. 310–312.

    "Sociological Effects of Manufacturing," pp. 314–315.

    "Bruckner Cycles, Migrations, and General Business," pp. 318–319.

    "Climatic Cycles and Politics," pp. 319–320.

    "Environment as a Key to the Contrasted Social and Religious Systems of Arabia and India," pp. 323–325.

    "Floods, Droughts, Famines, and Chinese Character," pp. 326–332.

    "The Economic and Social Cost of Water Barriers to New York City," pp. 337–343.

    "Regional Geography, and Sociology of the American Indians, pp. 346–356.

"The High Cost of Weather," *"The American Review of Reviews*, Vol. LXXV, No. 1, January, 1927, pp. 38–42.

The Human Habitat, D. Van Nostrand Co., New York, 1927, xii, 293 pp.

"Man and Nature in Hot Climates," *Asia*, Vol. 27, No. 10, October, 1927, pp. 822–829, and 868–871.

"Next Great Revolution will be Biological," *The Yale Scientific Magazine*, Vol. II, No. 1, November, 1927, pp. 19–22, & 50.

"The Quantitative Phases of Human Geography," *The Scientific Monthly*, Vol. 25, October, 1927, pp. 289–305.

"Religion and Who's Who," (with Leon F. Whitney), *The American Mercury*, Vol. XI, No. 44, August, 1927, pp. 438–443.

"Society and Its Physical Environment," *An Introduction to Sociology*, edited by Jerome Davis, Harry E. Barnes, D.C. Heath & Co., 1927, pp. 191–304.

"The 'Thing' in Families," (with Leon F. Whitney), *The Outlook*, Vol. 147, No. 1, September 7, 1927, pp. 21–23.

"The Tropical Plantation, which now yields luxuries but perhaps may some day help feed the world," *Asia*, Vol. 27, No. 11, November, 1927, pp. 918–925.

"The Weather and Human Progress," *Bulletin of the American*

Meteorological Society, Vol. 8, No. 11, November, 1927, pp. 159–164.

"The Weather of 1928," *Morrow's Almanack for 1928*, June, 1927, pp. 93–96.

"Why the American Woman is Unique," *The Nation*, Vol. CXXV, No. 3239, August 3, 1927, pp. 105–107.

"How Environment Strengthens Its Chains," *The American Schoolmaster*, Vol. 26, No. 6, June 15, 1928, pp. 204–211, State Normal College, Ypsilanti, Michigan.

"A Geographer's Idea of Mountaineers," *Mountain Life and Work*, Vol. IV, No. III, October, 1928, pp. 2–5.

"The Next Revolution," *Eugenics*, Vol. 1, No. 1, October, 1928, pp. 6–14.

"Temperature and the Fate of Nations," *Harper's Magazine*, Vol. 157, August, 1928, pp. 361–368.

"The Weather and Human Progress," *Stone and Webster Journal*, Vol. 42, No. 1, January, 1928, pp. 34–46.

"Babbitt and the Weather," *The Outlook*, Vol. 153, October 2, 1929, p. 186.

"Does Civilization Set Us Free," *Problems of Civilization*, comprising Volume VII in the series "Man and His World," edited by Baker Brownell, D. Van Nostrand Co., Inc., New York, 1929, pp. 11–39.

"Fire," *Encyclopaedia Britannica*, 14th edition, Vol. 9, 1929, pp. 262–266.

"Natural Selection and Climate in Northern Australia," *The Economic Record* (The Journal of the Economic Society of Australia and New Zealand), Vol. 5, No. 9, November, 1929, pp. 185–201.

"Who are Competent?," *Birth Control Review*, Vol. XIII, No. 7, July, 1929, pp. 187–189.

"Acclimatization," *Encyclopaedia of the Social Sciences*, Vol. I, 1930, pp. 401–403.

"The Effect of Climate and Weather," *Human Biology and Racial Welfare*, edited by Edmund V. Cowdry, Paul B. Hoeber, Inc., 1930 pp. 295–330.

"Weather and Health, A Study of Daily Mortality in New York City, *Bulletin of the National Research Council*, No. 75, April, 1930, 161 pp.

"The Matamek Conference on Biological Cycles, 1931," *Science*, Vol. 74, September 4, 1931, pp. 229–235.

"New Haven's Climate," *Health*, Vol. LVIII, No. 5, May, 1930, p. 11.

"The Stone Age in the Desert, *Home Geographic Monthly*, Vol. 1, No. 1, January, 1931, pp. 9–15.

"Capacity and Heredity," *Eugenical News*, Vol. XVII, No. 3, May-June, 1932, p. 78–80.

"Climate and City Growth," *Survey Graphic*, Vol. XXI, No. 7, October 1932, pp. 445–449.

"A Geographer's View of America's Queerness," *Education*, Vol. LII, No. 5, January, 1932, pp. 254–257.

Living Geography, 2 Vols. (with C. Beverley Benson and Frank M. McMurry), The Macmillan Company, 1932, Book 1, *How Countries Differ*, vi, 346 pp., and 28 plates; Book 2, *Why Countries Differ*, vi, 506 pp., and 38 plates.

"The Ebb and Flow of Human Population," *Comitato Italiano per lo Studio dei Problemi Della Popolazione*, Roma, 19 pp., 1932.

"The Origin of Racial Differences," *The University of Pennsylvania Bulletin*, Vol. XIX, March, 1932, pp. 482–485.

Economic and Social Geography (with F. E. Williams and Samuel Van Valkenburg), John Wiley & Sons, 1933, xi and 630 pp.

"The Geographic Background of the Revolution," *The New Russia Between the First and Second Five Year Plans*, edited by Jerome Davis, The John Day Co., New York, 1933, pp. 29–51.

"A Neglected Tendency in Eugenics," *Social Forces*, Vol. XII, No. 1, October, 1933, pp. 1–8.

"Russia's Worst Enemy," *New Outlook*, Vol. 161, April, 1933, pp. 36–39.

"America's Vanishing Middle Class," *Today*, Vol. 2, July 28, 1934, pp. 16–17.

"The Causes of Jewish Greatness," *Aryan and Semite: With Particular Reference to Nazi Racial Dogmas*, March 4, 1934, published by B'nai B'rith, Cincinnati, pp. 20–31.

"Eugenics in a Planned Society," (with George R. Andrews), American Eugenics Society (brochure), 3 pp., 1934.

"Foundations of Eugenic Science," American Eugenics Society publication, 1934, p. 5.

"Marginal Land and the Shelter Belt," *Journal of Forestry*, Vol. XXXII, No. 8, November, 1934, pp. 804–812.

"The Selective Action of Migration," *Memorial Volume of the Geographical Society of Lwow in Honor of Eugeniusz Romer*, edited by H. Arctowski, Lwow, 1934, pp. 495–517.

"The Adaptation of Corn to Climate," *Journal of the American Society of Agronomy*, Vol. 27, No. 4, April, 1935, pp. 261–270.

After Three Centuries: A typical New England family, (with Martha

Radsdale), The Williams and Wilkins Company, Baltimore, 1935, viii, 274 pp.

"Climatic Pulsations," *Geografiska Annaler*, 1935, Vol. 16, pp. 571–607.

Europe, (with Samuel Van Valkenburg), John Wiley and Sons, New York, 1935, x and 651 pp.

"Foundations of Eugenic Science," American Eugenics Society publication, New Haven, 1935, pp. 5–12.

"A Logical Geography Curriculum," *Journal of the National Education Association*, Vol. 24, No. 5, May, 1935, pp. 147–148.

"On Boundaries," *Annals of the Association of American Geographers*, Vol. 25, No. 3, pp. 134–135, September, 1935.

"The Success of Missionary Children," *The Missionary Review of the World*, Vol. 58, February, 1935, pp. 74–75.

Tomorrow's Children: The Goal of Eugenics, John Wiley & Sons, 1935, x, 139 pp.

"The Ultimate Goal of Birth Control," *Birth Control Review*, Vol. 2, No. 7, April, 1935, pp. 1–2.

"American Eugenics," Proceedings of the Annual Meeting of the American Eugenics Society, May 7, 1936, pp. 2, 6, 10, 31.

"The Conservation of Man," *Our Natural Resources and Their Conservation*, edited by A. E. Parkins, J. R. Whitaker, 1936, pp. 559–574.

"The Eugenic Point of View," *The Journal of Contraception*, Vol. 1, No. 8, June, July, 1936, pp. 109, 110.

"An Environmental Assistant of Eugenics, *Eugenical News*, Vol. XXII, November-December, 1937, pp. 101–104.

"Geography and History," *The Canadian Journal of Economics and Political Science*, Vol. 3, No. 4, November, 1937, pp. 565–572.

"Once More: What's in a Name" (read before a meeting of the Huntington Family Association, Norwich, Conn.), Huntington Family Association Publication, September 3, 1937.

"Ought I to Marry," *Good Housekeeping*, Vol. 105, No. 5, November, 1937, pp. 28–29, 232–236.

"Season of Birth and Mental Stability," *American Association on Mental Deficiency*, Vol. XLII, No. 2, pp. 116–124, 1937.

"Agricultural Productivity and Pressure of Population," *The Annals of the American Academy of Political and Social Science*, Vol. 198, July, 1938, pp. 73–92.

"Asia, Her Geography, *Carto Craft Comments*, Vol. III, No. 2, March, 1938, pp. 1–6.

"Farms and Villages of Sweden," *Journal of Geography*, Vol. 37,

March, 1938, pp. 85–90.

"The Philosophy of Climate," *Journal of Social Philosophy*, Vol. 4, No. 1, October, 1938, pp. 73–77.

"The Productivity of the Soil," *Comptes Rendus du Congres International de Geographie Amsterdam, 1938*, Tome Deuxième, Travaux de la section IIIb Geographie Economique, Leiden, E. Brill, pp. 200–210.

"The Season of Birth," *The Science Digest*, Vol. 4, No. 2, August, 1938, pp. 1–5.

Season of Birth: Its Relation to Human Abilities, March, 1938, John Wiley, vii, 473 pp.

"The Happy Family with Sufficient Children to Survive," *Living*, January, 1939, pp. 14–15.

"Climate," *Dictionary of American History*, Vol. I, James Truslow Adams, ed.-in-chief, New York, 1940, pp. 398–401.

Principles of Economic Geography, (not coauthors, but assisted by Frank E. Williams and Samuel Van Valkenburg, and Stephen S. Visher, John Wiley & Sons, x and 715 pp., 1940.

"Climatic Pulsations and an Ozone Hypothesis of Libraries and History," *University of Pennsylvania Bicentennial Conference on Conservation of Renewable Natural Resources*, pp. 94–147, 1941.

"Map of the Future," Letter to *Time*, Vol. XL, No. 5, August 3, 1942, p. 3, 4, and 6.

"The Quality of the People," *America At War, A Geographical Analysis*, ed. S. S. Van Valkenburg, Prentice-Hall, Inc., 1942, pp. 1–37.

"Solar Disturbances and Interdiurnal Variations of Atmospheric Pressure," *Bulletin of the American Meteorological Society*, Vol. 23, No. 10, December, 1942, pp. 388–399.

"What Next in Geography," *The Journal of Geography*, Vol. XLI, No. 1, January, 1942, pp. 1–9.

"Are We as Rich as We Think?," *Science Digest*, Vol. 14, July, 1943, pp. 25–31.

"The Geography of Human Productivity," *Annals of the Association of American Geographers*, Vol. XXXIII, No. 1, March, 1943, pp. 1–31.

"A Thousand Years of Eugenics in Iceland," *Eugenical News*, Vol. XXVIII, No. I, March, 1943, pp. 8–10.

"What Geography Does to America," *Transatlantic*, Vol. I, No. 1, September, 1943, pp. 37–42, and p. 60.

"Effect of Atmospheric Electricity on Business," *The Frontier*, Vol. 7, No. 4, December, 1944, pp. 6, 7, and 12.

"The Influence of Geography and Climate Upon History," *Compass of the World*, edited by Hans W. Weigert and Vilhjalmur Stefansson,, The Macmillan Co., New York, 1944, pp. 174–189.

"Season of Birth and Fame," *The Journal of Genetic Psychology*, Vol. 64, 1944, pp. 323–328.

"High Schools and Geographic Immaturity," *The Journal of Geography*, Vol. XLIV, No. 5, May, 1945, pp. 173–181.

Mainsprings of Civilization, John Wiley & Sons, May, 1945, xii and 660 pp.

"The Relation of Human Events, Especially Cycles to Extra Terrestrial Conditions," *Astrological Review*, Vol. XVIII, No. 3, March, 1945, pp. 29–41.

Letter under "Editorial Miscellany—Communications to the Editor," *American Scientist*, Vol. 33, No. 4, October, 1945, p. x, xiv, and xvi.

"Population, Peace or War," *Eugenical News*, Vol. XXX, No. 2, June, 1945, pp. 17–19.

"Broader Aspects of Environmental Cycles," *Foundation for the Study of Cycles, Foundation Reprint No. 16*, 1946.

"Cycles, Rhythms and Periodicities," *Foundation for the Study of Cycles, Foundation Reprint, No. 14*, 1946.

"Eugenics" in *How to Live*, edited by Irving Fisher and Haven Emerson, 21st edition, Funk and Wagnalls Co., New York, 1946, pp. 301–306.

"Storms—Spark Plugs of Civilization," *Reader's Scope*, Vol. 4, October, 1946, pp. 85–87.

"Two Intriguing Cycles," Foundation for the Study of Cycles, *Foundation Reprint No. 15*, 1946.

"Where Our Leaders Come From," *The American Magazine*, June, 1946, p. 38.

"Geography and Aviation," *Air Affairs*, Vol. II, No. 1, 1946, pp. 46–60.

"Cousins and Cousins and Kiths," Booklet of the Huntington Family Association, August, 1946.

Unpublished Manuscripts by Ellsworth Huntington

"Acclimatization," 4p., revised to 6p.

"Among the Druze Outlaws of Bashan," 12p.

"Arch Enemies of Bryan," 8p.

"Are There Any Real Rain-Makers?" 4p., 1 map.

"Asia in America," 14p.

"The Assorting of Racial Stocks in America and Australia," 17p.

"Atmospheric Electricity and the Stock Market," 4p.

"Atmospheric Moisture: Its Significance and Terminology," 2p.

"Barometric and Solar Variations," 20p.

"The Basins of Eastern Persia and Sistan: A Study of the Relation of Climate to Physiography," 12p.

"Birth Rates and Eugenics," 8p.

"Birth Selection for Racial Betterment," 11p.

"The Black Death and Influenza," 12p.

"Blond Horses and Blond Men," 8p., 1 diagram.

"Bread Making: An Ontographic Example," 3p.

"A Call on the Afghans," 22p.

"The Cause of Changes of Climate," 10p.

"The Cause of Climatic Variations," 11p.

"The Causes of Climatic Changes," 14p.

"Causes of Geological Changes in Climate and in Land Forms: An Electro-Tidal Hypothesis, 79p.

"Changes of Climate and History," 19p.

"Civilization and Geography," 7p.

"Climate and Colonial Policy," 21p.

"Climate and the Distribution of Disease," 25p.

"Climate, Health, and Racial Selection in Queensland," 12p.

"Climatic Changes as a Factor in Organic Evolution," 22p.

"The Climatic Relations of the Influenza," 10p.

"Clinching the Nails of Peace," 6p.

"The Comparative Geography of Mars and the Earth," 5p.

"The Conquest of Climate," 13p.

"The Content of Modern Geography," 15p., 2 diagrams.

"The Cultural Significance of Migration," 15p., 2 diagrams.

"The Cyclic Study of Climatic Changes," 8p.

"Death Valley and the Future of the United States," 15p.

"The Distribution of Civilization in the United States," 16p.

"Distribution of Famous Men—European," 13p.

"The Distribution of Human Ability in Europe," 4p.

"The Effect of Temperature and Humidity Upon the Death Rate,"
     20p., 1 diagram.

"Eugenics," 19p.

"Eugenics in History," 11p.

"The Evolution of Racial Differences," 16p.

"Far From the Track in Utah," 22p.

"The Historic Fluctuations of the Caspian Sea," 23p.

"The Function of Climate in the Determination of Geologic Syn-
     chronism, 55p.

"The Future Distribution of Population in the United States," 17p.

"The Future of Eugenics."

"The Geographical Engineer," 2p.

"Geography and Human Culture," 22p.

"The Geographical Evidences as to Primitive Civilization in Amer-
     ica," 11p.

"The Geography of the Election," 3p.

"Geology of the Harpoot Mountains, Asiatic Turkey," 3p.

"The Geology of the Harpoot Group of Mountains in Asiatic Tur-
     key," 10p.

"Germany and Russia in Turkey," 18p.

"The History of Lake Goljeuk, With a Brief Account of its Early
     Connection with the Euphrates and Tigris Rivers," 19p.

"Health and Business," 16p., 5 diagrams.

"Health and Climate," 10p, handwritten.

"Health and Energy," 22p.

"Health and Sanitation in Mexico," 22p.

"A Holdup Among the Druzes," 4p.

"How to Teach Climate to Children," 6p.

"Human Biology: The Influence of Climate," 3p. (some missing)

"Human Efficiency in Tropical Climates," 34p., 2 diagrams.

"The Ideal Distribution of Population," 7p.

"Illiteracy of Foreign-born Whites," 6p.

"The Infant League: A Parable," 1p.

"Inventions and Racial Character," 14p.

"Kashgar in the Heart of Asia," 15p.

"A Khojas Holiday Among the Kurds," 15p. Rewritten as "A Kurdish Holiday," 18p. Rewritten "My Friends the Kurds," 15p.

"A Logical Geography Curriculum," 12p.

"The March of Civilization," 17p.

"Marks at West Point and Annapolis," 3p.

"The Measurement of Civilization," 8p.

"The Migration of Intelligence," 16p.

"The Mind of the Mexican and the 'White Man'," 16p.

"A Mormon Summer," 19p.

"The Nature of Climatic Changes," 6p. handwritten.

"A New and Eugenic Aspect of Birth Control," 3p.

"New Clothes in Turkey," 2p.

"The New Dress of Turkey," 14p.

"The New Zealander in New Mexico," 14p.

"The Nomadism of Asia Minor," 3p. (some missing)

"Optimists of the Southwest," 14p.

"Our Climatic Flavor," 3p.

"The People of Villages," 7p.

"The Pilgrim Memorial Institute: A Proposal for the Pilgrim Tercentenary," 10p.

"Prepared for What?" 16p.

"Primitive Man and American Colonies," 19p.

"Pulsatory Climatic Changes," 44p.

"Rain, Horses and Diet," 5p.

"A Reconnaissance in Central Turkestan," 11p.

"The Relation Between Innate Ability and Literacy as Illustrated in Russia," 1p.

"The Role of Deserts in Evolution," 30p.

"Russian Geography and the Five-Year Plan," 19p.

"The Size of Families," 5p.

"Sliding," 4p.

"Solar activity, Cyclonic Storms, and Climatic Changes," 24p.

"Solar and Magnetic Changes as a Possible Factor in Crustal Deformation," 22p.

"Solar Changes and Barometric Pressure," 30p.

"Sub-Soil Irrigation," 4p. handwritten.

"Sunspots and Rainfall," 5p.

"Sunspots Previous to 1,600 A.D.," 4p.

"Notes and Ms. on the Tertiary Deposits of Central Asia and Their
    Relation to Climate," 11p. (incomplete) handwritten.

"A Theory of Climate and Civilization," 29p.

"The True Use of Location in Geography," 11p.

"The Turk as Ruler," 5p.

"The World Community," 17p.

"Two Rides in Mexico," 10p.

"The Ultimate Effect of Birth Control," 3p.

"The Utilization of Marginal Lands," 6p.

"Variability of Temperature," 27p.

"What does Java Mean?" 2p.

"What Geography Does to Us," 10p.

"What Kind of People are These?" 11p. handwritten.

"Where is our Middle Class?" 8p.

plus 140 pages of unidentified manuscripts.

A Note on the Spelling of Some Place-Names

Throughout chapters 2, 3, and 4 the spelling of place-names has followed Huntington's usage (although that occasionally varied). Below are listed some of the contemporary spellings of place-names mentioned in those chapters.

Anau—Annau

Andijan—Andizhan

Goljeuk—Gyoljuk

Harpoot—Harput

Heri Rud—Hari Rud

Issik Kul—Issyk Kul

Kuzzil Su—Kizil Su

Kwen Lun—Kunlun

Marsovan—Merzifon

Merv—Mary

Samsoon—Samsun

Sazanovka—Ananyevo

Sistan—Seistan

Tian Shan—Tien Shan

Vyernyi—Alma-Ata

Papers Presented by Ellsworth Huntington to the Association of American Geographers

(All references are to the *Annals of the Association of American Geographers*.)

1904   Philadelphia—"The Seistan Depression in Eastern Persia," Vol. 1, p. 101.

1906   New York—"Influence of Changes of Climate upon History," Vol. 1, p. 104.

1908   Baltimore—"The Climate of the Historic Past," Vol. 1, p. 113.

1909   Cambridge—"The Variety of Palestine," (special evening lecture).

1911   Washington—"The Big Trees of California as Recorders of Climatic Changes," Vol. 2, p. 115.
"The Effect of Barometric Variations upon Mental Activity," Vol. 2, p. 116.

1912   New Haven—"The Shifting of Climatic Zones as Illustrated in Mexico," Vol. 3, pp. 115–116.

1913   Princeton—"The Anthropography of Guatemala," Vol. 4, p. 139. "Climate and Human Efficiency," Vol. 4, p. 145.

1915   Washington—"Geographic Variables," Vol. 6, p. 127.

1916   New York—"Fluctuations of Our Southwestern Lakes," Vol. 7, pp. 77–78.

1920   Chicago—Memoir of Sumner Webster Cushing," Vol. XI, 1921, pp. 109–111 and p. 126.

1922   Ann Arbor—"Influenza, an Example of Statistical Geography," Vol. 13, pp. 210–211.

1923   Cincinnati—"Geography and Natural Selection," Vol. XIV, No. 1, March, 1924, pp. 1–16.

1930   Worcester—"A Cross Section of Northern Africa," Vol. XXI, June, 1931, pp. 125–126.

1931   Ypsilanti—"The Measurement and Geographical Distribution of Mental Activity," Vol. XXII, March, 1932, pp. 62–63.

1934 Philadelphia—"Caravan Cities, Climate, and History," Vol. XXXV, March, 1935, p. 45.

1936 Syracuse—"Season of Birth, and the Distribution of Civilization," Vol. XXVII, June, 1937, pp. 109–110.

1938 Cambridge (Mass.)—"Geography and History," Vol. XXIX, March, 1939, p. 78.

1941 New York City—"Geographical Distribution of Human Productivity," Vol. XXXII, March, 1942, pp. 121–122. Published as "The Geography of Human Productivity," Vol. XXXIII, No. 1, March, 1943, pp. 1–31.

Ellsworth Huntington—Memberships, Offices, Honors

1897 B.A.—Beloit College

1901 Gill Memorial Award of the Royal Geographical Society

1902 M.A. Harvard

1904 Charter Member Association of American Geographers

1907 Harvard Travellers Club Medal

1907 Charles Maunoir Medal

1907 Elected Fellow of the Geological Society of America

1907 Associate Editor—*Bulletin of the American Geographical Society*

1908 Resident membership in the Graduate Club Association (Yale)

1908 Listed in *Who's Who in America*

1909 Ph.D.—Yale

1909 Sigma Xi (elected to Yale Chapter)

1910 Contributing Editor—*Journal of Race Development*

1910 Research Associate—Carnegie Institution

1913 First Vice President—Association of American Geographers

1914 Honorary Membership in The Mining Society of the Sheffield Scientific School

1915 Kane Medal—Philadelphia Geographical Society

1915 Associate Member of the Society of American Foresters

1915 Elected Member of the American Genetic Association

1916 Elected at primaries . . . candidate for office of Representative fourth Norfolk district under the political designation of Prohibition

1916 Elected President—Ecological Society of America

1916 Member of Committee on Climatic Conditions as Related to Organisms, of the Ecological Society of America

1916 Honorary Member, Exposition Internationale De L'Alliance d'education Sociale et Civique

1918 Commissioned Captain, Military Division, U.S.A.

1918 Chairman, special committee of the National Institute of Social Sciences on U.S. Census

1919   Elected member of the Cosmos Club

1919   Major, Quartermaster Section Officers Reserve Corps of the
        Army of the U.S.A.

1919   Councilor of American Meteorological Society

1919   Member, National Research Council (Geology and Geography Division)

1920   Elected a Fellow of the American Meteorological Society

1920   Chairman of the Committee on Physiological Meteorology

1920   Appointed to Editorial Board of *Ecology*

1920   Awarded prize from Committee of Awards of the National
        Anaesthesia Research Society

1920   Vice President of "League of Independent Republicans"

1920   Member of The Armenia America Society

1921   Starred as a distinguished geologist in *American Men of
        Science*

1921   Chairman of Committee on Human Ecology of the National
        Research Council

1921   Elected to charter membership in the Stable Money League

1921   Member, National Research Council (Division of Biology and
        Agriculture)

1923   President of the Association of American Geographers

1923   Association of American Geographers, Yale, and National
        Research Council delegate to Second Pan-Pacific Science
        Congress, Melbourne and Sydney, Australia

1924   Elected Fellow of the Royal Geographical Society

1924   Councilor of the Association of American Geographers

1925   Elected Vice President of American Birth Control League

1925   President of the New Haven Council for Religious Education

1926   Member of Advisory Board of the American Society of Heating and Ventilating Engineers

1926   Member of the American National Council of The Institute
        of Pacific Relations

1926   Elected to the Committee on Family Records of The National
        Research Council

1927   Elected to Ends of the Earth (club)

1928   Member of Advisory Council of American Eugenics Society

1928   Councilor of the American Meteorological Society

1928   Advisory Committee—National Research Council Family Association Study (Sub-Committee on Family Records)

1928   Chairman of the New Haven Association of Near East Colleges

1928   Member of New Haven Committee for the Near East Relief
1929   Member of Council of Population Reference Bureau
1930   Listed in *The National Cyclopaedia of American Biography*
1932   Elected to College of Fellows of the Population Association of America
1933   Elected to Committee on Conservation and Land Utilization of American Association for the Advancement of Science
1933   Elected to National Council of Trustees of Lingnan University (Canton, China)
1934   Elected President of the American Eugenics Society
1935   Elected to Division of Geology and Geography of the National Research Council
1935   Elected to Phi Beta Kappa
1935   Membership on Advisory Board of the *Journal of Social Philosophy*
1935   Member of the Advisory Committee of The Motion Picture Foundation—(Division of Historical Pictures)
1935   Member of The Town Hall Club of New York
1936   Elected to Board of Directors of the Eugenics Research Association
1937   Elected to Pi Gamma Mu (The National Social Science Honor Society)
1937   Member—Advisory Board, National Society for the Legalization of Euthanasia
1937   Consulting Editor in Eugenics to *Birth Control Review*
1937   Committee on Preservation of Natural Conditions, National Research Council
1937   Member, Technical Advisory Committee on Climate and Season of the American Society of Heating and Ventilating Engineers
1938   Member, The Society of Daughters and Sons of The Clergy
1938   Elected to corresponding membership of the Finnish Geographical Society
1939   Elected to the Society of American Historians
1940   President of New Haven Harvard Club
1940   Sponsor, The Michigan Committee for Academic Freedom
1940   Member, Free McNamara Committee
1940   Member of the Connecticut Peace Conference
1941   Committee of the Foundation for the Study of Cycles
1941   President of the Connecticut Branch of the League of Nations Association

1941   Sponsor, Citizens' Committee for Harry Bridges

1942   National Council of Geography Teachers—"Distinguished Service to Geography Award"

1942   Listed in *Directory of American Scholars*

1943   Member of State Advisory Committee of the United War and Community Funds of Connecticut

1943   Advisor to the Climatic Section in the Quartermaster Corps of the Army

1945   Sponsor, National Committee to Combat Anti-Semitism

1946   Honorary Doctorate of Science, Beloit College

1946   Honorary D.Litt. Clark University

INDEX

303

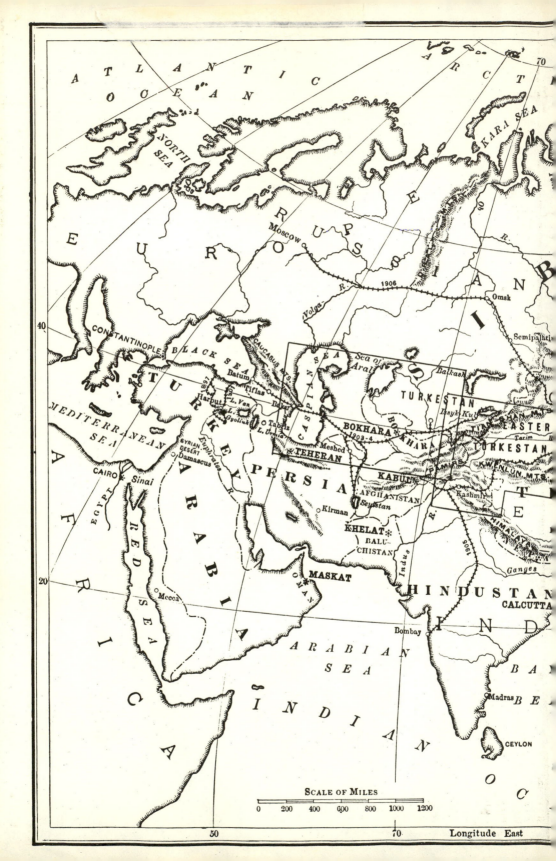

ATLANTIC
OCEAN

ARCTIC

70

KARA SEA

NORTH
SEA

Moscow

RUSSIAN

EUROPE

1906

Omsk

B

40

Semipalati

Volga R.

Balkash

CONSTANTINOPLE

BLACK SEA

Sea of
Aral

TURKESTAN

CASPIAN SEA

I

CAUCASUS MTS

Batum

Tiflis

MEDITERRANEAN
SEA

TURKEY

Harput

L. Van

Baku

EASTER

Gyolük

Tabriz

BOKHARA
1903-4

BOKHARA

KWEN-LUN MTS.

TURKESTAN

SYRIAN
DESERT

L. Urmia

Meshed

PAMIRS

Damascus

Euphrates R.

TEHERAN

KABUL

Isyk Kul

CAIRO

Sinai

PERSIA

AFGHANISTAN

T

E

EGYPT

ARABIA

Kirman

Seistan

Kashmir

RED SEA

KHELAT

BALU-
CHISTAN

HIMALAYA

Indus R.

1905

Ganges

MASKAT

Mecca

OMAN

HINDUSTAN

CALCUTTA

20

AFRICA

Bombay

IND

ARABIAN
SEA

BA

Madras

BE

INDIAN

CEYLON

O

SCALE OF MILES

0   200   400   600   800   1000   1200

50

70

Longitude East